The Role of Pleasure In Behavior

THE ROLE OF

PLEASURE

IN BEHAVIOR

A SYMPOSIUM BY 22 AUTHORS

Edited by ROBERT G. HEATH, M.D., D.M.Sc.,
*Professor and Chairman, Department of Psychiatry and Neurology,
Tulane University School of Medicine, New Orleans, Louisiana*

With 111 Illustrations

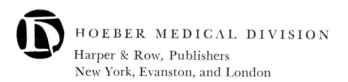

HOEBER MEDICAL DIVISION
Harper & Row, Publishers
New York, Evanston, and London

Library of Congress catalog card number: 64-21432

To the memory of
CHARLES ROSENBLUM,

late Director of the Louisiana State Department of Hospitals, who arranged for financial assistance and provided moral support to researchers and who promoted the symposium at which these papers were presented. It is fitting that *The Role of Pleasure in Behavior* be dedicated to this humanitarian who enjoyed life to its fullest and sought the same for others. His later years were devoted to the alleviation of pain by providing public services to the sick and indigent.

Contents

Contributors

L. M. N. BACH, PH.D., *Professor of Physiology, Tulane University School of Medicine, New Orleans, Louisiana*

IRWIN A. BERG, PH.D., *Professor and Chairman, Department of Psychology, Louisiana State University, Baton Rouge, Louisiana*

M. P. BISHOP, PH.D., *Assistant Professor of Psychology, Department of Psychiatry and Neurology, Tulane University School of Medicine, New Orleans, Louisiana*

NEIL R. BURCH, M.D., *Associate Professor of Psychiatry, Baylor University College of Medicine, Houston, Texas*

WINBORN E. DAVIS, M.S.W., *Acting Director, Louisiana State Department of Hospitals, Baton Rouge, Louisiana*

G. A. DENEAU, PH.D., *Assistant Professor of Pharmacology, University of Michigan Medical School, Ann Arbor, Michigan*

S. THOMAS ELDER, PH.D., *Assistant Professor of Psychology, Department of Psychiatry and Neurology, Tulane University School of Medicine, New Orleans, Louisiana*

JAMES K. FEIBLEMAN, *Professor and Chairman, Department of Philosophy, Tulane University, New Orleans, Louisiana*

DONALD M. GALLANT, M.D., *Assistant Professor of Psychiatry and Neurology, Tulane University School of Medicine, New Orleans, Louisiana*

E. GUERRERO-FIGUEROA, D.B.S., *New Orleans, Louisiana*

R. GUERRERO-FIGUEROA, M.D., *Assistant Professor of Neurophysiology, Department of Psychiatry and Neurology, Tulane University School of Medicine, New Orleans, Louisiana*

ROBERT G. HEATH, M.D., D.M.SC., *Professor and Chairman, Department of Psychiatry and Neurology, Tulane University School of Medicine, New Orleans, Louisiana*

RAUL HERNÁNDEZ-PÉON, M.D., *Director, Unidad de Investigaciones Cerebrales, Secretaría de Salubridad y Asistencia, Mexico City, Mexico, D.F.*

DONALD B. LINDSLEY, PH.D., *Professor of Psychology and Physiology, University of California, Los Angeles, California*

HENRY B. MURPHREE, M.D., *Assistant Chief, Section Neuropharmacology, Bureau of Research in Neurology and Psychiatry, Princeton, New Jersey*

JAMES OLDS, PH.D., *Professor of Psychology, University of Michigan, Ann Arbor, Michigan*

M. E. OLDS, PH.D., *Senior Investigator in Brain Research, University of Michigan, Ann Arbor, Michigan*

SANDOR RADO, M.D., D.POL.SC., *Professor of Psychiatry and Dean, The New York School of Psychiatry, New York, New York*

FRED W. SCHUELER, PH.D., *Professor and Chairman, Department of Pharmacology, Tulane University School of Medicine, New Orleans, Louisiana*

M. H. SEEVERS, M.D., PH.D., *Professor and Chairman, Department of Pharmacology, University of Michigan Medical School, Ann Arbor, Michigan*

LARRY STEIN, PH.D., *Senior Research Scientist, Wyeth Laboratories, Inc., Philadelphia, Pennsylvania*

T. YANAGITA, M.D., *Instructor in Pharmacology, University of Michigan Medical School, Ann Arbor, Michigan*

Foreword

WHEN ROBERT BURNS WROTE in *Tam O'Shanter:* "But pleasures are like poppies spread—/You seize the flow'r, its bloom is shed," he probably had no thought that scientists would one day devote serious study to what happens inside of man when he experiences pleasure. Yet before Burns's time, as today, *pleasure* and *pain* are the basic regulators of behavior, both in man and in lower animals. Pain moves man to seek shelter from the turbulent elements, sends him to the physician for treatment, and impels him to escape from harassment. Pleasure attracts man to the warmth of the fireside, to music, to good food, to high accomplishments, and to companionship.

From earliest experiences the child is guided by rewards and punishments designed to keep his behavior within acceptable limits and to help him find fulfillment and happiness. The rewards—whether a pat on the back, an affectionate hug, money, privileges, or special favors—are designed to provide pleasure and incentive to appropriate behavior and productiveness. The punishments are contrived to produce pain and thus to discourage unacceptable conduct.

What are the mechanisms operating inside a person when pain or pleasure is experienced? What are the physiologic, psychologic, pharmacologic, and dynamic phenomena involved? What happens at the cellular level when living mechanisms move toward pleasure and away from pain? The questions are not new, but knowledge of the subject is rapidly increasing through experimental observations. Studies of brain tissue and discovery that the pleasure-pain areas of the brain can be identified and stimulated in the laboratory are major steps forward.

The papers in this symposium represent latest experimental findings presented by distinguished pioneers in this field. The experimental data contained herein not only have proved highly interesting and informative to the scientist but also have raised further questions: What can be done with the newly identified phenomena? How can they be applied to the solution of human problems? These recent experimental observations may be explosive at the fundamental level in understanding man and may eventually have far-reaching effects on his daily living.

The quality of the presentations, the competence of those in attendance, and the high level of interest attest to the stimulus that cooperative university-state relations can give to research. For arranging the myriad details of programming and scheduling involved in a meeting of this type and for executing them smoothly, special thanks are due Miss Irene C. Dempesy, administrative assistant to Dr. Heath, and to Mrs. Anne L. Stroud, my secretary.

WINBORN E. DAVIS, M.S.W., ACTING DIRECTOR
LOUISIANA STATE DEPARTMENT OF HOSPITALS

Baton Rouge

Preface

OVER THE PAST SEVERAL YEARS interest has grown in the basic observation that a pleasurable response apparently can be induced by direct activation of the brain. In the increasing number of publications on the subject, numerous investigators have reported the phenomenon in studies with animals and a few in studies with human beings. The initially crudely designed experiments have recently become more complex and refined; in fact, rather ingenious technics have been developed to investigate the pleasurable response induced by discrete stimuli to the brain.

Research psychologists have carried out much of the basic work, and other basic scientists, recognizing the importance of this phenomenon, are now showing interest. Physiologists, long concerned with the physical basis of pain and cognizant of the interrelation between pain and pleasure, are vigorously pursuing these studies. The recent popularity of chemotherapeutic agents in the treatment of behavioral disorders has focused the attention of pharmacologists on behavioral mechanisms and has accelerated the search for compounds capable of positively alerting basic feelings without the undesirable side effects of older compounds which relieve pain and produce euphoria. Clinicians, especially psychiatrists, have been aware for some time that pleasure is an important determinant of behavior and have contributed voluminously to publications in the field. In most instances, however, they have handled the phenomenon at a metaphysical level. Except for the few investigators who have pioneered the work of relating pleasurable phenomena to activity of the brain, clinicians only recently have been inclined to apply the basic observation that pleasure and pain can be altered by direct manipulation of the brain to the understanding and treatment of disordered human behavior.

Researchers investigating pleasure and behavior have worked more or less within their own disciplines. Since technics are now available for long-term study of clinical problems in human subjects, it seemed timely to organize a symposium to permit leaders in the various disciplines to exchange ideas regarding mechanisms of the brain in pleasure and the role of pleasure in human behavior. Such a symposium was held in New Orleans,

Louisiana, on November 15 and 16, 1962, the second in a planned series con-
cerned with behavior and the nervous system and sponsored jointly by
Tulane University, Louisiana State University, and the Louisiana State
Department of Hospitals.

This monograph, which contains the papers presented at the symposium,
is divided into four sections: Psychophysiologic Studies, Pharmacologic
Studies, Physiologic Studies, and Psychodynamic Studies. During the symposium, discussions by participants and invited guests were encouraged and
valuable suggestions were made. Summary discussions, prepared by the
respective moderators, appear at the end of each section.

I am most grateful to all who contributed to this monograph and to the
discussants who enriched the proceedings. Special acknowledgment is made
of the assistance of Miss Irene C. Dempesy in the planning and synchronizing
activities during the meeting and in preparing the typescript. For the
financial assistance which made the meeting possible, I wish to express
appreciation to the Louisiana State Department of Hospitals, particularly
to the late Mr. Charles Rosenblum and to Mr. Winborn E. Davis who, at
the time of the symposium was Director of Training and Research for the
Department of Hospitals. I am indebted to Dr. Lois DeBakey for her most
valuable editorial assistance in preparing the book for publication.

ROBERT C. HEATH, M.D., D.M.SC.

New Orleans

PART I

Psychophysiologic Studies

DONALD B. LINDSLEY, PH.D.
University of California, Los Angeles

The Ontogeny of Pleasure: Neural and Behavioral Development

A DISCUSSION OF THE ONTOGENY of pleasure requires the identification and definition of (1) what is meant by pleasure and (2) the conditions which limit and regulate the development of behavior, of which pleasure may be assumed to be a partial manifestation. As to a definition of "pleasure," I confirm from a well-worn dictionary that pleasure has numerous synonyms, such as delight, joy, delectation, enjoyment, gratification, happiness. In the development of behavior, we shall look for certain stages of maturation of the nervous system, which is the prime integrator of behavior; for certain behavioral changes which are associated with neural maturation; and finally for those adaptations of behavior which we call learning. The behavioral adaptations undoubtedly have neural correlates, although we are not yet able to recognize them.

As scientists, we feel constrained to deal only with objective data, i.e., those which are observable or recordable. In this we may be justified, but we should not forget that behavior may be relatively immediate or delayed and readily overt or subtly covert; indeed, there may be instances in which we have no concurrent clue from body or brain to an observable or recordable response to stimulation, either because our measuring instruments are not sufficiently sensitive or because we have not looked in the right place for evidence of it. In the latter case, we can only infer that one or more stimuli have had an effect when a subject subsequently shows an adjustment in behavior or response to the stimulus, as in the instance of conditioning or learning, although control subjects are not so affected. And although the standard electroencephalogram will not record an evoked response to a single visual stimulus, such as a flash of light, an average-response computer will demonstrate the response strongly by averaging many stimulations whose responses are time-locked to the stimulus.

3

Although introspection fell into disrepute and disuse with the advent of behaviorism because the reporting of one's own experiences, feelings, and images was considered unreliable, the subjective report, which is simpler than the elaborate report of feelings and images, has continued to be a prominent part of psychophysical judgments. Certainly many psychologic phenomena are revealed initially by clues afforded through subjective reports, although they may later be identified by a more objective and independent procedure or measuring device. Thus, judicious use of introspections and subjective reports can be valuable in identifying the affect, feeling, or pleasure state of a human subject in terms of time of onset, cessation, and duration—and perhaps also in terms of intensity, provided suitable scaling procedures can be developed.

We must not forget that even observable behavior may be deceptive, as exemplified by the well-known poker face. Moreover, social behavior and facial expressions in China have different connotations from those in other countries. Thus behavior, however observable and however accurately recorded, is subject to misinterpretation. Although the variability of individual subjective reports may suggest lack of reliability, the underlying state which supports a subjective judgment or report may itself vary. In any case, some communality exists among reported feelings, and a degree of reliability can be assumed, since a common meaning for pleasure, joy, delight, and so forth could hardly have emerged without some common background of organismic and experiential conditions. Since it is even possible that common behaviors were learned in response to an earlier experienced affect or feeling state, responses to stimulation are recognized as having commonality and reliability.

To discuss the *ontogeny* of pleasure and behavior, we need not be overly concerned with the philosophic issue of whether introspection and subjective report can be used with, or in lieu of, behavior. In the case of the newborn and young infant, or the animal subject, the organism has either not yet acquired the language symbols necessary to communicate fluently or has not been endowed with speech. Thus we are restricted to the objective behavioral approach, except for the possibility of "tuning-in," as it were, upon electrical activities in the central nervous system, either to stimulate and induce behavioral changes or to record the ongoing and induced electrical activity, which is a by-product of, or occasionally an accessory to, processes intervening between the stimulus and the response.

Experimental work with animals or with newborn infants and young children calls for great ingenuity, since verbal instructions and responses are not possible. Thus, a range from simple to elaborate inferences must underlie the behavioral responses to natural or artificial stimuli regardless of how direct the stimulus-response sequences may be. The clever investigator can often incorporate into his experiment the checks and balances which constitute watertight logic for the inferences, but this may be difficult when the level of the psychologic and behavioral process must be elementary. The logic of a solution to a complex problem can more readily be implemented and evaluated at check points.

INVENTORIAL ASSESSMENT OF NEWBORN AND YOUNG INFANT

What is the status of behavior, reflexes, cerebral development, and manifestations of emotional life in the newborn and young infant? Where and how does behavior begin? Upon what does it depend? Do somatic and effector limitations preclude responsiveness to already functional sensory receptors and systems? Do central integrating networks or hierarchies determine the time at which certain stages of behavior or psychologic processes become manifest? What is the nature of the compounding of reflexes into behavior of involuntary and voluntary nature? When, how, and where does inhibitory control manifest itself, and how does it enter into behavior? Finally, what are the roots of pleasure, defined in terms of satisfaction and gratification and associated with attraction and approach, in contradistinction to displeasure, dissatisfaction, and aversion?

A century ago the great Russian physiologist, I. M. Sechenov,[31] addressed himself to questions of this kind in his *Reflexes of the Brain,* first published in 1863. Sechenov's classic experimental evidence was obtained from the intact and decapitated frog, in which he could demonstrate a variety of reflex actions, including involuntary and voluntary responses. He showed how responses could be augmented or inhibited by those parts of the central nervous system which intervene between sensory and motor fibers in the spinal cord, the brain stem, and the highest reaches of the nervous system of the frog. His logically sharp inferences accounted for differential responsiveness in the presence of sensory stimulation which varied in intensity and area of application. He extrapolated these to man and the newborn infant, emphasizing the important and necessary role of sensory stimulation in all behavior, stressing the role of habit in the modification of response, describing the potentiality of a central mechanism for augmenting as well as inhibiting reflexes, and elaborating the role of centers in the brain for determining whether the response to sensory stimulation would be augmented or inhibited. The counterbalancing of augmentative and inhibitory effects, he believed, is determined centrally by the interaction of reflexes at a given center. Basically, he held that since sensory activity, within limits, is a process which preserves life and is necessary to

it, there is a striving for it and an attraction to it (approach). Interference
with the process leads to dissatisfaction, displeasure, and avoidance or withdrawal from it (aversion).

Sechenov, in assessing the capacities of the newborn child, stated that
"man is born with a very small number of instinctive movements. . . . He
can open and close his eyes, suck, swallow, scream and cry, hiccough, sneeze.
. . . The sensory sphere in the new-born child is also very limited, for it
does not know how to look, listen, smell, and touch" (pp. 292–293). After
explaining how a child learns to see and hear, he summarized the development of the child thus: *"The child acquires consecutive reflexes in all
spheres of the senses by means of absolutely involuntary learning, and
thereby obtains a mass of more or less full conceptions of objects, i.e., elementary positive knowledge"* (p. 298). To the question whether the newborn child reacts passively or actively to external influences on his senses,
Sechenov replied that "it is known that the first condition for the maintenance of material integrity, i.e., for the maintenance of the function of all
nerves and muscles without exception, all organs must be adequately exer-
cised: the optic nerve must be subjected to the action of light, the motor
nerve must be stimulated and its muscles must contract, etc. On the other
hand, we know that if the exercise of any of these organs is forcibly prevented, the person experiences a strained feeling that compels him to perform the necessary action. It is clear, therefore, that the child does not react
passively to external influences. It is also obvious that the striving of the
child towards the outside world is an instinctive, involuntary phenomenon,
and that this striving, when it is satisfied,—i.e., when it calls forth some kind
of movement in the child,—is in all respects a real reflex. The child is
completely in the power of this instinctive striving, and that is the reason
of the particularly mobile character of childhood; the child is continually
passing from the exercise of one nerve to that of another. This instinctive
striving is also the source of the many-sided development of the organs of
senses and of movement" (p. 298). "Childhood is characterized by an ex-
ceptionally wide irradiation of reflex movements in response to such external sensory stimuli; . . . thus the reflexes from the eye and ear can spread
in the child to nearly all the muscles of the body. However, there comes a
time, when movements become, so to say, 'grouped.' . . . It is in this process
that the inhibitory mechanisms take part" (p. 318).

With regard to emotion, Sechenov said that "at the beginning of human
life, all psychical reflexes without exception are emotional, i.e., have augmented ends. Little by little the sphere of emotion becomes narrowed;
emotion is called forth, not by dull and monotonous images, but by brighter
and more mobile ones" (p. 325). "All this shows that emotion, in children,
is characterized by *great mobility,* i.e., is easily called forth and easily dis-

appears. . . . In the further development of the child, its conceptions (or more correctly the image connected with its conceptions) obtain an emotional character" (p. 326).

Thus Sechenov, even before Pavlov, had formulated the basis for conditioned reflexes and, having been exceedingly perceptive of human behavior from its simplest to its most complex social forms, had succeeded remarkably in using information gathered by sound physiologic methods in the formulation of explanations of more complex behavior. In particular, I should like to draw attention to two things which emerge from Sechenov's analyses: (1) that newborn animals and human infants *strive* for sensory stimulation and (2) that as searching or striving for more sensory stimulation broadens, the associated behavioral reflexes to greater stimulation in-

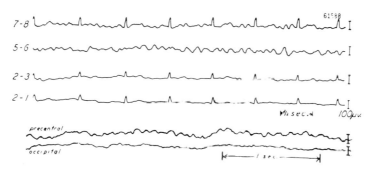

FIG. 1. Fetal and newborn electroencephalograms from same infant. Tracing 5-6 shows waves of 6- to 7-per-second frequency recorded from maternal abdomen when head of fetus was palpable in region of electrodes numbered 5-6. The same pattern and frequency were obtained from precentral region of head after birth, as shown in second tracing from bottom. (From Lindsley[20] by permission of author and publisher.)

crease (e.g., general activity and excitement, as actually observed by students of the neonate) until "psychical reflexes" and inhibition appear with the development of the cerebral cortex. Subsequent information on cortical development supports this order of development and apparently also the supplanting of concrete emotional expressions by more abstract forms of expression in concepts and images manifested by longings, desires, wishes, and perhaps fantasies, rather than by direct, overt expressions of approach and avoidance.

But let us now return to the behavioral inventory of the child and the relation of its development to the maturation and development of the brain. First, we must acknowledge that considerable behavior is in evidence and evolving steadily before birth of any given species. The first spontaneous activity observed in the human embryo appears to be the myogenic heart beat at about 3 weeks. (For a detailed survey of the work of Minkowski, Hooker, and others, see Carmichael.[4]) The first reaction to mechanical or electrical stimulation occurs at about 2 months and is largely limited to stimulation of the oral and facial regions. The earliest spontaneous movements occur at 9 weeks, and the grasp and plantar reflexes are observed at 11 weeks. According to Newbery,[28] mothers generally experience an internal bombardment beginning in the fourth month and increasing steadily thereafter until the last month of pregnancy. At birth and even 2 or 3 months previously, all sense modalities are responsive to stimulation. Their linkage reflexly to muscles is evidenced by the presence, by at least the seventh fetal month, of all reflexes seen at birth. Three of these—the Babinski, the grasp, and the Moro reflex—are especially notable because of their relative complexity and because of their reversibilty or complete disap-

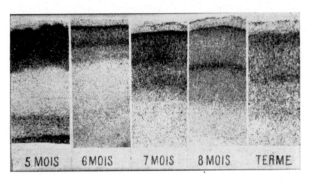

FIG. 2. Progressive changes in histologic development of cortex of human fetuses from fifth fetal month to term. (Courtesy of Dreyfus-Brisac and associates.[12])

pearance within the first few months of postnatal life. More will be said about these in relation to maturation of the neocortex.

I have recorded the fetal electroencephalogram in the seventh prenatal month through the maternal abdominal and uterine walls when the head of the fetus was properly oriented with respect to the electrodes on the maternal abdomen (Fig. 1).[20] The tracing labeled 5-6, from electrodes over the palpable head of the fetus, contains waves of 6- to 7-per-second frequency, similar in pattern and frequency to those recorded at birth for the same infant with electrodes over the precentral or motor region (lower tracing). Such rhythms from the sensorimotor region, according to Smith[33] are present in the newborn infant only during the most relaxed and drowsy state and seldom, if ever, during a waking or active state. The presence of such rhythms over the motor region of the newborn, and their absence over specialized sense zones, agrees with the histologic observations of Conel,[9, 10] which show that the motor area is considerably advanced in structural development over other areas of the cortex. Dreyfus-Brisac and associates[12] demonstrated diffuse and poorly regulated electrical activity in premature infants born in the seventh month. A comparison of the histologic development during the fetal period from 5 months to term (Fig. 2) seems to indicate that not until the seventh or eighth month is the laminar structure of the cortex of the fetus clearly differentiated; even after birth, considerable maturation and development has yet to take place, as shown by the work of Conel.[9, 10] As Dreyfus-Brisac[11] has pointed out: "The

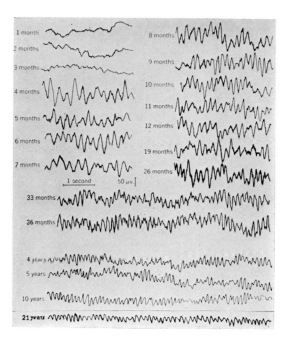

FIG. 3. Longitudinal electroencephalograms from the visual area of the same person over a span of 21 years. The alpha waves first appear regularly at 4 months at a frequency of 3 to 4 per second, increase to 5 or 6 per second by 1 year, and attain an adult frequency of 10 per second at 10 years. Note decrease in voltage with age. (From Lindsley[22] by permission of author and publisher.)

rhythmic potentials of the premature are very likely due to archaic structures which arrive precociously at a functioning level (central gray nuclei). In the full-term newborn, the development of the cortex, even though immature, probably reduces the likelihood of registering these potentials."

Smith[32, 34] and I[18, 19] have shown that a persistent alpha rhythm first appears over the occipital area of the brain of young infants by the third or fourth month. I have extended the longitudinal sequence in a single individual to 21 years of age (Fig. 3).[22] This series of tracings shows that the visual area has little or no regular rhythm during the first 3 months, but beginning in the fourth month there are alpha waves at a frequency of 3 to 4 per second which increases to 5 to 6 waves per second at 1 year and to adult frequency of 10 per second by 10 to 12 years of age; thereafter, frequency changes little, although voltage diminishes. The significant point here is that a functional change appears to occur in the third or fourth month, with the occipital region manifesting a persistent and continuing alpha rhythm thereafter. This undoubtedly indicates that the visual cortex has become functional (and apparently this is true of other sensory areas, as more recent evidence shows) in a way that has not existed before.

That the rhythmic electrical activity seen in the visual area in the third or fourth month is correlated with other signs of maturational and developmental change seems evident. Figure 4, from Conel's work,[9, 10] shows the histologic development in visual area OA of the *cortex* in a *newborn* child

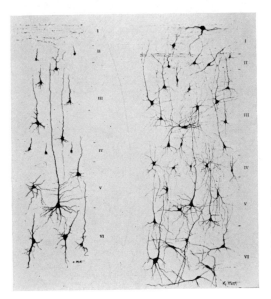

Fig. 4. Drawings from Golgi-Cox preparations of visual cortex area OA in human infants, at birth (left) and at 3 months (right). (From Conel[9, 10] by permission of author and publisher.)

by contrast with a 3-month-old child. As Conel has indicated, several criteria may be used to assess this change from birth to 3 months, but particularly evident are the greater length and ramification of basal and apical dendrites, which are believed to be the source of spontaneous cortical rhythms. In this connection, Purpura[29] and Voeller, Pappas, and Purpura,[38] studying the cortical development in the kitten by electron microscope, found the development of the axodendritic synaptic connections to be more advanced than the axosomatic.

In addition to a correspondence in time or stage between the onset of the alpha rhythm and certain features of histologic or structural development, behavioral tests of infant development, such as those of Cattell,[5] place the first integrated use of the visual mechanism at 3 months of age. For example, the standards of Cattell (1940) show that an infant of 3 months should be expected to regard a small cube placed before him. Also at that age he will inspect his fingers when they are held before him or follow a dangling ring as it moves back and forth in front of him.

The stages of maturation of the nervous system, as revealed by histologic data, correlate at least grossly with electroencephalographic data, and both of these correspond to the integrated use of the visual sense modality as revealed by developmental behavioral tests. Obviously, as pointed out long ago by Sechenov, the senses have been in use before the age of 3 months and even prenatally to some extent, but the postnatal use of the sense modalities during the first 2 or 3 months is probably associated primarily with reflex development and integration at a brain-stem level. This concept is supported by some unusual observations of Monnier and Willi[25, 26] on anencephalic monsters, i.e., human infants born without the cerebral cortex. In a mesorhombencephalic specimen which lived 57 days, they observed normal responses to exteroceptive stimuli: tactile, thermal, and nociceptive. They found little to distinguish the sensory and motor capacities of mesencephalic and diencephalic specimens from those of normal infants of the same age: Their posture; sensory responsiveness; spontaneous activity; and reflexes, including the Babinski, grasp, and Moro were about the same. Apparently in the normal newborn and young infant, perhaps to the age of 2 or 3 months, the cortex plays little role in the mediation of observed behavioral responses to sensory stimulation. Although the cortex has all its cell bodies or neurons at birth, these will clearly not mature for several months or perhaps even several years.

The fact that alpha-wave activity appears at 3 or 4 months of age and continues to grow in voltage at least during the first year and to increase in frequency to 10 years or so must have significance for the functioning of the brain in relation to perceptual and learning capacities. That both specific (axosomatic) and nonspecific (axodendritic) sensory projection mechanisms are involved in this process of maturation and development is apparent from extensive work now in progress with varied species. The spontaneous or autonomous rhythms (alpha-like waves) appear to be associated with the axodendritic mechanism, whereas the primary, specific evoked potentials elicited by sensory stimulation appear to be associated with axosomatic connections. Both mechanisms are apparently involved in the perceptual process, since removal of the ascending reticular activating system by lesion or by functional blockage with anesthetics or during sleep interferes with perceptual discrimination based on learned habits.

The electroencephalogram of the monkey,[6] when compared with that of man,[7] shows a similar pattern of frequency development of the alpha rhythm as a function of age. A persistent alpha rhythm first appears in the monkey at about 2 to 3 weeks of age, whereas in the human infant it begins at about 3 to 4 months; this difference corresponds to approximately a 1 : 6 ratio in life span and physiologic age. The frequency at onset in both monkey and man is about 4 waves per second, and there is a parallel increase in frequency to about 10 waves per second in each at the age of 2 years in the monkey and 10 to 12 years in man (Fig. 5).

Just as electroencephalographic changes are correlated with behavior in the human infant, the work of Harlow[13-15] suggests that stages of development of behavior, learning, and affectional responses bear a relation to the period at or immediately after onset of the alpha rhythm in the monkey.

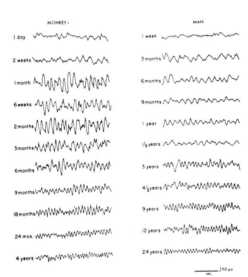

Fig. 5. Electroencephalograms of monkey and man at corresponding life-span ages. Alpha waves begin at 2 weeks in monkey and at 3 months in man (1:6 life-span ratio). Frequency of alpha waves increases as a function of age in essentially parallel fashion. (From Caveness[6] by permission of author and publisher.)

Marquis[23, 24] and Wenger[40] have shown in the human neonate that conditioning is possible in the early postnatal days but is exceedingly unstable; similarly, Harlow[13] has reported that infant monkeys can be conditioned to tone-shock combinations when the conditioning procedure starts at 3 days of age. It may be sheer coincidence, but the conditioning reaches its peak in about 15 to 20 days, when the alpha rhythm would normally have been established in monkeys. Other comparatively simple learning tasks, such as performance in a straight runway, black-white discrimination, and spatial discrimination in a Y-maze, also seem to reach an asymptote at about 15 to 20 days of age, an observation which suggests that such simple learning is related in some way to the functional capacity of the cerebral cortex as indicated by the development of alpha rhythm at that time. Peak performance of more complex learning tasks involving delayed response, discrimination in learning sets, and oddity problems is not attained until adolescence (in monkeys, 2 to 3 years of age) or later.

Harlow[14, 15] has outlined four stages in the development of monkey infant-mother affectional patterns: *reflex, attachment, security,* and *independence.* Reflex contactual and nursing patterns, as well as grasp, Babinski, and Moro reflexes, are evident from birth and extend to 15 or 20 days. Mowbray and Cadell,[27] in a more detailed study, investigated the rooting and subsequent behavior of the nursing pattern present at or shortly after birth and

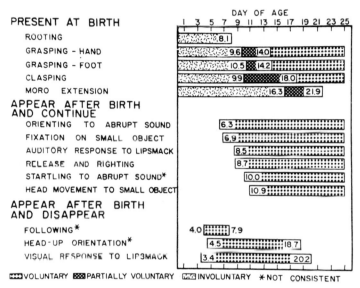

Fig. 6. Course of behavioral reaction in infant rhesus monkeys. Involuntary rooting, grasping, and Moro extension disappear by about 15 days; new responses of partially voluntary nature begin to appear by 8 to 10 days; other responses appear and disappear during first 20 days. (From Mowbray and Cadell[27] by permission of authors and publisher.)

for about 10 days thereafter. They found that grasping, clasping, and the Moro extension reflex are all present at birth (Fig. 6) and either change from a reflex to a voluntary activity or, as in the case of the Moro extension, disappear at about 20 days. Since the alpha rhythm is present at this time, it may be assumed that the cortex is functional and that inhibitory controls of lower brain-stem centers are probably responsible for the disappearance or modification of these reflexes as well as of the entire reflex stage. Orienting responses, fixation, and the startle reflex to sound begin to appear around the eighth to tenth day of postnatal life and persist thereafter.

Harlow[15] reported that the onset of the second, or attachment, phase of affectional development is accompanied by two nonaffectional patterns, *fear responsiveness* and *curiosity-manipulatory responses.* Removal from the mother causes the neonate monkey to whimper, cry, and show signs of distress. Although large, mobile, and brightly lighted objects elicit fear responses, they seem to excite in the neonate an insatiable curiosity of exploratory nature. As fear and distress mount while the infant is exploring, he races back to his mother or other objects which provide security, only to venture forth again later. Curiosity toward external objects as the infant matures leads to separation or "weaning" from the mother, whereas curiosity-manipulatory activities with the mother tend to perpetuate the maternal dependence. According to Harlow, the same stimuli which induce fear and aversion or avoidance at one stage of maturation may at another stage serve as an attraction and elicit approach responses. Thus, elementary fear responses, which evoke crying and apparent distress, may represent the initial phase in formulation of a concept of dissatisfaction and displeasure, whereas the magnetic attraction of external objects associated with a curiosity-manipulatory motive seems to lead toward "play" and the joy of activity, which eventually become identified and perpetuated as satisfaction and lead to approach behavior.

Harlow's experiments with various types of maternal surrogates, such as those made of wire and cloth, have led to clever investigations in the realm of the *security stage* and finally the *independence stage*, although fewer data are available on this more advanced phase.

Stratton,[35] following the lead of Wundt[39] with his tridimensional theory of feelings, proposed that *excitement* was an undifferentiated emotion, which formed a backdrop for all other emotions and feelings, whether pleasant or unpleasant. Excitement, he held, might precede or follow a more specific and defined emotion or feeling, such as anger, fear, depression, elation, or affection. Bridges[2] considered *excitement* to be the basic state from which feelings and emotions in children become differentiated and matured (Fig. 7). According to her scheme, the newborn child manifests only *excitement, distress* emerging at 1 month and *delight* by 2 months of age. Between 3 and 6 months, *anger, disgust,* and *fear* become part of the child's repertoire. To counterbalance these, between 6 and 12 months *elation* and *affection* appear. Between 12 and 18 months *jealousy* becomes differentiated from distress, and *joy* from delight. Excitement continues throughout as a base or modulator for each of the other emotions or feelings.

Whether newborn and young infants exhibit identifiable emotions has always been a controversial issue. Landreth[17] believes that little more can be said of emotional behavior at birth than that "resisting or rejecting stimuli by kicking, crying, and thrashing movements would seem reasonably

attributable to 'dissatisfaction' or distress while a turning toward or accept-
ing stimuli with relaxed passivity might equally reasonably be attributed to
'satisfaction.' As for the stimuli which elicit these generalized response patterns, the 'distress' or dissatisfaction response appears to be associated with
visceral tension, with pain, and with sudden intense stimuli, all of which
presumably upset the infant's state of equilibrium or homeostasis. The 'satisfaction' response is associated with relief of tension and with such feeding,
wrapping, and handling as restore and enhance equilibrium."

To go beyond Sechenov's view that an innate pattern of reflexes unfolds
and matures and that each of these requires stimulation and exercise to
remain effective and promote life, one would need to develop an elaborate
neurobiologic theory. Such a theory would be beyond the subject of this
presentation. However, Sechenov argued that sensory receptors and sensory
mechanisms are not a stand-by system, but that, on the contrary, through

FIG. 7. Schema showing approximate ages at which differentiation of emotions from initial generalized and undifferentiated excitement occurs. (From
Munn, N. L. *Psychological Development.* Boston, Houghton
Mifflin, 1938. By permission of
author and publisher. An adaptation from Bridges.[2])

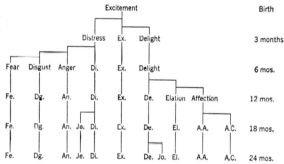

their reflex effector systems they lead to active striving for additional stimulation.

Certainly the generalized bodily activity of a newborn infant contributes
considerable sensory influx by way of proprioceptive, kinesthetic, and cuta-
neous stimulation. Any somatic activity gives rise to proprioceptive feedback; in turn, this, or any other sensory stimulation, effects excitation in the
brain-stem reticular formation. Consequently, through the ascending reticular activating system, all structures above, including the cerebral cortex,
stand to be activated and aroused. At the same time, the sensory impulses
from whatever source pass by way of the specific sensory system to their specific destinations in a primary receiving area, to spread and be elaborated
presumably in adjacent or widespread association areas. The confluence or
interaction of these specific and nonspecific effects of sensory stimulation is
essential to perception and undoubtedly to memory and learning as well.
One point of interaction is the cortex; another may be the limbic system,

especially the hippocampus, which itself is linked with neocortex, the reticular system, and other centers in the diencephalon.

Why is sensing an active process? Do animals and human beings strive for stimulation? Under what conditions is it satisfying? Do satisfaction and gratification lead to pleasure? Is pleasure synonymous with attraction and approach, and are these in turn synonymous with motivation and drive?

The answers to these questions are by no means clear, but some clues may be worth pursuing. First, let us examine a concept of Arnold,[1] who courageously attempted to review and integrate a mass of current neurophysiologic reports, as well as a number of older views, relative to the origins of feeling and emotion. She held, briefly, that "we can like or dislike only something we know. We must see or hear or touch something, remember having done so or imagine it, before we can decide that it is good or bad for us. Sensation must be completed by some form of *appraisal* [my italics] before it can lead to action. . . . Appraisal seems to be a process of evaluating and comparing sense impressions and memories from many sense modalities, and thus may take an appreciable time. But once a thing is evaluated, the experience of liking or disliking it follows immediately and automatically" (pp. 33-34). "We have now seen that an object or a situation is perceived, appraised, and liked or disliked; and that this liking or disliking arouses a tendency to approach or withdraw, to deal with this thing in some particular way. . . . According to our conception, the limbic system mediates liking or disliking, while the hippocampus seems to initiate the recall of memories, and also the impulse to a particular action" (p. 82). Arnold held that sensory and motor appraisals are mediated by special systems. Sensory appraisal receives relays from the sensory system and includes afferent connections from sensory receptors to the brain-stem reticular formation, the intralaminar and midline thalamic nuclei, and the cortex of the limbic lobe. She called this the *estimative system* because it serves the evaluation of incoming sensations. Unfortunately, the reader is never told what an appraisal or evaluation of sensation really is or what constitutes a basis for sensory and motor activity. Admittedly, these are not easy questions to answer.

In attempting to determine the interaction between intraorganic physiologic state and external stimulation in relation to motivation, I outlined some factors basic to drive states,[21] quoting at some length corroboration from Child[8] and Herrick.[16] Physiologic state, as Child viewed it, includes residua from previous reactions; simultaneous excitations from different sources; metabolic, respiratory, endocrine factors; periodicities; and, in fact, all external and internal factors which impinge upon the nervous system. Cannon[3] emphasized a steady state or equilibrium, which he called *homeostasis*; Child[8] referred to physiologic *regulation* or *equilibration*; and

Herrick[16] spoke of *behavior regulation*. However described, the steady state of chemical or physiologic systems is continually susceptible to disruption and imbalance. Reflex reaction to this produces movement which can only increase proprioceptive, tactual, and kinesthetic stimulation and often will expose other sensory receptors to external stimulation. The more activity and excitement manifested by the newborn or young infant, the more regulatory control and balancing of homeostatic and equilibratory mechanisms are involved. Similarly, the more active the child, the more stress is placed upon the mechanism concerned, e.g., the respiratory, circulatory, or metabolic systems. Ordinarily each system has its own safe-tolerance limits, and the combined activity of systems in the restoration of an appropriate balance would seem to constitute a state of well-being and, presumably, satisfaction. If, on the other hand, the stress is excessive, or if it is increased by greater activity, or if there is lack of attention to physiologic needs, limits of tolerance may be exceeded, and competition of adjusting systems may temporarily delay homeostasis and recovery. This would lead to distress or pain, additional struggling, and crying.

The general conclusion is that activity within limits is rewarded by satisfaction and a sense of pleasure in activity, whereas the more severe stress and struggle lead to discomfort and displeasure. One often notes the almost convulsive struggling, quivering, tremulousness, and excessive flushing of the face of a neonate who is in distress from gas or whose activities have been hampered by restraining garments or bed clothes which have become twisted or disarrayed. In contrast, mild activity of the limbs or body, patting, rolling, or vocal stimulation by the mother or a nurse usually elicits mild excitement, apparent contentment, cooing, and later, by the third or fifth month, smiling. Thus there seems to be a basis for differential responsiveness in the form of hyperactivity, restlessness, distress, and apparent discomfort, or of relaxed contentment with mild excitement and moderate activity suggesting pleasure and satisfaction. Although conditioning is unstable at such an early age, there is every opportunity for it to be repeatedly reinforced under normal conditions of maternal love, attention, and affection. In addition, the fact that even prenatally the mouth and face are sensitive to stimulation suggests that whatever neural mechanisms have developed are more mature with respect to these peripheral zones than to other sensory areas. Consequently, with a lower threshold and with opportunity to root with the head and obtain a nipple, there is good reason why the reflex mechanism for sucking is quickly put to use. Furthermore, the warm, sweet milk undoubtedly stimulates taste and temperature receptors, in addition to gradually filling the stomach and assisting in this way in physiologic homeostasis. Thus a pattern of stimulation involving several modalities quickly becomes conditioned to the sights, sounds, temperature, and tactual experiences which accompany the feeding experience, and even though unstable, day-to-day reinforcement tends to perpetuate the conditioning.

Ribble[30] emphasized that early mothering should provide a comfortable posture for the infant, gentle motion and rocking, soothing voices, ample opportunity to suck at the mother's breast or upon a nipple without sudden or strenuous interruption. The whole concatenation of sensory events, including sucking, swallowing, gentle holding and rocking, soft auditory and gentle vestibular stimulation, she believed, is not only pleasurable and favorable to temporary development but is significantly related to later social and emotional adjustment. She contended that "ruthless repression of pleasure-getting impulses of the baby results regularly in disorganization and in anxiety or tensional states with the resulting formation of such habits as thumb-sucking, persistent crying, repetitive activities, and masturbation, all of which apparently serve to relieve this anxiety or tension to some degree" (p. 647). In the newborn and young infant she noted confirmation of Freud's broadened view of infantile sexuality as an undifferentiated biologic form which requires adaptive striving. Satisfaction of these strivings associated with basic bodily functions results in pleasurable feelings. She concluded that "sexuality contributes to the primary orientations of the organism and to the infant's first awareness of himself and his body security and his well-being" (p. 623). When satisfaction of strivings for sensory stimulation are not permitted by adequate mothering, there are often dire consequences, such as negativistic excitement or regressive quiescence and lack of reactivity.

Many of the publications on this subject cite evidence of a "sensory hunger" or striving in human infants. The nature of the activity of the infant suggests that it is partly to satisfy a striving for sensory stimulation. Reduction of sensory stimulation when an infant is wide awake often leads to crying and restlessness, as if he were struggling to attain more stimulation. Restoration of mild and gentle stimulation usually quickly restores the equanimity of the infant. Harlow's[14] studies of affectional behavior in infant monkeys suggest that cloth or wire surrogate mothers, unlike true mothers, do not provide sufficient opportunity for affection or sensory stimulation; the infants at various ages were starved not only for affection but also for stimulation, at times rubbing their noses against the wire to the point of soreness and rawness. There was also some evidence of hyperactivity.

Thompson and Heron[37] reported that the most noticeable feature of the behavior of dogs removed from restricted environment after 8 to 10 months is extreme hyperactivity, which may persist for several years, according to Thompson.[36] The hyperactive behavior takes the form of nuzzling, hand-licking, tail-chasing, yelping, barking, and growling. Much of this behavior may be interpreted as the result of deprivation of sensory stimulation. Wundt and associates,[39] after rearing newborn monkeys in darkness for 16 months (except for 1 hour daily of unpatterned exposure to prevent blindness), allowed them to press a bar for a brief period of stimulation by light. The bar-pressing rates were extremely high and persistent in comparison with those of nondeprived monkeys and indicated an insatiable drive for stimulation by light. In human subjects who have undergone deprivation or isolation, visual and auditory hallucinations, as well as hyperactivity and restlessness, have been reported to develop. These experiments involving deprivation resulting from restricted environment indicate that sensory need or sensory hunger develops in the subjects, a phenomenon which is probably related to the sensory striving observed in the neonate; they suggest that satisfaction and pleasure are derived from sensory stimulation, whereas lack of it leads to hyperactivity and to attempts to induce stimulation.

SUMMARY

It is postulated that the *ontogeny of pleasure* begins with the first manifestations of reflex responsiveness and is related to the satisfaction derived from sensory stimulation and response. Reflex behavior, as well as later voluntary behavior, in addition to providing exercise, produces sensory stimulation of tactual, kinesthetic, and proprioceptive varieties and increases the chances of stimulation of other sensory modalities. An elementary pleasure or satisfaction is believed to derive from sensory stimulation and behavioral response; displeasure, discomfort, and distress, with associated withdrawal or avoidance behavior, are believed to develop as a result of sensory deprivation, restricted environment, and lack of affectional manipulation. As the affective and emotional world expands for the young child, basic pleasurable reactions of aversion or avoidance become conditioned to an ever-expanding personal and social environment, molding the personality in accordance with early experience.

The early stages of development in the human infant (and in the monkey) are characterized by lack of maturation of the cortical mantle, which is reflected in part by absence of persistent alpha rhythms until the age of 3 or 4 months in the human and 2 or 3 weeks in the shorter life-spanned monkey. Associated with this delay in electroencephalographic or physiologic development of the cortex is a corresponding delay in the structural and histologic maturation of the cortex. Both the electroencephalographic and histologic developments are paralleled by certain behavioral advances.

The progressive maturation of the cerebral cortex, with its potential inhibitory control and its relations with the reticular activating system and the limbic system, greatly enhances the range of reflex and voluntary behavior and provides for perception, memory, learning, and emotional and affectional reinforcements, of which pleasure appears to be one important aspect. Whether the limbic system, and more specifically the hippocampal portion, constitutes an important link in the mechanism underlying pleasure remains to be seen.

REFERENCES

1. ARNOLD, M. B. *Emotion and Personality,* Vol. II, *Neurological and Physiological Aspects.* New York, Columbia, 1960. Page references for quotations are given in parentheses after the passage cited.
2. BRIDGES, K. M. B. A genetic theory of the emotions. *J. Genet. Psychol. 37:*514, 1930.
3. CANNON, W. B. *Bodily Changes in Pain, Hunger, Fear, and Rage: An Account of Recent Researches into the Function of Emotional Excitement,* 2nd ed. New York, Appleton, 1929.
4. CARMICHAEL, L. (ed.). *Manual of Child Psychology,* 2nd ed. New York, Wiley, 1954.
5. CATTELL, P. *The Measurement of Intelligence of Infants and Young Children.* New York, Psychological Corporation, 1940.
6. CAVENESS, W. F. *Atlas of Electroencephalography in the Developing Monkey: Macaca Mulatta.* Reading, Mass., Addison-Wesley, 1962.
7. CAVENESS, W. F., VAN WAGENEN, G., and LINDSLEY, D. B. Comparison of monkey and human EEG development from birth to puberty. (Scientific Exhibit.) *Trans. Amer. Neurol. Ass. 85:*246, 1960.
8. CHILD, C. M. *Physiological Foundations of Behavior.* New York, Holt, 1924.
9. CONEL, J. L. *The Postnatal Development of the Human Cerebral Cortex,* Vol. I, *Cortex of the Newborn.* Cambridge, Mass., Harvard, 1939.
10. CONEL, J. L. *The Postnatal Development of the Human Cerebral Cortex,* Vol. III, *Cortex of the Three-Month Infant.* Cambridge, Mass., Harvard, 1947.
11. DREYFUS-BRISAC, C. The electroencephalogram of the premature infant. *World Neurol. 3:*5, 1962.
12. DREYFUS-BRISAC, C., SAMSON, D., BLANC, C., and MONOD, N. L'électroencéphalogramme de l'enfant normal de moins de 3 ans: Aspect functionnel bio-électrique de la maturation nerveuse. *Etudes néo-natales 7:*143, 1958.
13. HARLOW, H. F. The development of learning in the rhesus monkey. *Amer. Sci. 47:*459, 1959.
14. HARLOW, H. F. "Affectional Behavior in the Infant Monkey," in *Conference on the Central Nervous System and Behavior, Transactions of the Third Conference,* ed. by Brazier, M. A. B. New York, Macy, 1960, pp. 307–357.
15. HARLOW, H. F. "Development of Affection in Primates," in *Roots of Behavior,* ed. by Bliss, E. L. New York, Harper, 1962, pp. 157–166.

16. HERRICK, C. J. *Neurological Foundations of Animal Behavior.* New York, Holt, 1924.

17. LANDRETH, C. *Psychology of Early Childhood.* New York, Knopf, 1958, p. 173.

18. LINDSLEY, D. B. Electrical potentials of the brain in children and adults. *J. Genet. Psychol. 19*:285, 1938.

19. LINDSLEY, D. B. A longitudinal study of the occipital alpha rhythm in normal children: Frequency and amplitude standards. *J. Genet. Psychol. 55*:197, 1939.

20. LINDSLEY, D. B. Heart and brain potentials of human fetuses in utero. *Amer. J. Psychol. 55*:412, 1942.

21. LINDSLEY, D. B. "Psychophysiology and Motivation," in *Current Theory and Research in Motivation,* Vol. V, ed. by Jones, M. R. Lincoln, Neb., University of Nebraska Press, 1957, pp. 44–106.

22. LINDSLEY, D. B. "Attention, Consciousness, Sleep and Wakefulness," in *Handbook of Physiology,* Vol. 3, ed. by Field, J. Washington, D.C., American Physiological Society, 1960, pp. 1553–1593.

23. MARQUIS, D. P. Can conditioned responses be established in the newborn infant? *J. Genet. Psychol. 39*:479, 1931.

24. MARQUIS, D. P. Learning in the neonate: The modification of behavior under three feeding schedules. *J. Exp. Psychol. 29*:263, 1941.

25. MONNIER, M., and WILLI, H. Die integrative Tätigkeit des Nervensystems beim normalen Säugling und beim bulbo-spinalen Anencephalen (Rautenhirn-wesen). *Ann. Paediat. 169*:289, 1947.

26. MONNIER, M., and WILLI, H. Die integrative Tätigkeit des Nervensystems beim meso-rhombo-spinalen Anencephalus: II. Anatomischer Teil. *Mschr. Psychiat. Neurol. 126*:259, 1953.

27. MOWBRAY, J. B., and CADELL, T. E. Early behavior patterns in rhesus monkeys. *J. Comp. Physiol. Psychol. 55*:350, 1962.

28. NEWBERY, H. Studies of fetal behavior. IV. The measurement of three types of fetal activity. *J. Comp. Psychol. 32*:521, 1941.

29. PURPURA, D. P. Analysis of axodendritic synaptic organizations in immature cerebral cortex. *Ann. N. Y. Acad. Sci. 94*:604, 1961.

30. RIBBLE, M. A. "Infantile Experience in Relation to Personality Development," in *Personality and the Behavior Disorders,* Vol. 2, ed. by Hunt, J. M. New York, Ronald, 1944, pp. 621–651. Page references for quotations are given in parentheses after the passage cited.

31. SECHENOV, I. M. "Reflexes of the Brain," in *Sechenov: Selected Works,* English tr. ed. by Subov, A. A. Leningrad-Moscow, State Publishing House for Biological and Medical Literature, 1935, pp. 263–336. Page references for quotations are given in parentheses after the passage cited.

32. SMITH, J. R. The electroencephalogram during normal infancy and childhood: I. Rhythmic activities present in the neonate and their subsequent development. *J. Genet. Psychol. 53*:431, 1938.

33. SMITH, J. R. The "occipital" and "pre-central" alpha rhythms during the first two years. *J. Psychol. 7*:223, 1939.

34. SMITH, J. R. The frequency growth of the human alpha rhythms during normal infancy and childhood. *J. Psychol. 11*:177, 1941.

35. STRATTON, G. M. "Excitement as an Undifferentiated Emotion," in *Feelings and Emotions: The Wittenberg Symposium*. Worcester, Mass., Clark University Press, 1928, pp. 215–221.

36. THOMPSON, W. R. "Early Environment—Its Importance for Later Behavior," in *Psychopathology of Childhood*, ed. by Hoch, P. H., and Zubin, J. New York, Grune & Stratton, 1955, pp. 120–139.

37. THOMPSON, W. R., and HERON, W. The effects of early restriction on activity in dogs. *J. Comp. Physiol. Psychol. 47*:77, 1954.

38. VOELLER, K., PAPPAS, G. D., and PURPURA, D. P. Electron microscope study of development of cat superficial neocortex. *Exp. Neurol. 7*:107, 1963.

39. WUNDT, R. H., LINDSLEY, D. F., ADEY, W. R., and FOX, S. S. Self-maintained visual stimulation in monkeys after long-term visual deprivation. *Science 139*: 336, 1963.

40. WENGER, M. A. An investigation of conditioned responses in human infants. *Univ. Iowa Studies Child Welfare 12*:7, 1936.

JAMES OLDS, PH.D.
M. E. OLDS, PH.D.
University of Michigan

The Mechanisms of Voluntary Behavior

W E MAY CONSIDER THE BASIC DIRECTIONS of behavior as toward some
things and away from others, and the basic modes of behavior as voluntary and reflex. The two directions may be designated as (1) homing reactions and (2) aversive reactions. In the present paper, the object of a homing reaction will be called a positive reinforcement; the object of an aversive reaction will be called a negative reinforcement. The modes of behavior may be identified as (1) reflex behaviors, which depend heavily on just-prior (i.e., antecedent) stimulation, and (2) so-called voluntary behaviors, which depend heavily on expected but not yet applied (i.e., reinforcing) stimulation. Following Skinner,[32] we shall call the second category operant and thereby include behaviors which look voluntary even though we cannot determine the volitions of the animals involved. Operant behavior is conceived by Skinner as being emitted randomly by the animal at first, its eventual "frequency" being determined by the application of positive or negative reinforcements after particular instances of behavioral emission. Positive reinforcements augment the later frequency of behavioral emissions, and negative reinforcements have the opposite effect.

Because the reflex behavior elicited by a positive reinforcement is often imperceptible, we will treat positive reinforcement behavior as if it were entirely operant. Because negative reinforcements elicit a larger variety of perceptible reflex consequences, we find it desirable to divide aversive behaviors into four categories, two of which represent reflex behavior and two operant behavior. On the reflex side, there are (1) the level of general activity, which is raised during negative reinforcement stimulation, and (2) the more or less specific aversive or withdrawal reflexes which occur at

Supported by grants from the U.S. Public Health Service, the National Science Foundation, the Atomic Energy Commission, and the Wallace Laboratories.

the same time. In the operant group, there are (1) the elimination from the behavior repertoire of responses followed by the negative reinforcement and (2) the selection for repetition of those behaviors followed by termination of the aversive stimulus.

The present discussion will focus on the operant behaviors: (1) the positive reinforcement behaviors and (2) the operant component of the negative reinforcement behaviors. The contentions will be that the mechanisms of operant behavior differ from those of reflex behavior and that a common mechanism may exist for the operant behaviors controlled by negative reinforcement and those controlled by positive reinforcement.

REINFORCEMENT EXPERIMENTS WITH ELECTRICAL STIMULATION OF THE BRAIN (ESB)

The present discussion depends heavily on the discovery that positive reinforcement may be produced by applying electrical stimulation to a large number of brain structures[20] and the earlier, cognate observation that negative reinforcement also may be produced by ESB.[7] In the present studies we have used mainly macroelectrodes for producing regions of electrical excitation or electrolytic lesion. The limits of the method and the particular data herein presented require brief explanation. Since we are certain that we can never maintain the effective electrical field entirely within a functionally homogeneous neural structure, we always stimulate or destroy parts of a variety of functional systems and can therefore expect only the gross analysis which such a method permits. Furthermore, at least three of the studies to be mentioned are still in progress, and the results therefore reveal only directions, not conclusive facts.

This discussion may be divided on the basis of a series of questions which have arisen sequentially: (1) In the wide system of neural structures that appears to be involved in positive reinforcement by ESB, is there a field and a focus? Is there a broad set of minor entities all projecting to some constricted central area that is essential to these positive reinforcement mechanisms? (2) Are the topographic relations of structures yielding positive reinforcement and structures yielding negative reinforcement meaningful? Are the areas clearly separated? If an overlap exists, does it lie on the topographic boundary between the two systems? (3) What are the functional relations between the substrates of positive and negative reinforcement? Do they inhibit one another? Does one mechanism in any way depend on the other? (4) What are the chemical sensitivities of these systems? Are they controlled mainly by excitatory or inhibitory neurohumors? Need one assume spontaneous activity in these mechanisms? (5) What are the pathways relating these mechanisms to behavior? Do these mechanisms control motor systems? If so, are these pyramidal or extrapyramidal motor systems?

POINTS OF REFERENCE IN THE BRAIN

To establish certain points of reference in the brain which will be repeatedly used, we shall review briefly the basic organization of the central nervous system. In most mammals, the following structures are found in front of the spinal cord: (1) the medulla oblongata or hindbrain; (2) the mesencephalon or midbrain; (3) the cerebellum, growing like a mushroom planted on the upper boundary between medulla and midbrain; (4) the diencephalon or between-brain, in front of the midbrain; and (5) the

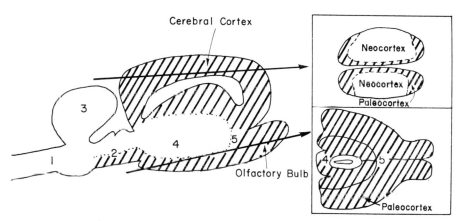

FIG. 1. Schematic picture of brain of rat showing (1) medulla, (2) midbrain, (3) cerebellum, (4) diencephalon, and (5) telencephalon. Olfactory-chemoreceptor systems shaded.

telencephalon or endbrain, located in front of the diencephalon and consisting of the olfactory bulbs, some subcortical nuclei, and the cerebral cortex (Fig. 1). The cerebral cortex may be conceived of as blossoming above the boundary between diencephalon and olfactory bulbs in a fashion similar to that in which the cerebellum sits above the medulla and midbrain. The cerebral cortex, however, is far larger and hence spreads out over many of the previously mentioned structures, covering many of them completely. In the cortex, the main distinction is between the borders which compose the paleocortex (also called the rhinencephalon) and the larger (in-between) parts of the cortex which compose the neocortex. The paleocortex is phylogenetically related to the olfactory system and may still be involved in processing information derived from special receptors for detecting chemical changes in the blood and cerebrospinal fluid. The rest of the cortex is related mainly to somesthetic, auditory, visual, and motor systems. In the diencephalon, a similar distinction exists between the lower (ventral) part, the hypothalamus, which is heavily related to olfaction and chemoreception and to the paleocortex, and the upper (dorsal) part, the thalamus, which is similarly related to the neocortex. The same dorsal-ventral relation has also been shown recently in the midbrain, where in dorsal areas (in lemniscal and reticular activating and tectal systems) somesthetic, auditory, and visual information is processed, but where in ventral areas are fibers from olfactory, rhinencephalic, and hypothalamic systems.[19]

FOCUS OF POSITIVE REINFORCEMENT

Positive reinforcement produced by ESB was originally discovered with electrodes in a boundary region between the rhinencephalic systems of the telencephalon and the related systems of the hypothalamus.[20] It was first thought to be mainly related to the rhinencephalon; experiments showed the positive reinforcing effects could be produced by stimulating some parts of almost all rhinencephalic structures.[15] In rats, it became clear that more than half the electrodes placed at random in the rhinencephalon would yield positive reinforcement.

Later studies showed that the focus of the phenomenon, if maximum responding for a minimum stimulation could be taken to indicate a focus, was not in the rhinencephalon but rather in the hypothalamus or midbrain or possibly even farther back.[15, 22, 25] In fact, a pair of long tubes extend from the olfactory bulbs and rhinencephalon and pass along the two outer edges of the hypothalamus into similar (ventrolateral) areas of the midbrain. Whereas much of the area between these tubes and surrounding them seems to yield positive reinforcement when electrical stimulation is applied, the tubes themselves are the focus of the phenomenon, if maximal effects from minimal stimulation is used as the criterion (Fig. 2).

A number of differences have been observed between the positive reinforcement produced by hypothalamic stimulation and that produced by rhinencephalic stimulation. Since these differences appear to be important for an understanding of both the internal organization of the positive reinforcement mechanism and its integration into larger cerebral systems, we shall list and discuss four of them here. (1) In experiments in which each response was followed by one ESB reward, response rates were far higher with hypothalamic than with rhinencephalic stimulation. Animals pressed a lever 10,000 times an hour to stimulate the lateral hypothalamus but only about 500 times an hour under the same conditions to stimulate the septal or amygdaloid areas, both of which are subdivisions of the rhinencephalon.[22] (2) The animals' "appetites" for lateral hypothalamic stimulation often seemed relatively insatiable, whereas definite satiation was usually reached in experiments with rhinencephalic stimulation. Animals stimulated themselves several thousand times in the septal area and then stopped for the day; animals stimulated themselves hour after hour in the lateral hypothalamus, maintaining a rate of several thousand responses per hour and stopping only when a state of physical exhaustion appeared.[17] (3) The reward produced by hypothalamic stimulation seemed to be accompanied by a heightened level of general activity,[28] whereas the reward produced by

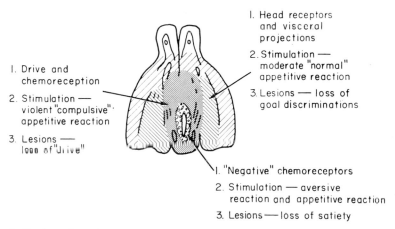

1. Drive and chemoreception

2. Stimulation — violent "compulsive" appetitive reaction

3. Lesions — loss of "drive"

1. Head receptors and visceral projections

2. Stimulation — moderate "normal" appetitive reaction

3. Lesions — loss of goal discriminations

1. "Negative" chemoreceptors

2. Stimulation — aversive reaction and appetitive reaction

3. Lesions — loss of satiety

FIG. 2. Horizontal section through central telencephalon of rat. At top are olfactory bulbs; at bottom on the sides is pyriform cortex, next is amygdala, and darkly shaded area in middle is hypothalamus. Hypothalamic nuclei are represented by stippled area at center (surrounding ventricle); negative reinforcement, but also positive reinforcement, is produced by stimulation here. Lateral hypothalamic tubes are represented by darker shading; this is region of medial forebrain bundle; purely positive reinforcement is produced by stimulation here.

rhinencephalic stimulation seemed often to be accompanied by more or less complete inhibition of general activity.[16] (4) Whereas there was some apparent relief of pain or anxiety by reward produced by rhinencephalic stimulation, such effects were not evident in some hypothalamic areas.[3]

These differences are possibly best understood when compared with earlier data from lesion and ablation experiments which seemed to indicate that the effects of rewarding stimuli in the environment are lost if rhinencephalic parts of the system are ablated,[10, 30] whereas control of the system by chemical or hormonal states or by visceral conditions of drive or satiety are lost if diencephalic parts of the system are destroyed.[33, 34] Such data might suggest that the rewarding stimuli from the environment are projected first to rhinencephalic systems of the telencephalon and from there have influence over a hypothalamic focal point. However, they also seem to indicate that states of organic need have influence mainly through the hypothalamus, a phenomenon which might suggest that the hypothalamus, like the rhinencephalon, represents an input stage to the system and that both influences are combined at a third focal point not yet localized.

In an effort to establish relative priority of different parts of the system, a series of ablation experiments has been carried out to determine whether one "ESB reinforcement" area is essential to production of the phenomenon by stimulation at another, similar area. The first such series of experiments was performed by Ward,[37, 38] who showed that extensive ablations in various rhinencephalic structures did not adversely affect the positive reinforcement produced by stimulation in the ventrolateral regions of the tegmentum (Fig. 3).

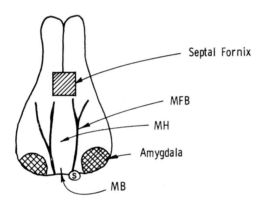

FIG. 3. Horizontal section showing experiments of Ward.[37, 38] Lesions were placed either in amygdala or in area of septal fornix. Positive reinforcement behavior was produced by stimulation (S) near boundary between diencephalon and midbrain; lesions were without important effect. Abbreviations: MFB, medial forebrain bundle; MH, midhypothalamus; MB, mammillary bodies.

We have recently extended this work by experiments intended to discover whether anterior or posterior parts of the lateral hypothalamic tube could be considered essential to the process of positive reinforcement by electrical stimulation. Because the tube runs in anterior-posterior direction all the way from the telencephalon through the diencephalon, and because stimulation of all parts appears to yield strong positive reinforcement, one cannot help wondering whether the effects of the stimulation have access to mechanisms of behavioral control through the outflow directed toward the rhinencephalon and cortex or through the outflow directed toward the midbrain.

Electrodes were implanted in anterior and posterior parts of the tube, and their position was verified by means of tests for positive reinforcement. In cases in which these tests indicated that both electrodes were in the positive reinforcement system, large electrolytic lesions were made at either the anterior or the posterior point. In each case, a companion lesion was made at a site directly opposite that point in the contralateral side of the brain.

Lesions of approximately 1 mm. were made by passing 2 ma. of direct current for 15 seconds.[11] The electrode site used for making the lesions was no longer tested. Tests were made for positive reinforcement from stimulation

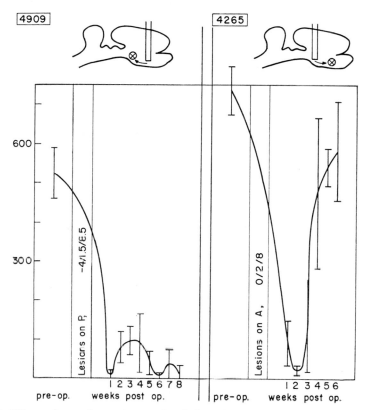

FIG. 4. Effects of anterior and posterior lesions in lateral hypothalamic tubes. Each vertical line represents range of five scores taken over period of 1 week. Each score indicates response output for 8-minute period on positive reinforcement behavior test. In case on left, stimulation in anterior part of lateral tube served as reinforcement, and lesions were placed in posterior part (lesions on P); in case on right, stimulation was in posterior part, and lesions were placed in anterior part (lesions on A). In both cases, positive reinforcement behavior dropped sharply for 2 to 3 weeks. In case of anterior lesions, however, recovery occurred in fourth week; behavior at upper limits of the range was of same order of magnitude as that preceding lesions. For further analysis (Fig. 5) each animal was given a score representing peak of his fourth-week range as percentage of low point of his range during week before lesion.

of the remaining (anterior or posterior) electrode site; in all animals, positive reinforcement behavior did not appear for 2 or 3 weeks (Fig. 4). In 7 of 10 animals with anterior lesions, however, performance recovered, so that positive reinforcement behavior rates were of the same order of magnitude as those before the lesions existed. In none of the animals with posterior lesions was there similar recovery (Figs. 4 and 5).

Results appear to indicate that the phenomenon has a posterior focus; at least, the posterior part of the lateral hypothalamic tube is essential in some way to the positive reinforcement produced by stimulation of the anterior part. The anterior part, however, is not similarly essential. One may specu-

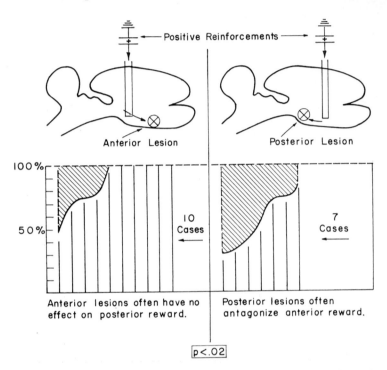

Fig. 5. Positive reinforcement performance after anterior and posterior lesions were produced in lateral hypothalamic tube. In each case, best performance 4 weeks after production of lesion is given as percentage of worst performance the week before lesion existed (Fig. 4). Difference between the two groups is significant when tested by Mann-Whitney U test.[31]

late that information must make its exit in the direction of the midbrain before the positive reinforcement phenomenon can appear.

AMBIVALENT REACTIONS AND SIGN INVERSIONS

The next series of studies was prompted by the observation, originally made by Roberts,[28] that electrical stimulation in many areas of the brain yielded both positive and negative reinforcement. Observations of this kind have now been made by many others.[2, 5, 12, 18] We believe that these ambivalent reactions divide into two types; one is that in which the animal responds by turning the stimulus on sparingly in an experiment in which stimulation depends on a response. In other experiments, however, in which the animal is stimulated repeatedly by the apparatus, the stimulus appears to be "on" too much of the time, and the animal responds by turning it off part of the time.[12] One may conclude that in extremely small doses the stimulus is positively reinforcing, but in excessive doses it is negatively reinforcing.

However, the more common kind of ambivalent reaction we have observed[25] is more conflicted. The animal responds by turning the stimulus on even though each application of the stimulus appears to be aversive. The stimulus appears to be both rewarding and aversive in the same durations and at the same current levels. The animal will often press the pedal regularly in the positive reinforcement experiment but at the same time will struggle to escape from the field. If the animal succeeds in escaping from the test chamber, it will not return voluntarily. But if it is brought back and forced to remain in the test chamber, it will maintain a substantial rate of positive reinforcement behavior (still struggling to escape). Such behavior we have labeled "mixed reactions." It is difficult to avoid the conclusion that two normally incompatible patterns are being elicited simultaneously.

Since two mutually inhibitory systems were apparently stimulated simultaneously in these experiments, we assumed that the electrodes in these cases must be placed on a boundary between locations yielding positive and those yielding negative reinforcement. To test this assumption, we studied the topographic distribution in the diencephalon of points yielding positive reinforcement, negative reinforcement, ambivalent responses, and neutral reactions.[25] Test points were spaced 1 mm. apart from rat to rat, and each point was tested first for positive reinforcement and second for negative reinforcement produced by electrical stimulation.

Results did not agree with our expectation that ambivalent reactions would be elicited by stimulation in boundary regions between areas yielding purely positive and those yielding purely negative reinforcement; they showed instead an unexpected and considerably more interesting distribution. As expected, certain points yielded purely positive or purely negative reinforcement; other points yielded ambivalent reactions, but these did not fall on a topographic boundary.

To understand the organization discovered, one may imagine a black box with two large, multichanneled cables entering from different sides, along with innumerable smaller cables. The black box appears to be mainly a point of juncture between the two very large cable systems. Stimulating one of the cables yields purely positive reinforcement; stimulating the other cable yields purely negative reinforcement; and stimulating the black box itself yields mixed responses. The black box represents the midline system of the hypothalamic nuclei, all of which appear to be involved. The two large cables represent the medial forebrain bundle and the periventricular system of fibers.[1] The medial forebrain bundle system is the lateral hypothalamic tube already mentioned. Its gross anatomic structure suggests that its main function is to connect the hypothalamic nuclei with the telencephalon, but it may have an even more extensive range of connections. It is commonly conceived as a two-way system, but its main direction of conduction is probably from telencephalon toward hypothalamus. The periventricular system of fibers, sometimes called the dorsal longitudinal fasciculus of

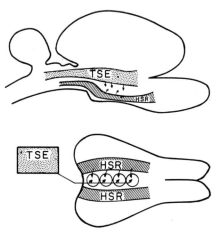

Fig. 6. Schematic sagittal and horizontal sections to show outcome of positive-negative reinforcement mapping study. Purely negative reinforcement behavior was produced by stimulation of periventricular system of fibers, here labeled TSE (for tegmentothalamic substrate of escape); purely positive reinforcement behavior was produced by stimulation of lateral hypothalamic tube, here labeled HSR (for hypothalamic substrate of reward). The nuclei (circled) into which both systems project yielded ambivalent, i.e., positive-negative, reactions.

Schütz, is mainly involved in relating the hypothalamic nuclei to the nonspecific systems of thalamus and midbrain. It too may be a two-way system, but its main direction of conduction is probably away from the hypothalamus toward the nonspecific systems. From the viewpoint of the present analysis, the hypothalamic nuclei might be thought to serve mainly as a way station for transfer of messages from the medial forebrain bundle to the periventricular system of fibers, or vice versa. In our experiments, stimulation of the medial forebrain bundle actually yielded purely positive reinforcement (Fig. 6); stimulation of the periventricular system of fibers yielded purely negative reinforcement; and stimulation of all medial hypothalamic junctional areas yielded mixed positive-negative effects.[25]

A striking difference between hypothalamus and thalamus demonstrated in these tests is incidental to the present discussion but deserves mention. Almost every electrode in the hypothalamus yielded positive reinforcement; i.e., the medial points yielded mixed positive-negative effects, and the lateral points yielded purely positive effects. In no instance, however, did hypothalamic points yield purely negative or neutral effects. In the thalamus, on the other hand, almost every electrode yielded some negative reinforcement. One cannot help wondering what is the evolutionary significance of a division in which thalamus seems more involved in aversive behavior and hypothalamus more involved in homing reactions. As for the impression that the whole hypothalamus seems to be involved in this kind of behavioral control, one may ask where the specific drive centers and the opposing autonomic centers of the hypothalamus appear in this analysis, if all the hypothalamus is shown to be a positive (or mixed positive-negative) reinforcement system. The answer is that this same hypothalamus, by other tests, yields drive and autonomic responses. But a common denominator of all these differentiated areas is their involvement in reinforcement of behavior, both positive and negative, but particularly positive.

INTERACTIONS

These studies have relevance to the apparent reversal of sign which occurs in the hypothalamic nuclei. Stimulation of the input yields reinforcement of one sign; stimulation of the output yields reinforcement of the other sign; and stimulation of the region that seems to contain the synapse between them yields a mixed effect. This anomalous sign inversion has led us in three directions: (1) to examine other data for similar inversions, (2) to imagine the neural matrix which would explain such an anatomic relation, and (3) to analyze the functional interaction between positive and negative reinforcement by ESB to discover the existing relation.

Possible sign inversions in other aspects of our data are not hard to find, although many of them are dubious because of the small number of cases studied, the small size of the tracts involved, and the consequent question whether stimulation of the tract or of the area through which it passes yields a given effect. The particular system involving a whole series of sign inversions is called alternately the Papez circuit[26] or the limbic system of MacLean.[13] The actual synaptic points need not be indicated for purposes of the present discussion; for those interested, we mention particularly the relay in the habenula, that in the mammillary body, and that between the dentate gyrus and the hippocampal gyrus (Fig. 7). The actual names are not important, but the structure of the system involved is. The Papez circuit might be conceived of in oversimplified fashion as involving four families of neurons, A, B, C, and D, each family located in a different area of the brain. Neurons of family A connect with B, B with C, C with D, and D with

A again to form a circuit. This has always been considered a circuit in which information could circulate, maintaining its form or character while being made available first to one and then another relevant system. If, as we now suspect, stimulation of A yields effects opposite to those caused by stimulation of B, and stimulation of B yields effects opposite to those for C, and so forth, then the idea of circulation of a simple message becomes unsatisfactory, and the possibility that inhibition rather than excitation occurs at these synapses becomes more likely. A wide variety of neuro-

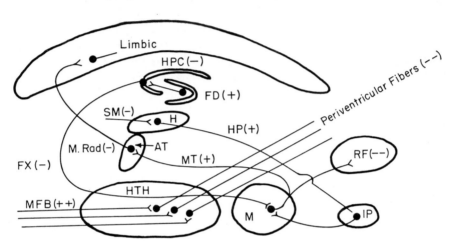

FIG. 7. Possible sign inversions in highly schematic picture of Papez-MacLean system as it might appear in sagittal section of brain of rat. Stimulation of fiber systems marked with plus signs is thought to yield positive reinforcement behavior; stimulation of those marked with minus signs is thought to yield negative reinforcement behavior. Abbreviations: Limbic, limbic cortex; HPC, hippocampus; FD, fascia dentata (dentate gyrus); SM, stria medullaris; H, habenula; HP, habenulo-interpeduncular tract; IP, interpeduncular nucleus; RF, reticular formation; M, mammillary bodies; HTH, hypothalamus; MFB, medial forebrain bundle; MT, mammillothalamic tract; AT, anterior thalamus; M. Rad, medial radiations to the cortex; FX, fornix.

inhibitory synaptic processes has been demonstrated in the last two decades.[8] It is perhaps congruous with our age that these should be explicitly incorporated into our theorizing about the functions of the gross anatomic pathways.

If indeed all synapses in a Papez circuit-like system were inhibitory, one might wonder how the system could function as a circuit at all, how it could get started, or for that matter, how it could yield any significant output. If A inhibited B, which was not operating anyway, then nothing would happen. If, however, B were spontaneously active, then A's activity on B could be effective. And if C, D, and A were also spontaneously active, then

A's activity on B could come full circle: A would inhibit B and this would release C, thereby inhibiting D and releasing A. The function of such a system might be unclear, but at least theoretically it would work. As for output, if each neuron acted only on its successor within such a circuit, there would be little hope of a wider range of consequences. We may, however, imagine that each member of the circuit has both extra- and intra-circuit efferents and afferents: The existence of an abundance of collaterals in the case of most neurons renders this possibility likely. If we grant spontaneous activity and a system of collaterals, such a circuit might well serve as a complicated system of interactions to mediate damping effects of positive and negative reinforcing mechanisms on each other.

We now turn our attention to more detailed analysis of the relation between the positive reinforcement induced by stimulation in the medial forebrain bundle and the negative reinforcement produced by stimulation in the periventricular fibers. Experiments intended to test for reciprocal inhibitory effects have led to the surprising discovery of antagonism in one direction but apparent synergism in the other[24] (Fig. 8).

Positive reinforcement behavior produced with electrical stimulation in the lateral hypothalamus was usually depressed or completely antagonized by a continuous, noncontingent application of stimulation in the periventricular escape system. This observed antagonism suggested possible inhibition of the positive reinforcement system by stimulation of the negative reinforcement system. We conjectured that an inhibitory synapse between periventricular fibers and medial forebrain bundle fibers might exist in one of the hypothalamic nuclei (e.g., the posterior nucleus of the hypothalamus). The main difficulty with this conjecture is that, on the basis of anatomic studies, the medial forebrain bundle appears to be primarily afferent and the periventricular system primarily efferent. It is difficult to see how the efferent could inhibit the afferent. Although relatively recent views[1] hold that both tracts are bidirectional, the relation is clearly not primarily one from periventricular system to medial forebrain bundle. Therefore some problem remains.

Negative reinforcement behavior produced with stimulation in the periventricular system was usually augmented by continuous application of stimulation in the lateral hypothalamic positive system.[24] This synergism suggested (1) that the positive reinforcing stimulus somehow augmented the negative reinforcing effects of the aversive stimulus, (2) that the positive reinforcing stimulus augmented the behavioral output involved in the escape behavior, or (3) that the positive reinforcing stimulus augmented the reinforcing effect of terminating the aversive stimulus. In any event, there was not the simple inhibition of the negative reinforcement behavior that might have been predicted by a simple reciprocal model.

A FINAL COMMON PATH?

We decided to examine the third possibility—that the positive reinforcing stimulus augmented the reinforcing effect which occurred when the negative stimulus was terminated. This led us to speculate that the basic motiva-

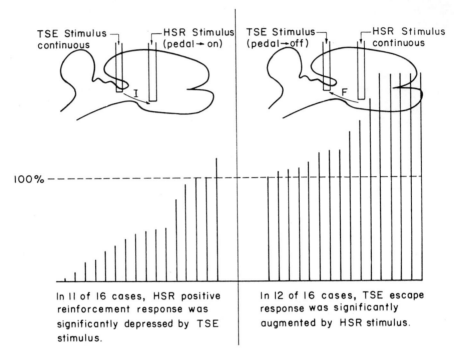

Fig. 8. The interaction experiment.[24] Two electrode pairs were implanted in each of 16 animals. One pair in tegmental substrate of escape (TSE) yielded purely negative reinforcement behavior; the other pair in hypothalamic substrate of reward (HSR) yielded purely positive reinforcement behavior. When a continuous train of TSE stimulation was introduced while positive reinforcement behavior resulting from HSR stimulation was underway, the behavior was significantly depressed. When, on the other hand, a continuous train of HSR stimulation was introduced while negative reinforcement behavior produced by TSE stimulation was underway, the behavior was significantly augmented. Thus an inhibitory relation (I) is hypothesized from TSE to HSR and a facilitory relation (F) from HSR to TSE.

tion for pedal-pressing in the negative reinforcement experiment might be not simple but complex. If the positive reinforcement mechanism of the medial forebrain bundle were made up of spontaneously active neurons inhibited by stimulation of the periventricular system, then cessation of the stimulus would result in a release phenomenon; i.e., a burst of activity would occur in the medial forebrain bundle system every time activity stopped in the periventricular system. Conceivably, therefore, a press of the pedal to terminate periventricular stimulation might be reinforced by the ensuing burst of activity in the positive system of the medial forebrain rather than directly by termination of activity in the negative system.

We do not contend that *all* aversive activity is controlled by the positive reinforcement system but only that this system possibly is involved in control of the organized or operant component of the aversive behavior, the component which seems directed toward stopping the ongoing negative stimulus by foresight rather than automatic means. In the case of a human subject, we should expect him to react strongly to a painful stimulus by withdrawing but to be guided in his voluntary behavior under enduring noxious stimulation by the "pleasant" feeling of relief rather than merely the cessation of pain. If the animal were really working for a release of activity in positive reinforcing substrates as well as, or instead of, for termination of activity in the negative ones, then, although the *actual* mechanism is still not obvious, it is conceivable that some mechanism might exist which would cause the animal to work even harder when a continuous electrical stimulus was applied to the positive substrates. This would explain the anomalous augmentation of escape behavior observed in the interaction experiment.

If operant behavior apparently motivated by termination of the negative stimulus were actually motivated by a burst of released activity in the positive substrate, then the operant aspect of this particular aversive behavior would be heavily dependent on the integrity of the positive mechanism for its maintenance. Lesions in the positive area might therefore attenuate or obliterate this aversive behavior. In the other direction, however, because of the inhibitory action from the negative substrate on the positive, there might even be augmentation of positive behavior after lesions had been produced in the negative substrate.

Experiments on this problem so far have been preliminary. In six animals we studied the effects of periventricular (escape) lesions on positive reinforcement; in another eight we studied the effects of lesions of the medial forebrain bundle (positive reinforcement) on negative reinforcement. Small bilateral electrolytic lesions were produced by means of electrodes previously tested for reinforcement; a second set of electrodes in the opposing system was used to test the effectiveness of the lesions. Results have been in the predicted direction (Fig. 9). In no single case did periventricular (escape) lesions produce a deficit in positive reinforcement behavior, whereas in two of six animals, the augmentation was great. On the other hand, in no case did lesions of the medial forebrain bundle (positive) produce appreciable augmentation of negative reinforcement behavior. In five of these eight animals, a major deficit in negative reinforcement behavior was observed; in three, escape behavior disappeared altogether. Although the numbers indicate only partial effects in some instances, the possibility remains that escape behavior is entirely dependent on the positive reinforcement mechanism, since the small electrolytic lesions might easily have

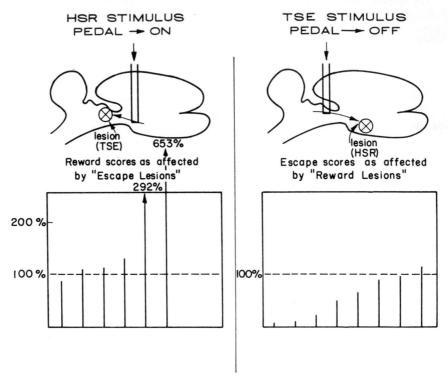

FIG. 9. Effects of lesions in areas producing positive and negative reinforcement on behavior produced by electrical stimulation in opposing area. Lesions in tegmental substrate of escape (TSE) did not depress positive reinforcement behavior; in fact, two animals showed augmentation. Lesions in hypothalamic substrate of reward (HSR) caused significant depression in negative reinforcement behavior.

missed the crucial area in certain cases; histologic verification of these lesions has not been accomplished as yet.

One must be cautious about interpreting such an outcome as a forceful validation of the instigating hypothesis, in this case the hypothesis that the operant escape behavior is positively reinforced only when positive reinforcement mechanisms are released from inhibition—the inhibition produced by the periventricular fibers. This is but one of a number of possible interpretations of the outcome and deserves no special attention because it happened to precede the experiment. Juxtaposing the observations of the previous interaction experiments and of the present lesion experiment, however, seems appropriate.

First, stimulation at the "reward" point caused an increment in the aversive behavior; second, lesions at the reward point caused a decrement in the aversive behavior. Therefore, it is difficult to imagine that neural activity emanating from this lateral hypothalamic reward point had any neutralizing effect on (any tendency to counteract) aversive behavior; on the contrary, it somehow appeared to abet and possibly to be essential to the aversiveness. Third, stimulation at the "escape" point, on the other hand, caused a decrement in the lateral hypothalamic reward behavior; and fourth, lesions at the escape point sometimes yielded an increment in reward behavior. Therefore, it seemed possible that neural activity emanating from this periventricular escape point had a tendency to counteract reward behavior, and it appeared possible that an inhibitory relation might exist.

INHIBITORY CHEMICAL CONTROLS

In the preceding sections we conjectured that a positive reinforcement mechanism in the lateral hypothalamus might be inhibited by stimulation in the periventricular system and that a release of the suppressed neural activity might occur on termination of the periventricular stimulation. Clearly this implies not a dormant system in the lateral hypothalamus but one that is spontaneously active. Perhaps a level of spontaneous neural activity might be temporarily suppressed by inhibitory input, to return suddenly to normal or even yield a supernormal burst upon termination of the inhibitory input. The activity might be analogous to that of the "off" fibers in the retinal ganglion.[9] Study of the effects of excitatory and inhibitory transmitter substances directly applied to the positive reinforcement substrate has shed some light on the problems of spontaneous activity and inhibitory control.[23]

Many attempts to stimulate the central nervous system by direct application of the supposed neurotransmitters, acetylcholine, epinephrine, and serotonin, failed in our laboratory after the volume of directly applied substances was reduced below that which permitted stimulation by means of saline alone. With these small volumes, however, stimulation was achieved by means of various substances which caused a depletion of ionic calcium in the interstitial fluid. Most neural fiber systems may be conceived of as prone to continuous spontaneous discharge were it not for the presence of ions which control activity, just as an atomic pile would be in continuous activity except for the rods which control the reaction. In the case of neural fibers, the "rods" which control activity are most often calcium ions; any momentary reduction in these results in a burst of activity similar to that which accompanies application of a depolarizing current.[4] A depletion of ionic calcium may be effected merely by use of a substance which unites with calcium to form a precipitate or to form a soluble complex. A wide variety of such substances has been used in our laboratory to stimulate the hypothalamus, including, in ascending order of efficacy as stimulators and of tendency to withdraw ionic calcium from the interstitial fluid, sodium phosphate, sodium citrate, sodium pyrophosphate, and sodium versenate (EDTA).

After completing these experiments with calcium-binding substances, we tried the neurohumors again for excitatory and inhibitory effects in the lateral hypothalamic (reward) substrate, mixing them with sub- and supra-threshold concentrations of sodium pyrophosphate. In these experiments, serotonin and epinephrine, the neurohumors found in extremely high concentrations in this area of brain,[36] counteracted strongly the excitation produced by high concentrations of pyrophosphate (Fig. 10). The supposedly neuro-inhibitory substance, gamma aminobutyric acid, had similar (but weaker) action. Acetylcholine did not have any remarkable capacity to counteract the effects of suprathreshold pyrophosphate or to augment the action of subthreshold concentrations. None of these chemicals had any excitatory power when mixed with subthreshold pyrophosphate injections or when mixed with saline or distilled water. The possibility that the main neurotransmitters in this area (serotonin and epinephrine) have inhibitory function must therefore be considered seriously.

Absence of any excitatory transmitters, however, has certainly not been demonstrated. Failure to stimulate or inhibit with acetylcholine suggested that possibly this substance was being counteracted effectively by cholinesterase. For this reason, the acetylcholine-like compound carbamylcholine, which resists cholinesterase, was tested. It produced effective chemical activation when applied to the lateral hypothalamus, whether mixed with subthreshold concentrations of pyrophosphate or merely with enough saline to make an isotonic solution (Fig. 10).

Results of these experiments, therefore, suggest (1) that the substances especially related to the hypothalamus possibly have inhibitory action but (2) that the area may also yield excitatory responses related to acetylcholine. We might suppose that this area of the hypothalamus, like the transcallosal system of Marrazzi and Hart,[14] is positively sensitive to cholinergic substances and negatively sensitive to the catecholamines. Because the amines are heavily distributed in this area, however, inhibitory input to the area may play a large part in its control. And because acetylcholine is perhaps

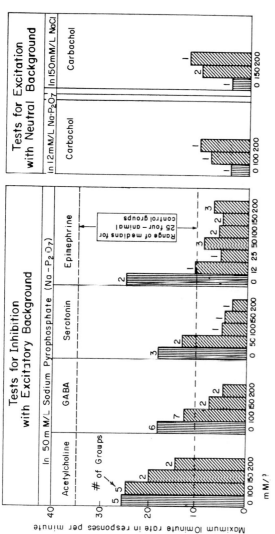

Fig. 10. Inhibitory effects of epinephrine, serotonin, and gamma aminobutyric acid (GABA) in experiments involving direct chemical stimulation; excitatory effects of carbachol. Chemical stimulation was effected by use of 50 mM. per liter of sodium pyrophosphate, 3-mμl. volume, pH 7.0. (All solutions were rendered equally hypertonic by addition of propanediol.) Chemical was applied directly to hypothalamic substrate of reward by implanted cannulae; one injection was applied after each lever response. The fastest 10-minute rate of positive reinforcement behavior in a 3-hour test period was assigned as score to each animal. Each animal was tested on one solution only. Animals were tested in groups of four; number of groups tested with each solution is indicated by numbers above columns. Neurohumors were added to stimulating solutions in quantities shown below each column. Osmolarity was maintained by subtracting propanediol. Heights of columns represent median scores for all animals tested on a given solution. Epinephrine proved to be most efficacious, having significant inhibitory effects in concentrations of 25 mM. per liter; serotonin was second, and GABA third. Carbachol had excitatory effects in concentrations of 100 mM. per liter.

more moderately present in this area according to histochemical maps, excitatory input may be less important.[6]

STRUCTURE AND FUNCTION OF A REINFORCEMENT MECHANISM

In the final section of this paper we shall treat briefly the main point at issue: What is the nature of the reinforcement of behavior? How does neural activity in these areas act upon mechanisms of behavioral control to augment the frequency of some behaviors and deplete the frequency of others? We do not yet have an answer. The approach we have taken to a solution is to delimit a system of cerebral areas within which such control seems to take place and to give careful analysis to the neuroanatomic structure of the system and the physiologic nature of the various synaptic, spontaneous, and propagated processes involved.

The areas so far mentioned have been (1) the paleocortical positive reinforcement areas, (2) the hypothalamic nuclei of mixed results, (3) the periventricular system of purely aversive effects, and (4) the lateral hypothalamic (medial forebrain bundle) area of purely positive effects. The hypothalamic nuclei themselves appear to deserve first place in a search for an integrative mechanism. Possibly the lateral hypothalamic area comes second. If these two areas are matched, two possible modes of integration might be involved. In the hypothalamus there appears to be a system of extremely small neurons embedded among cellular bodies of longer-axoned neurons and among their fibers.

The Hypothalamic Nuclei

All the main differentiated nuclei of the hypothalamus are grouped along the midline; there are several of them, and they have widely diversified functions, being related to such matters as eating, water control, and thermal regulation, as well as to various autonomic adjustments.[1] From the viewpoint of the present analysis, however, these nuclei are relatively homogeneous, all yielding mixed positive-negative reinforcing effects when electrical stimulation is applied and all representing anatomic points for synapse between elements of the periventricular system and elements of the medial forebrain bundle system. We shall label them collectively as the midhypothalamus and distinguish them from the lateral hypothalamic tube, to which we have referred previously. The lateral tube contains mainly the medial forebrain bundle and, as may be seen, we have used the terms lateral hypothalamus and medial forebrain bundle more or less interchangeably.

The question of polarity becomes prominent when we consider the synapses between medial forebrain bundle and periventricular fibers in the midhypothalamus. Which direction do they conduct? In discussing direction, we shall use the term "downstream" to refer to the paleocortex–medial forebrain bundle–midhypothalamus–periventricular direction, and "upstream" to refer to the opposite direction. Older anatomic views suggested that the medial forebrain bundle and periventricular systems were mainly downstream channels, and although newer views[1] make it clear that both systems are bidirectional, it still seems likely that the main direction of conduction in this family of systems is downstream.

Our data, however, suggest only one relation, an upstream, inhibitory one, and we have found no evidence so far to suggest any downstream relation at all. Our observations suggest the presence of a set of inhibitory synapses with the periventricular (escape) system fibers as afferents and the medial forebrain bundle (positive) system units as efferents. Thus far, however, we have been able to determine no function for the downstream relations which must also exist between these two systems.

One possibility is that the medial forebrain bundle contains three kinds of elements: (1) fibers coming down from paleocortical sensory analysers (possibly from the rhinencephalic positive system), (2) fibers representing paleocortical and extrapyramidal motor systems (possibly determining the gross direction of behavior), and (3) small interstitial elements with both origin and termination in the hypothalamus itself (possibly making up the lateral hypothalamic positive system). If we assume that the main fiber system originating in the midhypothalamus is the periventricular escape system and that it is a downstream system, then conceivably it might have elements of class 1 as its own inhibitory afferents and elements of class 3 as elements inhibited by its recursive collaterals; i.e., the rhinencephalic reward system would inhibit the periventricular escape system in the midhypothalamus, and the periventricular system would inhibit the lateral hypothalamic reward system in the same midhypothalamic nuclei but at a different system of synapses. The stimulation of periventricular fibers then would activate these fibers antidromically, thereby exciting the collateral system and bringing inhibition to bear on the lateral hypothalamic positive mechanism.

One implication of this suggested arrangement is that a stimulation of the *rhinencephalic* positive mechanism would cause inhibition of the periventricular escape system rather than augmentation, as was observed in the case of *lateral hypothalamic* positive stimulation. To test this possibility, we repeated the interaction experiment which we mentioned earlier: Negative reinforcement behavior was produced with electrical stimulation in the periventricular system as the aversive stimulus. Tests were made for modification of this behavior by continuous application of stimulation in the positive system. But this time, in Routtenberg's[29] experiment in our laboratory, the rhinencephalic rather than the lateral hypothalamic positive system was used for application of the positive stimulus. And in this case, the behavior produced by the aversive stimulus was not augmented but was, in fact, suppressed or inhibited. This makes the difference between the two positive systems so prominent that it cannot be ignored, whatever the eventual interpretation may be. Stimulation in the earlier discovered, milder paleocortical area yields positive reinforcement combined with suppression or inhibition of aversive behavior; stimulation in the more active focus in the lateral hypothalamus yields positive reinforcement combined with augmentation of aversive behavior.

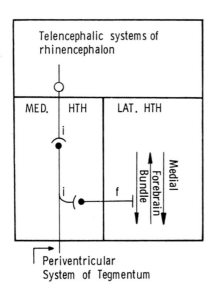

FIG. 11. Schematic diagram showing supposed synapses in hypothetical hypothalamus. Positive reinforcement mechanisms of rhinencephalon are supposed, in this diagram, to have inhibitory synapses on periventricular neurons which originate in medial hypothalamus. Recursive collaterals of periventricular neurons are supposed to inhibit interneurons, which have positive reinforcing effects in lateral hypothalamus.

   The possibility exists, therefore, that one positive system (A) inhibits the periventricular system of fibers (B), and the other positive system (C) is inhibited by it (B). If this should be so, then the paleocortical positive points (A) may conceivably have their effect on the final common path of operant behavior reinforcement (C)—the lateral hypothalamic positive system—by virtue of this double inhibitory relation. By inhibiting B, A would cause a release of activity in C, and the latter event would account for reinforcement of the ongoing behavioral patterns. We consider it possible that, if these events occur, they all take place in the midhypothalamus, the A–B synapses being the main downstream synapses occupying this area and the B–C synapses having a status involving recursive collaterals of the B (periventricular) fibers (Fig. 11).

THE LATERAL HYPOTHALAMIC TUBE

Possibly the most striking anatomic feature of the lateral hypothalamic area, the tube which seems to be the core of the positive reinforcement system, is that it contains or is bounded by a large number of downward coursing (motor?) fiber systems, both myelinated and unmyelinated. In the medial forebrain bundle itself are long-axoned fibers from the olfactory area, others from the rhinencephalic cortical systems, and still others from the extrapyramidal motor systems. Bounding the medial forebrain bundle dorsally is a second large component of the extrapyramidal motor system, the component which runs through the subthalamus; bounding the medial forebrain bundle laterally is the remainder of the forebrain's motor outflow, the pyramidal tract itself.[1]

Several other facts should be mentioned to give perspective to the following discussion. (1) The medial forebrain bundle system actually runs from its cortical origin all the way to, and possibly through, the ventrolateral midbrain; however, it is not always accorded the same name through its whole extent, and it is not clear that any single fiber group runs the whole length of the system. Phylogenetically, this system derives from a tract connecting the olfactory bulb to the tegmentum; at some stages in phylogenic development it seems almost as if the olfactory bulb and this long connecting tube constitute the whole of the forebrain.[1] (2) Along its whole course are interposed small granule cells and short-axoned cells as well as the longer-fibered cells.[27] (3) Juxtaposed to this system along its telencephalic course is a system of nuclei much like, and continuous with, the hypothalamic nuclei which bound it medially in the hypothalamus. This whole system of nuclei yields the mixed positive-negative reinforcing effects which are characteristic of the hypothalamic nuclei when electrical stimulation is applied. (4) Arising more or less on the other boundary of this tube (the dorsolateral boundary in the diencephalon) is the system of extrapyramidal nuclei, nuclei which often yield neutral effects on electrical stimulation.[1]

In forming hypotheses about the relation of structure and function in this long tubular and double-bounded system, two preliminary assumptions seem reasonable: (1) that the general function is relatively homogeneous over the whole extent, with the posterior pole having priority only in the fact that much of the output of the system must pass through this point; and (2) that the paleocortical and extrapyramidal systems under discussion have an organization not totally unlike that of the neocortex, with some neurons specialized to reception of incoming sensory input, as in layer 4 of the neocortex, and others specialized to determination of behavioral direction, as in layer 5.

If fibers from both kinds of neurons travel in the medial forebrain bundle, those of the first type (sensory) may possibly enter the midline nuclei to form the inhibitory afferents of the periventricular fibers which compose the connection previously mentioned. The motor fibers, on the other hand, might continue to travel downstream to influence the basic directions of behavior (Fig. 12).

If this kind of organization exists, interaction between the short, or granular, neurons of the medial forebrain bundle and the longer-axoned motor fibers might be at the crux of the reinforcement process, provided the me-

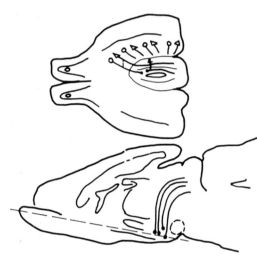

FIG. 12. Sections of brain showing approximate organization of medial forebrain bundle, periventricular systems of fibers, and granule cells in telencephalon, medial and lateral hypothalamus, and dorsal tegmentum. Paleocortical sensory (round) and motor (triangular) neurons are suggested as passing through area of medial forebrain bundle. The hypothesis is indicated that paleocortical sensory fibers innervate periventricular system through medial hypothalamic nuclei but that motor fibers bypass medial nuclei on their way farther downstream in lateral tubular area. Periventricular fibers as seen in sagittal (lower) section originate in medial hypothalamus and rise dorsally into midthalamus and tegmentum. In horizontal section, these same fibers are imagined as having recursive collaterals, which innervate granule cells of medial forebrain bundle. Although these granule cells are here indicated as being entirely in lateral hypothalamic tube, they might conceivably be better imagined as crossing over from medial to lateral hypothalamus, as indicated in more schematic Figure 11.

dial forebrain bundle motor fibers were the entities to be reinforced and the smaller units of the medial forebrain bundle did the reinforcing. Even so, it is, of course, still not apparent why the *axons* of the reinforced fibers would mingle with the granule and short-fibered reinforcing neurons. Since the extrapyramidal motor system has sources of origin of its fibers distributed repeatedly along the axis of this system, nearby small fibers at each level might possibly act upon the somadendritic systems of the extrapyramidal neurons originating at that level (Fig. 13). But it is also feasible that the spontaneous activity of the longer-fibered neurons might be controlled at the axonal level. The notion of activity triggered at the initial segment or at the first node of Ranvier in axonal systems is currently gaining wide acceptance.[8] This idea should encourage serious consideration of the possibility that activity might be generated or modulated at other axonal stages.

REINFORCEMENT OF UNIT RESPONSES

If the medial forebrain motor fibers are reinforced, and if the medial forebrain smaller units perform the reinforcing, then these relations should

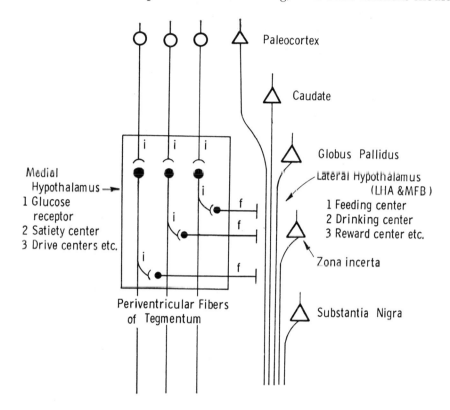

FIG. 13. Schematic diagram indicating possible origin of motor systems of medial forebrain bundle in paleocortical and extrapyramidal structures, as well as possible identity of medial hypothalamic drive systems with ambivalent medial nuclei, and lateral hypothalamic consummatory centers with lateral hypothalamic positive reinforcing tube.

be demonstrable at the elementary, or unit, level. Furthermore, whether or not these speculations have any validity, experiments in which various responses of the brain are used as operant responses to be reinforced by stimulation in the lateral hypothalamic tube are appealing because they suggest a possible method of separating the voluntary from the involuntary systems of the brain. At least they should allow classification of cerebral responses (and possibly also cerebral systems) into those that are and those that are not controllable by methods of operant reinforcement. Such a classification would certainly contribute toward an understanding of the reinforcement process.

The experiments involving reinforcement of a neural response must be viewed with caution because the phenomenon is not readily duplicable at this stage. Furthermore, from a technical point of view, because of the infrequent occurrence of a reinforceable neural response, it is difficult to demonstrate that any augmentation in response frequency yielded by operant conditioning is a consequence of positive reinforcement rather than direct elicitation or toning up of the brain by background stimulation.

Nevertheless, careful efforts to overcome these problems suggest that a method for further work is indicated. Animals for long-term study were prepared with a positive reinforcing macroelectrode in the lateral hypothalamic tube. Behavioral tests were performed to validate the location of the electrode. Then the animals were anesthetized with pentobarbital and placed in a stereotaxic instrument. Exploration was then made by means of two microelectrodes glued together, with a separation of about 100μ at the tips.[35] These were inserted into a trephine opening and advanced through the brain by means of a micromanipulator. The potential differences between each microelectrode and a large ground electrode in the brain were amplified by a two-channel capacitor coupled system and displayed on a twin-beam cathode ray oscilloscope; differences were also recorded on a two-channel magnetic tape recorder. Movement of the microelectrodes was continued until neural responses of constant form and repetitive character were observed on both channels. These were considered to be extracellular responses of single brain cells if (1) they were negative with respect to ground, (2) the duration was in the 0.3- to 1.5-millisecond range, (3) their amplitude was of 300 μv. or more, and (4) their amplitude was changed radically by micromovement of the electrode tips (in the 30- to 100-μ range).

When two different unit responses of this sort were indicated by recordings from the two proximal microelectrodes, reinforcement tests were made while the animal was still anesthetized.

Two kinds of control tests were used to differentiate between elicited and reinforcing effects: (1) Cessation of responding as well as responding itself were reinforced at a given point in the brain, so that the animal was reinforced first for stopping the unit response and later for making the response. (2) While one unit response was reinforced, the second, recorded from a nearby point, served as a control. If a unit response rate increased during the appropriate period and if no similar augmentation occurred during the period of reinforcement for stopping or during the period of reinforcement of the other unit response, then the unit response rate in question was considered to be under operant control. In several instances, two neighboring unit responses have been shown by this method to be under operant control. Many animals failed this test. In two cases there was satisfactory histologic localization of the brain points yielding such operantly controlled unit responding. In one animal, the two microelectrodes were in fibers of the limbic system; in the other, they were in fibers of the extrapyramidal system. In both instances, each of the two neighboring unit responses appeared to be under operant control (Fig. 14). In these as well as many previous experiments in our laboratory, electrodes were often histologically determined to be in neocortex. For these cases, failure of control of unit responses by reinforcing methods seemed to be the rule.[21]

Although results are far from conclusive, it is conceivable that response frequencies of paleocortical and extrapyramidal motor fibers are determined somehow by electrical stimulation in the lateral hypothalamic tube, provided that this stimulation is correlated in a reinforcing fashion relative to the neural responses in question.

SUMMARY

This report is concerned with recent experiments on the hypothalamic and paleocortical mechanisms which control the basic directions of behavior: toward some things and away from others. A common denominator of the otherwise diversified drive systems of the hypothalamus and the older cortical areas is that their electrical stimulation yields positive or negative reinforcement or sometimes a complex positive-negative effect. The anatomic and physiologic relations among the areas yielding the three effects suggest a chain or circuit of fibers with alternate members yielding positive or negative reinforcement on stimulation, and with the nuclei which contain synapses between fibers giving positive and negative effects yielding the complex positive-negative reinforcing effects. Two hypotheses become attractive on the basis of these observations: (1) that negative mechanisms of reinforcement have control over instrumental behavior by means of their inhibitory power over spontaneous mechanisms of positive reinforcement, and (2) that a complex circuit of mutually inhibitory relations mediates a systematic interaction of positive and negative reinforcement mechanisms, yielding perhaps an automatic computer-like system for the making of hedonistic calculi.

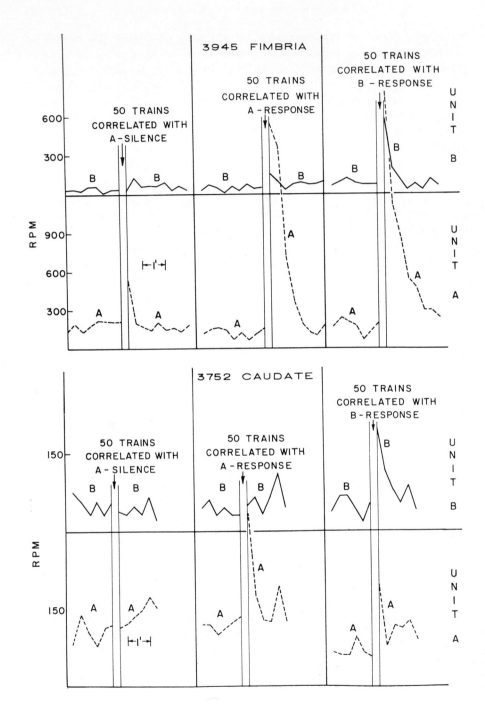

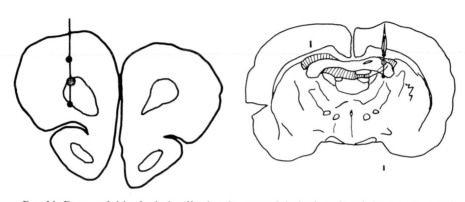

3752　　　　　　　　3945

FIG. 14. Data and histologic localization in successful single-unit reinforcement experiments. Each curve indicates changing response rate of single unit response in responses per minute (RPM). Points were determined every 20 seconds and were converted to RPM by multiplying response output by 3. Each gap indicates an interposed period during which fifty 0.5-second trains of 50-μa. (60-cycle sine wave) stimulation were applied by way of lateral hypothalamic (positive reinforcing) electrodes. Curves for B and A units were generated simultaneously. Three procedures were applied successively: (1) reinforcement for stopping A response, (2) reinforcement for making A response, and (3) reinforcement for making B response. In each case, a 3-minute recording was made before and after a series of stimulations. Electrical stimulation always had its first major effect in augmenting a unit response rate when it was used to reinforce the animal for making that response. In other words, the *first* large increment in each response rate appeared during the time the stimulus was correlated (as reinforcement) with that response. The 3-minute period immediately after a reinforcement period regularly contained a decline from a high level of responding that resembled a normal operant extinction curve. The previously reinforced A response showed a second large increment when the B response was reinforced. This may be interpreted as "superstitious" behavior;[32] a similar effect has been observed in our laboratory when two skeletal operants were used.

REFERENCES

1. ARIËNS KAPPERS, C. U., HUBER, G. C., and CROSBY, E. C. *The Comparative Anatomy of the Nervous System of Vertebrates, Including Man.* New York, Macmillan, 1936.
2. BOWER, G. H., and MILLER, N. E. Rewarding and punishing effects from stimulating the same place in the rat's brain. *J. Comp. Physiol. Psychol. 51*:669, 1958.
3. BRADY, J. V. "Motivational-Emotional Factors and Intracranial Self-Stimulation," in *Electrical Stimulation of the Brain: An Interdisciplinary Survey of Neuro-behavioral Integrative Systems,* ed. by Sheer, D. E. Austin, Tex., University of Texas Press, 1961, pp. 413–430.
4. BRINK, F. Role of calcium ions in neural processes. *Pharmacol. Rev. 6*:243, 1954.
5. BROWN, G. W., and COHEN, B. D. Avoidance and approach learning motivated by stimulation of identical hypothalamic loci. *Amer. J. Physiol. 197*:153, 1959.
6. BURGEN, A. S. V., and MACINTOSH, F. C. "The Physiological Significance of Acetylcholine," in *Neurochemistry: The Chemical Dynamics of Brain and Nerve,* ed. by Elliott, K. A. C. Springfield, Ill., Thomas, 1955, pp. 311–389.
7. DELGADO, J. M. R., ROBERTS, W. W., and MILLER, N. E. Learning motivated by electrical stimulation of brain. *Amer. J. Physiol. 179*:587, 1954.
8. ECCLES, J. C. The mechanism of synaptic transmission. *Ergebn. Physiol. 51*:299, 1961.
9. HARTLINE, H. K., WAGNER, H. G., and RATCLIFF, F. Inhibition in the eye of *Limulus. J. Gen. Physiol. 39*:651, 1956.
10. KLUEVER, H., and BUCY, P. C. Preliminary analysis of functions of the temporal lobes in monkeys. *Arch. Neurol. Psychiat. 42*:979, 1939.
11. KRIEG, W. J. S. Accurate placement of minute lesions in the brain of the albino rat. *Quart. Bull. Northwest. Med. Sch. 20*:199, 1946.
12. LILLY, J. C. "Learning Motivated by Subcortical Stimulation: The Start and Stop Patterns of Behavior," in *Reticular Formation of the Brain,* ed. by Jasper, H. H. Boston, Little, Brown, 1958, pp. 705–727.
13. MACLEAN, P. D. Psychosomatic disease and the "visceral brain": Recent developments bearing on Papez theory of emotion. *Psychosom. Med. 11*:338, 1949.
14. MARRAZZI, A. S., and HART, E. R. "An Electrophysiological Analysis of Drugs Useful in Psychotic States," in *Tranquilizing Drugs,* ed. by Himwich, H. E. Washington, D.C., American Association for the Advancement of Science, 1957, pp. 9–21.
15. OLDS, J. A preliminary mapping of electrical reinforcing effects in the rat brain. *J. Comp. Physiol. Psychol. 49*:281, 1956.
16. OLDS, J. Runway and maze behavior controlled by basomedial forebrain stimulation in the rat. *J. Comp. Physiol. Psychol. 49*:507, 1956.
17. OLDS, J. Satiation effects in self-stimulation of the brain. *J. Comp. Physiol. Psychol. 51*:675, 1958.
18. OLDS, J. Approach-avoidance dissociations in rat brain. *Amer. J. Physiol. 199*:965, 1960.

19. OLDS, J. Hypothalamic substrates of reward. *Physiol. Rev. 42*:554, 1962.

20. OLDS, J., and MILNER, P. Positive reinforcement produced by electrical stimulation of septal area and other regions of rat brain. *J. Comp. Physiol. Psychol. 47*:419, 1954.

21. OLDS, J., and OLDS, M. E. "Interference and Learning in Paleocortical Systems," in *Brain Mechanisms and Learning: A Symposium,* ed. by Delafresnaye, J. F. Oxford, Blackwell, 1961, pp. 153–187.

22. OLDS, J., TRAVIS, R. P., and SCHWING, R. C. Topographic organization of hypothalamic self-stimulation functions. *J. Comp. Physiol. Psychol. 53*:23, 1960.

23. OLDS, J., YUWILER, A. H., OLDS, M. E., and YUN, C. GABA microinjection in hypothalamic reward centers. *Fed. Proc. 21*:353, 1962. (Abst.)

24. OLDS, M. E., and OLDS, J. Approach-escape interactions in rat brain. *Amer. J. Physiol. 203*:803, 1962.

25. OLDS, M. E., and OLDS, J. Approach-avoidance analysis of rat diencephalon. *J. Comp. Neurol.* In press.

26. PAPEZ, J. W. A proposed mechanism of emotion. *Arch Neurol. & Psychiat. 38*:725, 1937.

27. PAPEZ, J. W. Visceral brain: Its component parts and their connections *J. Nerv. Ment. Dis. 126*:40, 1958.

28. ROBERTS, W. W. Both rewarding and punishing effects from stimulation of posterior hypothalamus of cat with same electrode at same intensity. *J. Comp. Physiol. Psychol. 51*:400, 1958.

29. ROUTTENBERG, A., and OLDS, J. The attenuation of response to an aversive brain stimulus by concurrent rewarding septal stimulation. *Fed. Proc. 22*:515, 1963. (Abst.)

30. SCHREINER, L., and KLING, A. Behavioral changes following rhinencephalic injury in cat. *J. Neurophysiol. 16*:643, 1953.

31. SIEGEL, S. *Nonparametric Statistics: For the Behavioral Sciences,* New York, McGraw-Hill, 1956.

32. SKINNER, B. F. *The Behavior of Organisms: An Experimental Analysis.* New York, Appleton, 1938.

33. TEITELBAUM, P. Sensory control of hypothalamic hyperphagia. *J. Comp. Physiol. Psychol. 48*:156, 1955.

34. TEITELBAUM, P., and STELLAR, E. Recovery from the failure to eat produced by hypothalamic lesions. *Science 120*:894, 1954.

35. VERZEANO, M., and NEGISHI, K. Neuronal activity in cortical and thalamic networks: A study with multiple microelectrodes. *J. Gen. Physiol. 43* (6) *Suppl:* 177, 1960.

36. VOGT, M. Sympathomimetic amines in the central nervous system: Normal distribution and changes produced by drugs. *Brit. Med. Bull. 13*:166, 1957.

37. WARD, H. P. Basal tegmental self-stimulation after septal ablation in rats. *Arch. Neurol. 3*:158, 1960.

38. WARD, H. P. Tegmental self-stimulation after amygdaloid ablation: Results of studies in rats. *Arch. Neurol. 4*:657, 1961.

M. P. BISHOP, PH.D.

S. THOMAS ELDER, PH.D.

ROBERT G. HEATH, M.D., D.M.SC.

Tulane University School of Medicine

Attempted Control of Operant Behavior in Man with Intracranial Self-Stimulation

PROGRESS IN UNDERSTANDING RELATIONS between brain function and behavior has been facilitated by continued development in experimental technics and methodology. Intracranial self-stimulation (ICSS) serves as a recent case in point. Although widely used for only a few years, this technic has earned a prominent position among available research tools for experimental analysis of brain-behavior relations. Thus far, reported self-stimulation work under controlled laboratory conditions has been confined to subhuman species. The present report describes exploratory efforts in the extension of such studies to man.

Olds and Milner[28] first demonstrated in 1954 that rats will press a lever in order to obtain brief electrical stimulation to various subcortical regions by way of permanently implanted electrodes. It is this set of operations which has become known as intracranial self-stimulation. Subsequently, this phenomenon has been reproduced many times in rats,[1, 4, 5, 8, 9, 15–18, 22, 24, 25, 28–30, 32, 33, 35, 37, 39, 41, 42] and its species generality has been extended in controlled studies to include the goldfish,[6] bottlenose dolphin,[20] guinea pig,[40] cat,[7, 23, 34] dog,[36] and monkey.[7, 10, 11]

Beginning in 1952, reports have appeared describing subjective experiences of an apparently pleasurable nature accompanying electrical stimulation of subcortical structures in human subjects.[12-14, 31] Only two previous attempts have been made, however, to apply self-stimulation technics to human subjects. Sem-Jacobsen and Torkildsen[31] have reported self-stimulation in human patients, and Heath describes elsewhere in this symposium (p. 222) an innovation in which a patient with depth electrodes wore a

55

portable transistorized stimulator on his belt while pursuing daily activities over an extended period of time.

The report of Sem-Jacobsen and Torkildsen indicates that patients with implanted electrodes stimulated deep structures by means of a button switch which continued to deliver the stimulus as long as the button was depressed. A bipolar, biphasic pulse, with a duration of 1 millisecond, a repetition rate of 60 pulse pairs per second, and current varying from 60 to 500μa., was reportedly used for most patients. Unfortunately, little was reported regarding the characteristics or properties of the self-stimulation behavior of these patients. It was noted that the duration of the stimulus train (controlled by the patient) varied from almost constant stimulation in some regions of the brain to brief intermittent stimulation in others, and these regions were reportedly consistent from one subject to another. These brain areas were not identified, however, and no information was given regarding the possible interaction of brain site and current level in the production of such effects. It was further reported that the most rapid rate of pressing and releasing the button was obtained when a patient's "level of consciousness was altered" so that he "appeared unresponsive," and it was noted that patients would sometimes stimulate themselves into a grand mal seizure. These investigators maintain that the positive response described in studies with animals can be subdivided, on the basis of their experience with human subjects, into "ease and relaxation," a "feeling of joy with smiling," and a sexually toned "great satisfaction." They note, however, with respect to self-stimulation by their subjects that "the motives seem complex, ranging from curiosity and funny tickling to relaxation and pleasure." As will be seen, our own work thus far with intracranial self-stimulation in human subjects raises some even more serious questions regarding the motivation underlying this behavior in neuropsychiatric patients and underscores the importance of stringent control over variables other than the electrical stimulus itself which may influence a subject's behavior.

The purpose of the present study, as initially formulated, was simply to determine whether a lever-pressing response could be adequately conditioned and later modified in human subjects through the application of brief electrical stimuli to a number of subcortical regions where such stimulation is known to have reinforcing properties in subhuman organisms. Two subjects were available for this exploratory work, each with a large number of implanted electrodes in various cortical and subcortical structures. On the basis of animal work, we assumed that demonstrating genuine self-stimulation behavior would be a simple matter of finding the right combination of electrode site and current level. Once a stable pattern of lever-pressing behavior had been established, it was further assumed that this could be readily modified, as is the case with animals, by changes in stimulus intensity or in schedules of reinforcement, to provide the sort of quantitative data in support of human intracranial self-stimulation that has been repeatedly obtained in studies with animals. Unexpected developments, however, necessitated gross changes in the proposed methodology. The revised procedures and results obtained with them will be outlined after our subjects and apparatus have been described.

MATERIALS AND METHOD

SUBJECTS

Early in July 1962 depth electrodes were implanted in the two subjects used in the study. Details of implantation, types of electrodes, and connecting plugs are given elsewhere in this symposium (p. 84).

Subject No. B-12 is a 35-year-old divorced white man with a diagnosis of chronic schizophrenic reaction, catatonic type. Duration of illness probably extends back to childhood, as he was reportedly extremely withdrawn, had no friends, and quit school in the sixth grade to stay home with his mother. Florid psychotic symptoms developed in 1945, when he was 18 years old. First psychiatric hospitalization occurred 4 years later after attempted suicide. He has been continuously hospitalized for the past 9 years and has failed to respond to electroshock therapy, insulin coma therapy, group psychotherapy, and various tranquilizing drugs. At times in the past, he has displayed pronounced paranoid symptoms, but during the past few years catatonic features have been predominant. He is autistic and withdrawn, has extreme difficulty in communicating, rarely speaks unless spoken to, and seldom responds with more than one or two words. He admits having almost constant auditory hallucinations. During the period of our work with him, he has been relatively rational and unusually cooperative, considering the extent of his illness.

Subject No. B-10, a 25-year-old single white man, reportedly showed no evidence of abnormal behavior until the age of 18 years. He did poorly in school and quit after the sixth grade. He spent 4 months in military service, receiving a medical discharge after a suicidal gesture. He has a history of 13 psychiatric hospitalizations from 1957 to 1962, most of these occasioned by rage reactions and uncontrolled behavior. An original diagnosis of schizophrenic reaction, simple type, was changed in 1959 to schizophrenic reaction, paranoid type. However, electroencephalographic evidence of temporal lobe abnormality was obtained in 1961, and the patient has since been regarded as having psychomotor epilepsy with possible underlying schizophrenia. His psychomotor episodes are frequently triggered by frustration or perceived rejection. They are characterized by initial increasing anger with hostile verbalization, followed by apparent loss of contact with the environment and a glazed, wide-eyed stare. He then may alternate between expressions of rage and extreme fearfulness and trembling. He is amnesic for these episodes but frequently has a vague recollection of having killed someone, usually his parents, after these seizures. He has experienced only two severe episodes of this type since implantation of depth electrodes 4 months ago and has usually been in high spirits. In our work with him, however, he proved a difficult subject, with frequent demanding or sullen behavior and almost no patience or tolerance for frustration.

APPARATUS

Apparatus consisted of a complex of stimulating, recording, and programming equipment, together with a large lever and microswitch hand button and a two-unit intercom system. The subject was seated in a small, electrically shielded, semisoundproof room with the lever, hand button, and intercom unit on a table before him. A speaker beneath the table delivered continuous masking noise. All other apparatus was situated outside this room. A one-way vision window allowed observation of the subject. Lights were dimmed in the control room so that the subject could not see the experimenters, and special shielding was devised to eliminate visual cues associated with flashing lights from the control panels and relays.

Stimulation equipment included two Grass S-4 stimulators with stimulus isolation units as well as a locally constructed stimulator which delivers a fixed biphasic rectangular wave form with pulse duration of 0.5 millisecond and fixed repetition rate of 100 cps. The latter device (the T.A. stimulator*), is equipped with a stepping switch arrangement similar to that previously described by Stein and Ray[39] and by Stein,[37] which allows successive increases or decreases in delivered current with repeated lever presses through a series of 21 steps, which may be preset to the levels desired. The unit has a jack connector, which also permits use of an external stimulator through the stepping switch system. With the latter feature not in operation, the unit functions like any other stimulator except that frequency and pulse duration are fixed.

A stimulus-monitoring device, the Model B Stimulus-Monitor[2, 3] permitted simultaneous monitoring of both current and voltage. Aside from providing a constant check on stimulation received by the subject, this device has the advantage of complete safety to the subject, regardless of component failure.

Automatic recording of lever-pressing performance was achieved by

---

* Manufactured to the authors' specifications by Technical Associates of New Orleans.

means of Gerbrands cumulative recorder with a chart speed of 30 cm. per hour. Each lever press by the subject moves the pen up one notch (four responses per millimeter). With maximal excursion at roughly 500 responses,

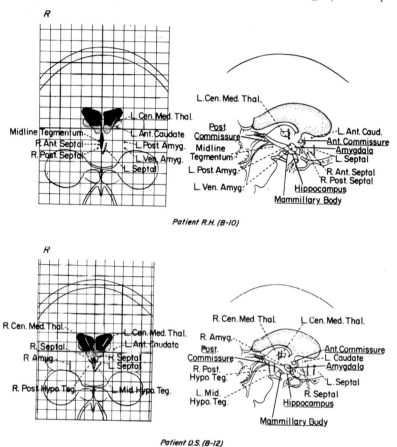

FIG. 1. Location of electrodes used to deliver stimulation in this study. Regular silver ball electrodes are shown as solid black circles; multiple electrodes indicated are miniature stainless steel arrays, each containing six electrodes 2 mm. apart. These are numbered 1 through 6 from bottom to top. Thus, reference in text to electrode left septal SS 2-4 indicates bipolar stimulation between this pair, 4 mm. apart, on the stainless steel array in the left septal area.

the pen automatically resets to zero and continues. The resulting saw-tooth record provides clear visual presentation of the subject's rate of responding during an experimental session and of any changes in response pattern which may occur spontaneously or as a function of changes in experimental variables introduced by the experimenter.

A Varian G-10 recording potentiometer was used with the T.A. stepping stimulator in exploratory work with self-determined reward thresholds in one patient. Details of this technic and instrumentation have been described by Stein and Ray[39] and Stein.[38]

Diagrams of subcortical electrodes through which stimulation was delivered in our work with each of the subjects are presented in Figure 1. Electrode placement shown in these diagrams was taken directly from final postoperative roentgenograms. Semiautomated operation of equipment was provided through use of an assembly of Foringer control panels. A partial view of the control room and equipment is shown in Figure 2. Figure 3 shows subject B-12 engaged in lever-pressing.

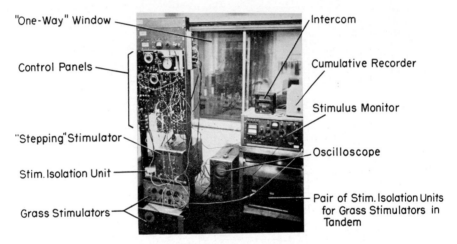

FIG. 2. Control room apparatus.

PROCEDURE

Because of the exploratory nature of this work and the necessary modifications in procedure as the experiments progressed, only general statements regarding technic and methods will be presented here. More detailed descriptions of procedure for technics that have yielded reportable data will be given in chronologic fashion in conjunction with the appropriate observations.

STIMULUS PARAMETERS. For most of the work reported here, the stimulating wave form was a monophasic rectangular pulse 0.2 millisecond in duration delivered at 100 pulses per second for a stimulus train of 0.5 second. Unless otherwise specified, these parameters apply to all reported data. This stimulus was provided by a single Grass S-4 stimulator and delivered through a Grass 4A stimulus isolation unit and the stimulus monitor to the subject. At the outset, a pair of Grass stimulators was coupled to provide biphasic rectangular pulses of 1 millisecond each, with a repetition rate of

100 pulse pairs per second. This system proved impractical for our purposes because it required independent control of "up" and "down" current amplitude. It was replaced by the T.A. stimulator, which produces biphasic rectangular pulses of 0.5 millisecond each, at 100 pulse pairs per second, with externally timed stimulus trains ranging from 0.15 to 0.5 second. Maximal current output with the T.A. stimulator was found to be insufficient for work with septal and caudate placements, and the single Grass S-4 system was introduced for almost all later work.

All these wave forms are considered to be noninjurious to brain tissue

Fig. 3. Subject No. B-12 pressing lever for brain stimulation. View through one-way vision window.

with brief intermittent stimulation such as was used in this study.[19] The monophasic rectangular wave form with parameters as previously described is a commonly used stimulus in animal self-stimulation studies and thus has the additional advantage of permitting direct comparison of our data with some of the data obtained from subhuman species.

Both the lever and the hand button, when pressed by the subject, delivered a brief stimulus with train duration automatically controlled. Thus, with the train setting at 0.5 second, the subject received a stimulus of this duration whether he merely tapped the switch or depressed it for more than 0.5 second. In the latter case, he had to release the switch and press again to receive another stimulus.

CONDUCT OF EXPERIMENTAL SESSIONS. The schedule for self-stimulation work with the subjects was irregular and influenced by other commitments of both the patients and experimenters. In general, we tried to allow at least 1 day between sessions for a given subject. Sessions varied in length up to a maximum of about 6 hours, with a break for lunch and other short breaks. Subject No. B-12, the schizophrenic patient, was extremely cooperative and worked for hours without complaint or apparent discomfort. Subject No. B-10, the epileptic patient, was generally much less cooperative. Besides frequent sullen and demanding behavior, he feigned adverse reactions to the stimulation (even on occasion with the current turned off). Few usable data were collected from him. Because this patient was intellectually intact, we had hoped he could provide verbal description of any "pleasurable" sensations accompanying self-stimulation. He became increasingly uncooperative and unreliable, however, and we terminated work with him after seven sessions, focusing our efforts on the remaining subject.

During sessions the subject was seated alone in the experimental room, as shown in Figure 3. He was unable to see or hear anything outside the room but could communicate with the experimenters, if he wished, through the intercom system. Instructions to him were delivered verbally over the intercom or by means of special tone signals. No external cues were available to him by which he might detect changes in experimental conditions introduced by the experimenters, such as alteration of stimulus intensity or shift of the current-delivering circuit from the lever to the hand button or vice versa. It was necessary, however, to enter his room in order to change from one pair of stimulating electrodes to another.

For some procedures, frequent contact with the subject through the intercom system was necessary; for others, he would work alone for as long as 3 hours with no contact whatever. In either case, extreme care was taken not to influence the behavior being studied by any means other than manipulation of experimental variables.

INITIAL ATTEMPT TO ESTABLISH LEVER-PRESSING BEHAVIOR AND MODIFY IT THROUGH CHANGES IN STIMULUS INTENSITY OR SCHEDULES OF REINFORCEMENT

An ideal means of demonstrating reinforcing properties of intracranial stimulation in man would be to condition a lever-pressing response, just as this would be done in work with animals, by the usual shaping technic, i.e., by reinforcing orientation or movement toward the lever with delivery of brief stimulation to the brain and then successively requiring more direct approaches to the lever for such reinforcement until the subject eventually presses the lever and begins self-stimulation. With an active animal and good electrode placement, this procedure can frequently be accomplished in only a few minutes. Several considerations, however, militated against our attempting this with our first human subjects. We had no guides regarding effective current level, with our stimulus parameters, in human subjects. In addition, the schizophrenic subject, No. B-12, was catatonic and might have sat for hours without making a movement that could be reinforced. In the case of the other easily irritated and unpredictable subject, externally de-livered stimulation, coming without warning, might have frightened or an-gered him. It was thus decided to forego the conditioning procedure and to use other technics for establishing self-stimulation with these subjects.

The initial procedure used was aimed toward rapid exploration of several subcortical structures and electrode combinations within these structures. With a selected pair of electrodes connected through the lever to the stimu-lation circuit, the subject was instructed to respond to a tone signal by pressing the lever. If he felt nothing or a neutral sensation, he was to press three more times; if he felt "bad," he was to press only once or twice; if he felt "good," he was to press repeatedly until he wished to stop. Each series began with zero current and was followed by small increases in current with each tone signal. This was continued as long as the subject indicated by his three responses that the stimuli were either not perceived or neutral, until a level was reached which produced either continued responding beyond three lever presses or less than three responses, signifying an aversive effect. Self-stimulation responding, when it occurred, was allowed to continue and was automatically recorded. After a stable base-line response record was obtained, any or all of the following changes were successively introduced: (1) gradual increase or decrease of stimulus intensity, (2) switching the cur-rent off entirely, and (3) shifting from the continuous-reinforcement (CRF) schedule (stimulation with every response) to a fixed-ratio (FR) schedule, in which stimulation was delivered only with every fifth lever press, or tenth, or at any ratio set by the experimenters.

Abundant self-stimulation data are available from animal studies to dem-onstrate that each of these changes in stimulus conditions produces charac-teristic alterations in the pattern of responding. Moreover, the effects of such changes upon response patterns are consistent from one animal species to another.[27] Human subjects performing a simple response for more con-ventional rewards, e.g., trinkets and pennies,[21] show the same characteristic changes in response pattern as do animals, following changes in magnitude of reward, shift to a fixed-ratio schedule, or withholding of the reinforcing agent. There would seem, then, to be ample grounds for generalizing that such changes, introduced while a human subject is pressing a lever for brain stimulation, should produce definite alterations in mode of responding. Production of such changes would provide sound evidence for the reinforcing or rewarding properties of the intracranial stimulation.

We had no difficulty whatever in obtaining self-stimulation behavior. This appeared, in fact, with the first pair of electrodes tested (left septal SS 1-6 in Subject No. B-10) and recurred repeatedly with stimulation in several subcortical structures in both subjects. Modification of the response pattern, however, through changes in stimulus conditions as previously described, was by no means as simple. Figure 4 compares sample lever-pressing response records for each of our patients with records illustrating the lever-pressing behavior of a typical animal working for intracranial self-stimulation.

In the animal records reduction of stimulus current produces a distinct slowing of response rate, with immediate recovery of the original rate when the initial current level is reinstated. A shift from continuous reinforcement (stimulation with each lever press) to the fixed-ratio (in this case FR-3) schedule of reinforcement effects an initial drop in rate with notable pauses between periods of responding and then a gradual adjustment to the new condition. When the current is turned off, the animal quickly stops responding. The rapidity of this extinction process appears to be a special characteristic of operant behavior for intracranial stimulation as contrasted to more conventional rewards, such as food.[16, 28, 32] These, then, are the sorts of changes in manner of responding which we should expect to find in human subjects if the intracranial stimulation is indeed rewarding or reinforcing. The human records in Figure 4 are characteristic of most such data obtained from our subjects. No appreciable change in response rate occurred with either current changes or shifts to fixed-ratio schedules. Even more disturbing, when the current was turned off, both subjects continued to press the lever at essentially the same rate until the experiment was terminated by the experimenter after hundreds of unrewarded responses.

These observations are puzzling, especially since we had taken extra precautions against creating any extraneous rewards for lever-pressing (e.g., verbal reinforcers, approving head nods) with these subjects. As work with each electrode pair was begun, verbal instructions for response to the tone were repeated, and these concluded with, "If it feels good, press until you want to stop." A sign on the wall immediately in front of the subject also conveyed the instructions and concluded with these same words. On occasion, after long periods of continuous responding for zero current, the subjects were asked why they were pressing the lever (or the hand button, as the case might be). The schizophrenic patient (No. B-12) would invariably state that it felt "good"; the epileptic subject (No. B-10) would say that he was trying to cooperate with us, that he assumed we must want him to press it, since he had been placed there. Despite fairly forceful reminders in his

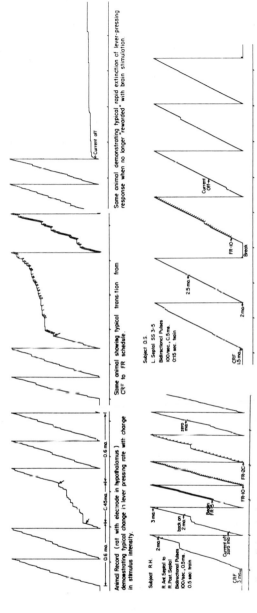

Animal Record (rat with electrode in hypothalamus) demonstrating typical change in lever pressing rate with change in stimulus intensity.

Same animal showing typical transition from CRF to FR schedule.

Same animal demonstrating typical rapid extinction of lever-pressing response when no longer "rewarded" with brain stimulation.

Human subject records showing continuous responding but no rate change following current or schedule changes and no evidence of extinction.

FIG. 4. Comparative animal and human response records.

case of the actual instructions, the same behavior recurred repeatedly, and the same sort of explanation was invariably given.

The most reasonable interpretation of records such as these is that the continued lever-pressing behavior was established or, at any rate, maintained by means of some reinforcement other than the intracranial stimulation. Certainly, they would seem to provide dubious evidence of genuinely rewarding effects of such stimulation in these instances. On the other hand, no other human data of this sort are available for comparison, and it must be remembered that these are neuropsychiatric patients rather than normal persons. In any case, the evidence of continued responding in the absence of apparent reward serves to underscore the need for strict controls in brain stimulation work with human subjects.

STUDY OF DIFFERENTIAL RESPONDING FOR DIFFERENT INTENSITIES OF STIMULATION

As noted earlier, our technic for initial exploration of electrode sites was to use a tone signal with successive increases in current and instructions to the subject to press his lever three times if, upon pressing, he felt either nothing or a neutral sensation, less than three times if he felt "bad," and until he wished to stop if he felt "good." As a first approach to other procedures which might elucidate intracranial self-stimulation behavior in human subjects, this admittedly crude technic was simply standardized in such a way as to provide reliable data concerning rewarding or aversive properties of the various subcortical structures.

The following method was used for this work. Available electrode pairs in a given area of the brain were informally explored as before, and a promising pair was selected. A current level which produced continued responding was determined. In all areas except the amygdala, which was studied first, the subject was then allowed to continue self-stimulation for a period of about 15 minutes, so that thresholds might become stabilized. The rewarding current level was again informally checked several times against zero current and adjusted, if necessary. Current was then increased gradually above the reward level with successive tone signals in order to reveal any level which produced indication of an aversive effect (less than three lever presses). This level, when found, was further checked against the previously established reward level and against zero current. Precise stimulator voltage dial settings for the selected current levels were recorded, and at this point the controlled experimental series was begun.

Instructions to the subject were as before, except that if the stimulus felt "good," he was to continue pressing either until he wished to stop or until he was told to stop by the experimenter. With successive tone cues, the three selected current levels were made available to the subject on a random basis for as many as 60 trials, 20 at each current level. (Order of presentation was derived from a table of random numbers.) An arbitrary limit of 10 responses to a given tone cue was set, the experimenter always terminating responding at this point. Number of lever presses was recorded for each trial.

To date, this procedure has been used only with Subject No. B-12. Summarized raw data for the five areas thus far studied in this patient are presented in Tables 1, 2, and 3. Stimulus parameters (other than intensity) were identical for all areas, i.e., monophasic rectangular pulses of 0.2 millisecond delivered at 100 pulses per second with a stimulus train of 0.5 second.

As noted earlier, no warm-up period of self-stimulation was used preceding experimental work in the amygdala, the first area studied with this

TABLE 1. DIFFERENTIAL SELF-STIMULATION FOR THREE
LEVELS OF CURRENT IN AMYGDALA[a]

Number of lever presses					
Series I			Series II[b]		
0 ma.	0.15 ma.	0.4 ma.	0 ma.	0.4 ma.	0.8 ma.
3	10	2	3	10	2
3	10	2	6	10	2
3	10	2	3	10	2
10	10	2	4	10	2
3	5	2	3	10	2
3	10	2	3	10	2
3	10	2	3	10	2
3	4	2	3	10	
3	3	2	3	10	
4		6		10	
10		10		10	
3		6			

[a] Subject instructed to press lever in response to a tone signal as follows: If he felt nothing or if the stimulus felt neither "good" nor "bad," he was to press three times; if the stimulus felt "bad," he was to press less than three times; if it felt "good," he was to continue responding until he wished to stop or was stopped by examiner. (Responding was arbitrarily terminated by examiner after 10 lever presses.)

Presentation of the three current levels was on a random basis. Above data are summarized in chronologic order for each current level.

Stimulus parameters: Monophasic rectangular pulses of 0.2-millisecond duration delivered at 100 pulses per second. Train duration: 0.5 second.

[b] Series II began about 5 minutes after completion of series I, following further exploration of current levels during this interval.

TABLE 2. DIFFERENTIAL SELF-STIMULATION FOR THREE
LEVELS OF CURRENT IN SEPTAL AREA AND
IN CAUDATE NUCLEUS[a]

Number of lever presses					
Septal area[b]			Caudate nucleus[c]		
0 ma.	3.5 ma.	6 ma.	0 ma.	8 ma.	10 ma.
3	10	10	3	10	1
3	10	10	3	10	1
10	4	10	3	10	1
4	10	10	3	10	1
3	10	10	3	10	1
3	3	10	3	10	1
3	10	10	10	10	1
4	10	10	3	10	2
3	3	10	3	1	1
3	3	10	3	10	1
3		10	4	10	2
		10	3	10	2
		10	10	10	2
			10	10	2
			10	10	10
			10	10	2
			10	10	2
			10	2	2
			10	10	2
			3	10	2

[a] Instructions to subject and stimulus parameters as in Table 1.
[b] No aversive current level obtained at site of stimulation. Intermediate current of 3.5 ma. selected because it appeared to be at reward threshold.
[c] Monopolar stimulation with indifferent electrode on leg.

technic. Table 1 demonstrates the resulting difficulty encountered. A single series was planned, but about midway through it, it became obvious that the subject's thresholds were shifting, with the apparent effect that the previously aversive current was becoming rewarding and the formerly rewarding current was becoming neutral. We felt justified in terminating the series and initiating a second series with higher current levels. It is apparent, especially in the second series, that the subject responded differentially for no current, the rewarding current, and the aversive current and that his performance under each of these conditions was reasonably consistent, particularly in view of his schizophrenia and extreme tendency toward perseveration, as evidenced by the occasional continued responding for zero current, more noticeable in Tables 2 and 3.

TABLE 3. DIFFERENTIAL SELF-STIMULATION FOR THREE LEVELS OF
CURRENT IN CENTRAL MEDIAN THALAMUS AND
IN MIDHYPOTHALAMUS[a]

Number of lever presses

Central median thalamus			Midhypothalamus		
0 ma.	1.25 ma.	2.5 ma.	0 ma.	0.2 ma.	0.4 ma.
5	10	2	3	10	2
10	10	2	3	10	1
3	10	2	10	10	1
3	10	2	10	10	1
3	10	2	10	10	1
3	10	2	3	10	1
4	10	2	3	10	3
3	9	10	10	3	1
10	3	2	4	10	2
10	8	10	3	10	2
3	10	8	10	10	2
5	10	10	10	3	2
3	10	6	5	10	2
3	3	2	10	10	2
3	10	2	10	10	2
3	10	2	4	10	2
3	4	2	4	10	2
4	10	2	4	10	2
3	10	2	3	10	2
3	3	5	4	10	2

[a] Instructions to subject and stimulus parameters as in Table 1.

Table 2 presents the data obtained with this procedure for the septal area and caudate nucleus. For the septal area, with the electrode pair selected, no aversive current level could be detected up to 12.5 ma. We thus used as an intermediate level in this instance a current which appeared to be precisely at reward threshold. Observations indicated that this was the case, as responding at this current level alternated between evidence of reward and of a neutral effect. In the caudate nucleus, despite a preliminary warm-up period for stabilization of threshold, the pattern of responding definitely changed toward the end of the series. This change may be attributable to changing thresholds or to a satiation effect, or the patient simply may have been drifting out of contact, with impairment of attention and increased perseveration. The cluster of trials showing continued responding for zero current supports the latter interpretation. In any event, general results for both the septal area and the caudate nucleus appear to provide evidence for reward properties with relatively high currents in these areas.

Interestingly, in the stimulation of the caudate, a small relative increase of current above the reward level produced a clearly aversive effect.

Table 3 suggests rewarding and aversive current levels also for both the central median thalamus and the midhypothalamus. As before, the records are not perfect, but general performance appears to justify such an interpretation. Again, it must be remembered that this patient had a severe schizophrenic illness and had difficulty following instructions on even the simplest psychologic tests. We were surprised at even the limited degree of consistency of his self-stimulation performance with this three-level technic.

STUDY OF CHOICE BEHAVIOR UNDER FREE-CHOICE AND FORCED-CHOICE CONDITIONS

An additional technic used with Subject No. B-12 was to have him alternate between use of the lever and of the button during continuous responding. The experimenters attempted to control his selection through differential reinforcement, a rewarding current being made available on one device but not on the other.

FREE-CHOICE PROCEDURE

In the free-choice experiment, the subject was instructed to continue self-stimulation as long as he wished and to shift whenever he wished from the lever to the button or vice versa. A rewarding current was made available to him on one of these devices and either no current or an aversive current on the other. Without further instruction to the subject, these currents were reversed by the experimenters in the course of his responding. In addition, the current was sometimes switched off entirely, so that he was unable to receive brain stimulation from either device. Under conditions of reward current versus aversive current, the subject's choice behavior was easily controlled by this procedure. Because of his strong perseverative tendencies, however, most attempts to control such behavior under conditions of rewarding current versus no current were unsuccessful. Figure 5 illustrates one of the few successful results with this procedure. These records were obtained with self-stimulation in the amygdala (right amygdala, SS 1-3), with a reward current of 0.4 ma., an aversive current of 0.8 ma., and remaining stimulus parameters as in Table 1. The first record shows performance for rewarding as opposed to aversive current. The subject initially continued to press the lever, which was delivering rewarding current, except for seven brief shifts to the button and back. When the current was turned off, he continued to respond as in the earlier records. Conditions were then reversed in the course of his responding, with aversive current introduced on the lever and reward current available with the button. He quickly switched to the button. Conditions were reversed once more, and the subject again switched accordingly.

The lower record in Figure 5 is a continuation of the one above except that conditions were changed to provide the subject with a choice between

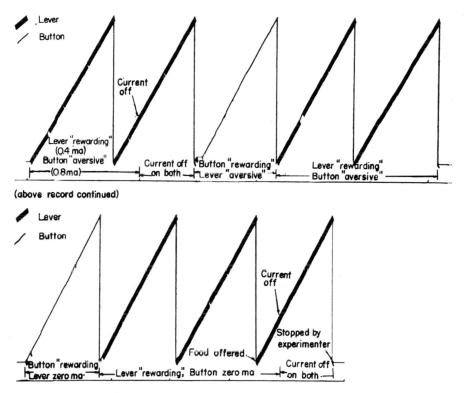

FIG. 5. Free-choice intracranial self-stimulation responding by Subject No. B-12 for stimulation to amygdala: Rewarding current (0.4 ma.) versus aversive current (0.8 ma.) and versus zero current. Copyright 1963 by the American Association for the Advancement of Science.

the rewarding current (again, 0.4 ma.) and no current. Rewarding current was initially available on the button, during which time the subject stayed with the button. With shift of reward to the lever after about 500 responses, he shifted appropriately to the lever and continued with this for more than 1,000 responses, with occasional brief spontaneous shifts to the button and back again. At this point, it was well past lunch time, and the subject had not eaten for 7 hours. While he was responding for the rewarding current, an attractive tray of food was placed beside him. As the record indicates, this produced no break in responding, although he repeatedly glanced over at the food. Even under these conditions he continued to respond without change in rate after the current was turned off, until he was finally instructed to stop. When questioned, he indicated that he had considered pressing the lever with one hand and eating with the other but had decided that he could wait. Once he was told to stop pressing the lever, he ate heartily.

FORCED-CHOICE PROCEDURE

As noted earlier, the free-choice procedure involving a rewarding current versus no current was seldom successful because of the subject's tendency to respond perseveratively for no current. In order to circumvent this perseveration, we introduced a modification which forced the subject to make a choice between the lever and the button whenever a signal was given by the experimenters. The subject was instructed to continue responding as long as he wished and was permitted to shift at will from one device to another, as before. In addition, however, he was instructed that whenever a tone signal was sounded, he was to shift immediately to the other device, and that he could then either stay with that one or return to the one he had been pressing. In other words, in addition to spontaneous shifting, he was forced with each tone signal to test the other device and decide which he preferred. In this procedure a rewarding current was made available on one device and zero current on the other. In conjunction with some tone signals, the rewarding current would be shifted by the experimenters to the other device; at other times, the tone signal would be given without such a change.

With this forced-choice procedure, the subject demonstrated fairly consistent preference for rewarding currents in several subcortical structures. Figure 6 shows his performance under these conditions with stimulation in the septal area (right septal SS 4-6) at a current level of 5 ma. versus no current. With reward initially available on the lever, both spontaneous shifts and forced shifts (in response to the tone signal) were followed by rapid return to the rewarding device. On the three occasions when the tone was associated with shift of reward to the other device, the subject's preference shifted accordingly. These data appear to provide sound evidence of the reinforcing or rewarding properties of intracranial stimulation at this site. Again, however, when the current was turned off entirely, this subject vacillated back and forth a few times and then continued to press the lever without reinforcement for about 1200 responses and more than half an hour, until stopped by the experimenter. This behavior has been consistent for this patient throughout all experimental work with him thus far.

OTHER PROCEDURES UNDER CURRENT
INVESTIGATION

At present, our only available subject for self-stimulation studies is the schizophrenic patient, No. B-12. We have been impressed not only by the failure of his self-stimulation response to extinguish upon removal of reinforcement but also by the remarkable stability and inflexibility of his response rate. Aside from a stair-step pattern of responding and pausing with stimulation at higher current levels in the septal area (Fig. 7), his lever-pressing behavior has been extremely stereotyped and consistent at about 40 responses per minute.

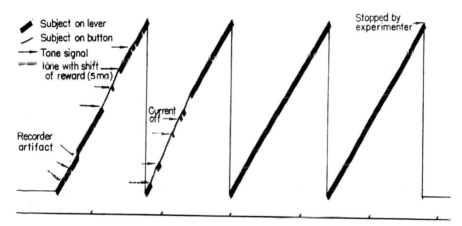

Fig. 6. Forced-choice intracranial self-stimulation responding by Subject No. B-12 for stimulation to septal area: Rewarding current (5 ma.) versus zero current. Copyright 1963 by the American Association for the Advancement of Science.

In animal work, stimulant and depressant drugs have been shown to have striking effects upon response rate.[38] One attempt has been made to test the effect of a stimulant drug in our subject. Figure 8 illustrates his rate of responding on an FR-10 schedule before and after intravenous injection of 10 mg. of methamphetamine. Aside from absence of occasional pauses in the postinjection as compared with the preinjection record, this drug produced no detectable change in response rate. Such changes might conceivably be produced by a higher dose of this drug or by other drugs, and no conclusion should be drawn on the basis of this lone record. In any case, the record illustrates the machine-like precision and stability of this patient's lever-pressing behavior.

Subject No B-12

R. Septal SS 4-6
Bidirectional Pulses
0.2 ms., 100 / sec.
0.3 sec. train

Adjusting
Current

2 ma.

3 ma.

4 ma.

4 ma. with polarity reversed

Fig. 7. Alteration of response pattern with changes in intensity of current and direction of current flow. Only instance of rate change observed with Subject No. B-12.

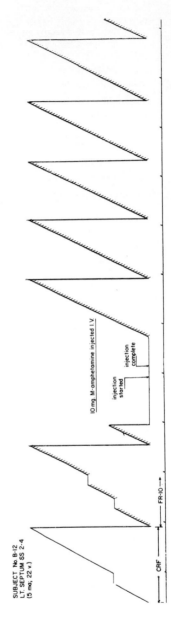

SUBJECT No B-12
LT. SEPTUM SS 2-4
(5 ma; 22 v.)

CRF

FR-10

10 mg. M-amphetamine injected I.V.

injection
started

injection
complete

Fig. 8. Intracranial self-stimulation responding on a fixed-rate schedule for stimulation to septal area before and after intravenous administration of methamphetamine to Subject No. B-12.

Clinical effects of psychoactive drugs in patients and effects of such drugs upon the performance of animals under conditions of intracranial self-stimulation suggest that abnormal functioning of reward centers in the brain may be a factor in various mental disorders.[26, 38] For this reason, data concerning the effects of psychoactive drugs upon reward thresholds of certain subcortical structures in psychiatric patients might be of considerable value. A technic developed by Stein and Ray[39] has been used with the rat to obtain self-determined reward thresholds. In brief, the animal presses a lever to obtain brain stimulation, but with each response the current is reduced slightly through a series of several equal steps between a moderately rewarding top value and zero current. When the animal is "no longer satisfied" with the current received, it can reset the current back up to the top step by pressing a second lever. Each reset thus provides a measure of reward threshold, and these can be automatically charted in such a way during an extended period of performance as to demonstrate any change in threshold resulting from injection of a drug. Animals undergo considerable training at this task before they are used for evaluation of pharmacologic effects, because performance is typically erratic initially and gradually stabilizes with repeated training.

We attempted to ascertain whether this self-determined threshold technic would be practicable with human subjects. Because our schizophrenic subject (No. B-12) was so perseverative, we seriously doubted that it would be suitable for him, but it has shown some promise. Figure 9 illustrates his initial performance on this task with stimulation in the posterior hypothalamic-tegmental region. The points at which successive resets occur are indicated by the lower excursions of the pen. The training period lasted 80 minutes, during which time there were roughly 3,000 responses on the lever for brain stimulation and 225 resets.

As was expected, the patient's perseveration is reflected in his frequent pressing of the lever for brain stimulation down to zero current, but there appears to be gradual improvement with time and promise of reasonable stabilization of base-line threshold measurements in the vicinity of 0.3 ma. This closely resembles animal records obtained in the first few hours of training. We plan to pursue the technic further in the hope that it may prove a direct and effective means of studying the action of pharmacologic compounds in various subcortical structures of chronic psychotic patients.

REWARDING AND AVERSIVE CURRENT LEVELS
IN VARIOUS REGIONS OF THE BRAIN

Table 4 presents our observations to date concerning rewarding and aversive current levels in various subcortical structures for our schizophrenic

subject, No. B-12. This material is based on the data obtained through use
of the three current levels, free-choice, and forced-choice technics previously
described. The current levels specified should not be interpreted as firmly
established even for this subject; they are intended rather as representative
differential thresholds in the various brain areas. Brady[7] has shown that
prior stimulation in one area can affect response rate, and presumably reward threshold, in a second area. Our exploratory work was not adequately
controlled for this variable. If the material in Table 4 is accepted as

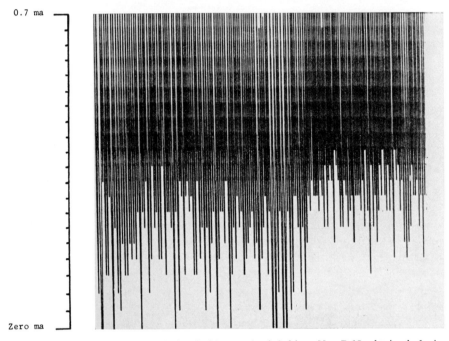

FIG. 9. Self-determined reward threshold record of Subject No. B-12 obtained during
initial training session on this task, with stimulation to hypothalamic-tegmental area (right
posterior hypothalamus–tegmentum SS 3-4).

roughly accurate, however, two features are impressive. First, current requirements for both rewarding and aversive effects appear to be generally
much higher in the septum and caudate than in the hypothalamic-tegmental
area. This would be expected on the basis of available animal data, although the degree of difference for this patient seems considerably greater
than that observed in animals. The current requirements indicated for the
caudate nucleus raise some question whether the rewarding and aversive
properties can be ascribed to the caudate or whether they result from spread
of the field of excitation to other structures.

The current values given for structures other than the caudate are for a specific pair of electrodes in an array of six, the pair having been selected because it looked promising in casual exploration of that area. Other electrode pairs in the same array and the same distance apart (usually 4 mm.)

TABLE 4. COMPARATIVE CURRENT INTENSITIES FOR REWARD AND AVERSIVE INTRACRANIAL SELF-STIMULATION RESPONDING WITH VARIOUS SUBCORTICAL PLACEMENTS: SUBJECT NO. B-12[a]

Structure	Rewarding	Aversive
Caudate (head) (L. reg.)	8.0 ma.	10.0 ma.
Septal area (R. SS 4-6)	3.5 ma. and above	—[b]
Amygdala (R. SS 1-3)	0.4 ma.	0.8 ma.
Central median thalamus (L. SS 4-6)	1.25 ma.	2.5 ma.
Midhypothalamus (L. SS 4-6)	0.2 ma.	0.4 ma.
Posterior hypothalamus (R. SS 4-6)	0.5 ma.	0.7 ma.
Posterior hypothalamus-tegmentum (R. SS 3-4)	0.5 ma.	0.7 ma.
Tegmentum (R. SS 1-3)	—[c]	0.2 ma.

[a] Stimulus parameters: Unidirectional rectangular pulses of 0.2 millisecond duration delivered at 100 pulses per second. Train duration: 0.5 second. Bipolar stimulation between electrodes 4 mm. apart in all areas except caudate nucleus (monopolar) and posterior hypothalamus-tegmentum (electrodes 2 mm. apart).

[b] Stimulation apparently rewarding and nonaversive up to 12.5 ma. Not tested above this level.

[c] Not tested below 0.2 ma. (apparatus limitations).

frequently gave apparently significantly different values, although these were not rigorously tested.

The second interesting feature of these data is the indication for all electrode sites formally studied, with the exception of the septal pair, of an aversive current in the range of 25 to 100 per cent above the rewarding level. (Although no aversive level was found up to 12.5 ma. with the septal pair used, monopolar stimulation of another septal electrode, and with a different wave form, appeared to be aversive at a current level equivalent to about 11 ma. with the present stimulus parameters.) This rather consistent observation of rewarding and aversive properties in the same brain sites does not correlate well with most animal data. Olds[25] has reported similar observations in rats, but these have been restricted to the middle hypothalamic area. (But see Olds and Olds, p. 23.) Olds has shown, moreover, that with further increases in current, the rewarding effects become predominant again. He postulates that the field of excitation around the electrodes extends with increasing current through a lamina of negative cells and into more positive ones.[25] In our work, we have never increased the current significantly above a level indicated by the subject as aversive. We therefore cannot determine whether the phenomenon described by Olds might have been demonstrated by these placements.

Another possible explanation of this consistent observation of positive and negative effects in the same areas has occurred to us. Little has been said about the behavior of our subjects during self-stimulation. The state of frenetic excitation and apparent eagerness which is typical in animals during self-stimulation was never observed in our human subjects. In fact, no gross behavioral expressions of pleasure or excitement were ever noted, and only occasionally did the subjects show any visual evidence of autonomic arousal. On one occasion, we increased the current gradually for our schizophrenic subject (No. B-12) during self-stimulation in the posterior hypothalamus. For the first time, his response rate increased slightly, and his breathing became more rapid. With current held at this level, he continued to press the lever for only a few seconds and then stopped. Observing his behavior in the light of extensive experience with animal subjects, we had the distinct impression that an animal under the same circumstances not only would have continued, but would have increased its response rate. We have wondered whether the current levels judged aversive by our subject are really those at which the rewarding properties of the stimulation become intense enough to produce autonomic arousal. Such arousal might, upon conscious reflection, be frightening to a human subject but not to an animal. Interestingly, our schizophrenic patient has used only two terms to describe the stimulation: "good" and "too much."

SUMMARY AND CONCLUSION

Attempts to establish, modify, and extinguish a simple lever-pressing response under conditions of intracranial self-stimulation in two human subjects have proved largely unsuccessful. These early efforts have been of value, however, in demonstrating that patients' verbal reports of effects of brain stimulation may be grossly unreliable and probably should not be accepted as valid unless supported by behavioral data obtained under conditions of stringent control.

With revisions of procedure, data were obtained which suggest the presence of subcortical areas in the human brain in which brief electrical stimulation appears to have rewarding or reinforcing properties. The areas of the brain thus far found to have such apparent properties are the head of the caudate nucleus, the septal area, the amygdala, the central median thalamus (intralaminar thalamic nuclei), the midhypothalamus, the posterior hypothalamus, and the boundary of the hypothalamus and tegmentum. With our electrode placements and stimulus parameters, relatively small increases in current above the rewarding level produced an apparently aversive effect. In the septal placements studied, the range of rewarding currents appeared to be significantly wider than in other areas, but too few electrode sites have been carefully explored to provide definite evidence on this point.

Since most of our findings are based on the intracranial self-stimulation behavior of one clearly non-normal subject, they should be interpreted with caution. Much additional research in this area is needed before any firm conclusions can be drawn.

REFERENCES

1. Asdourian, D. Interaction effects of intracranial stimulation with rewarding and aversive solutions. *J. Comp. Physiol. Psychol.* *55*:685, 1962.
2. Becker, H. C. "A Stimulus Monitor: Its Use in Electrophysiology." Unpublished master's thesis, Department of Physics, Tulane University, 1953.
3. Becker, H. C., Peacock, S. M., Jr., Heath, R. G., and Mickle, W. A. "Methods of Stimulation Control and Concurrent Electrographic Recording," in *Electrical Stimulation of the Brain*, ed. by Sheer, D. E. Austin, Tex., University of Texas Press, 1961, pp. 74–90.
4. Beer, B., and Valenstein, E. S. Discrimination of tones during reinforcing brain stimulation. *Science* *132*:297, 1960.
5. Bower, G. H., and Miller, N. E. Rewarding and punishing effects from stimulating the same place in the rat's brain. *J. Comp. Physiol. Psychol.* *51*:669, 1958.
6. Boyd, E. S., and Gardner, L. C. Positive and negative reinforcement from intracranial stimulation of a teleost. *Science* *136*:648, 1962.
7. Brady, J. V. "Motivational-Emotional Factors and Intracranial Self-Stimulation," in *Electrical Stimulation of the Brain: An Interdisciplinary Survey of Neurobehavioral Integrative Systems,* ed. by Sheer, D. E. Austin, Tex., University of Texas Press, 1961, pp. 413–430.
8. Brady, J. V., and Conrad, D. G. Some effects of limbic system self-stimulation upon conditioned emotional behavior. *J. Comp. Physiol. Psychol.* *53*:128, 1960.
9. Brodie, D. A., Moreno, O. M., Malis, J. L., and Boren, J. J. Rewarding properties of intracranial stimulation. *Science* *131*:929, 1960.
10. Bursten, B., and Delgado, J. M. R. Positive reinforcement induced by intracerebral stimulation in the monkey. *J. Comp. Physiol. Psychol.* *51*:6, 1958.

11. DELGADO, J. M. R., and BURSTEN, B. Attraction and avoidance evoked by rhinencephalic stimulation in the monkey. *Fed. Proc. 15*:143, 1956.

12. DELGADO, J. M. R., and HAMLIN, H. "Spontaneous and Evoked Electrical Seizures in Animals and in Humans," in *Electrical Studies on the Unanesthetized Brain,* ed. by Ramey, E. R., and O'Doherty, D. S. New York, Hoeber-Harper, 1960, pp. 133–151.

13. HEATH, R. G., and the Department of Psychiatry and Neurology, Tulane University. *Studies in Schizophrenia.* Cambridge, Mass., Harvard, 1954, p. 348.

14. HEATH, R. G., and MICKLE, W. A. "Evaluation of Seven Years' Experience with Depth Electrode Studies in Human Patients," in *Electrical Studies on the Unanesthetized Brain,* ed. by Ramey, E. R., and O'Doherty, D. S. New York, Hoeber-Harper, 1960, pp. 214–247.

15. HODOS, W., and VALENSTEIN, E. S. Motivational variables affecting the rate of behavior maintained by intracranial stimulation. *J. Comp. Physiol. Psychol. 51*:502, 1960.

16. HOWORTH, C. I., and DEUTSCH, J. A. Drive decay: The cause of fast "extinction" of habits learned for brain stimulation. *Science 137*:35, 1962.

17. KEESEY, R. E. The relation between pulse frequency, intensity, and duration and the rate of responding for intracranial stimulation. *J. Comp. Physiol. Psychol. 55*:671, 1962.

18. KLING, J. W., and MATSUMIYA, Y. Relative reinforcement values of food and intracranial stimulation. *Science 135*:668, 1962.

19. LILLY, J. C. "Learning Motivated by Subcortical Stimulation: The 'Start' and the 'Stop' Patterns of Behavior," in *Electrical Studies on the Unanesthetized Brain,* ed. by Ramey, E. R., and O'Doherty, D S. New York, Hoeber-Harper, 1960, pp. 78–105.

20. LILLY, J. C., and MILLER, A. M. Operant conditioning of the bottlenose dolphin with electrical stimulation of the brain. *J. Comp. Physiol. Psychol. 55*:73, 1962.

21. LONG, E. R., HAMMACK, J. T., MAY, F., and CAMPBELL, B. J. Intermittent reinforcement of operant behavior in children. *J. Exp. Anal. Behav. 1*:315, 1958.

22. MARGULES, D. L., and OLDS, J. Identical "feeding" and "rewarding" systems in the lateral hypothalamus of rats. *Science 135*:374, 1962.

23. NEILSON, H. C., DOTY, R., and RUTLEDGE, L. Motivational and perceptual aspects of subcortical stimulation in cats. *Amer. J. Physiol. 194*:427, 1958.

24. NEWMAN, B. L. Behavioral effects of electrical self-stimulation of the septal area and related structures in the rat. *J. Comp. Physiol. Psychol. 54*:340, 1961.

25. OLDS, J. Effects of hunger and male sex hormones on self-stimulation of the brain. *J. Comp. Physiol. Psychol. 51*:320, 1958.

26. OLDS, J. "Differentiation of Reward Systems in the Brain by Self-Stimulation Techniques," in *Electrical Studies on the Unanesthetized Brain,* ed. by Ramey, E. R., and O'Doherty, D. S. New York, Hoeber-Harper, 1960, pp. 17–49.

27. OLDS, J. Hypothalamic subtrates of reward. *Physiol. Rev. 42*:554, 1962.

28. OLDS, J., and MILNER, P. Positive reinforcement produced by electrical stimulation of septal area and other regions of rat brain. *J. Comp. Physiol. Psychol. 47*:419, 1954.

29. OLDS, J., TRAVIS, R. P., and SCHWING, R. C. Topographic organization of hypothalamic self-stimulation functions. *J. Comp. Physiol. Psychol. 53*:23, 1960.
30. REYNOLDS, R. W. The relationship between stimulation voltage and rate of hypothalamic self-stimulation in the rat. *J. Comp. Physiol. Psychol. 51*:193, 1958.
31. SEM-JACOBSEN, C. W., and TORKILDSEN, A. "Depth Recording and Electrical Stimulation in the Human Brain," in *Electrical Studies on the Unanesthetized Brain*, ed. by Ramey, E. R., and O'Doherty, D. S. New York, Hoeber-Harper, 1960, pp. 275–290.
32. SEWARD, J. P., UYEDA, A., and OLDS, J. Resistance to extinction following cranial self-stimulation. *J. Comp. Physiol. Psychol. 52*:294, 1959.
33. SEWARD, J. P., UYEDA, A., and OLDS, J. Reinforcing effect of brain stimulation on runway performance as a function of interval between trials. *J. Comp. Physiol. Psychol. 53*:224, 1960.
34. SIDMAN, M., BRADY, J. V., BOREN, J. J., CONRAD, D. G., and SCHULMAN, A. Reward schedules and behavior maintained by intracranial self-stimulation. *Science 122*:830, 1955.
35. SPEAR, N. E. Comparison of the reinforcing effect of brain stimulation on Skinner box, runway, and maze performance. *J. Comp. Physiol. Psychol. 55*:679, 1962.
36. STARK, P., and BOYD, E. S. Self-stimulation by dogs through chronically implanted electrodes in the hypothalamus. *Fed. Proc. 20*:328, 1961.
37. STEIN, L. Secondary reinforcement established with subcortical stimulation. *Science 127*:466, 1958.
38. STEIN, L. "Effects and Interactions of Imipramine, Chlorpromazine, Reserpine, and Amphetamine on Self-Stimulation: Possible Neurophysiological Basis of Depression," in *Recent Advances in Biological Psychiatry*, Vol. IV, ed. by Wortis, J. New York, Plenum Press, 1962, pp. 288–309.
39. STEIN, L., and RAY, O. S. Self-regulation of brain-stimulating current intensity in the rat. *Science 130*:570, 1959.
40. VALENSTEIN, E. S. Changes in response rates for brain stimulation in septum pellucidum following amygdalectomy. Presented at the Eastern Psychological Association Meetings, 1958.
41. VALENSTEIN, E. S., and BEER, B. Reinforcing brain stimulation in competition with water reward and shock avoidance. *Science 137*:1052, 1962.
42. WARD, H. P. Stimulus factors in septal self-stimulation. *Amer. J. Physiol. 196*: 779, 1959.

ROBERT G. HEATH, M.D., D.M.SC.

DONALD M. GALLANT, M.D.

Tulane University School of Medicine

Activity of the Human Brain during Emotional Thought

ONLY RECENTLY HAVE TECHNICS been developed to permit collection of data concerning the relation between central neural mechanisms and behavior. Although animal data are extensive, interpretation is difficult in the absence of subjective reporting. Information concerning participation of various systems of the brain in emotional behavior, collected from parallel studies in animals and human subjects, has been presented previously,[6, 9] The present report concerns a larger series of human subjects for whom data have been obtained from a larger number of areas of the brain.

Neural systems prominently mentioned in published reports as being most involved in emotional behavior are the reticular, the limbic, and the diencephalic. We have previously reported observations which demonstrate the association between structures of the limbic system and emotion.[7, 8, 12, 14, 18] Lindsley[19] postulated an executive role for the reticular system in emotional expression. Brady's[3] recent review is exhaustively documented. The electrode implantation methods[1, 2, 10, 11, 15] developed at Tulane University permit recording of electrical activity from these deep systems and from the surface of the scalp simultaneously with subjective mental activity. In addition to the recording of neural activity with fluctuations in behavior, a variety of stimuli have been introduced into the different systems to alter their function. The response of patients to stimulation of the brain is the subject of the paper by Heath in this monograph. Data reported here will demonstrate recordings obtained (1) with spontaneously developing behavior and behavioral states induced by environmental stimuli and (2) with parenteral administration of some pain-reducing and euphoria-inducing drugs.

Supported by a grant-in-aid from The Commonwealth Fund, funds provided through the Louisiana State Department of Hospitals, and U.S.P.H.S. Grant No. M-6075.

MATERIAL AND METHODS

Since 1950, 54 patients have been studied with depth electrode technics at Tulane University. Studies have been discontinued in 51 of these, 41 of whom were psychotic, 37 undeniably schizophrenic by all accepted clinical criteria. Six of the 51 subjects were epileptic; 2 were afflicted with seizures only, whereas the other 4 displayed serious behavioral symptoms in addition to seizures. Eight of the 51 patients had diseases other than psychiatric disturbances, including Parkinsonism, carcinoma with intractable pain, severe advanced rheumatoid arthritis, and narcolepsy. Diagnosis of the 3 patients still under study are schizophrenic reaction, catatonic type; schizophrenic reaction, paranoid type; and psychomotor epilepsy. Each subject was thoroughly evaluated by psychiatric study and psychologic testing. With additional data regarding medical and social history, a broad background of information was available for use during interviews with patients.

Methods for implanting electrodes and cannulae with the stereotaxic instrument and for maintaining them in position for prolonged periods have been detailed previously. During the first year of our studies, technics permitted the electrodes to remain in place for only a few days to a few weeks. Procedures were gradually developed to hold the electrodes in place for longer and longer periods, and since 1952 they have remained in patients for 1 to 2 years.

Three types of electrodes have been used. The "regular" electrode consists of a spherical silver ball, 0.05 in. in diameter, welded to a length of silver-plated, No. 34-gauge copper wire insulated with vinyl chloride acetate. In some patients a "triple" electrode was implanted, consisting of a smaller ball, 0.02 in. in diameter, welded to two strands of the silver-plated, No. 34-gauge copper wire. Three such wires were intertwined so that the silver ball contact points were 2 mm. apart. The "stainless steel" electrode consists of six (type No. 316) stainless steel wires, 0.003 in. in diameter, with quad Teflon-coated leads. Each stainless steel electrode has six contact points 2 mm. apart. Resistances of the three types of electrodes vary considerably, the regular electrode having a resistance of 2 K ohms, the triple electrode 20 K ohms, and the stainless steel electrode approximately 60 K ohms. It has proved valuable to use the regular electrode in conjunction with the triple and stainless steel electrodes during recordings because of the widely different resistances.

In the 51 patients prepared with regular electrodes, recordings were obtained from over the pia of the cortical areas (frontal, parietal, temporal, and occipital) and from the following deep structures: septal region, caudate nucleus, hippocampus, amygdala, thalamus, globus pallidus, hypothalamus, mesencephalic tegmentum, and cingulate gyrus. In most of the patients studied, scalp recordings were also made synchronously with the deep recordings. The silver ball electrodes are clearly visible in the roentgenogram of Patient No. B-11 (Fig. 1), one of three patients currently under study, but the stainless steel wires are so small that they cannot be detected without assiduous study of the film. The elongated metallic tips of

TABLE 1. ELECTRODE PLACEMENTS IN SCHIZOPHRENIC
PATIENT NO. B-11[a]

Site	Electrodes
L. temporal cortex	8 regular
R. temporal cortex	6 regular
L. occipital cortex	4 regular
R. occipital cortex	4 regular
L. frontal cortex	2 regular
R. frontal cortex	2 regular
L. parietal cortex	2 regular
R. parietal cortex	2 regular
L. auditory cortex	1 regular
R. auditory cortex	1 regular
L. centromedian	1 stainless steel[b]
R. centromedian	1 stainless steel
L. caudate	1 regular
R. caudate	2 regular
L. hippocampus	1 regular + 1 stainless steel
R. hippocampus	1 stainless steel
L. hypothalamus	1 regular
R. hypothalamus	1 stainless steel
L. septal region	2 regular + 1 stainless steel
R. septal region	1 regular + 1 stainless steel
L. amygdala	1 stainless steel
L. globus pallidus	1 regular

[a] White woman, aged 33 years.
[b] Each stainless steel electrode has six contact points 2 mm. apart.

the cannulae used for introduction of chemicals into the brain are also easily seen. Electrode placements in this patient are listed in Table 1.

The recordings herein presented were obtained on one or multiple (up to four) Grass electroencephalographs. Recordings with multiple machines were synchronized with a multi-electroencephalographic synchronizing apparatus. Implanting electrodes with multiple leads is highly advantageous, since important activity is proving to be focal, even within specific anatomic nuclei or cerebral regions.

RESULTS

RECORDINGS OBTAINED DURING SPONTANEOUS BEHAVIOR AND WITH BEHAVIORAL STATES INDUCED BY ENVIRONMENTAL STIMULI

The patients prepared with depth electrodes were studied psychologically while physiologic data were recorded synchronously from a large number of regions of the brain. In 14 of our 54 patients, we were able to correlate some types of reproducible electrical activity in specific areas of the brain

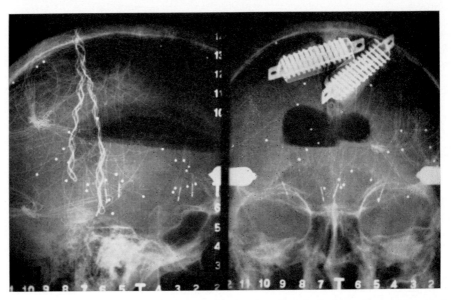

FIG. 1. Roentgenogram of Patient No. B-11 showing silver ball electrodes, stainless steel wires, and cannulae implanted into and over the surface of the brain.

with patterns of thought activity. We have previously reported this phenomenon in a smaller series of patients.[7, 8, 14, 18] The distinct, reproducible change in pattern of electrical activity, an amplitude and frequency alteration in rhinencephalic structures, was associated with an intensely emotional reaction, usually rooted in memories. The recording change could be induced through direction of the interview by the psychiatrist into specific associations. When the electrical phenomenon occurred spontaneously, inquiry consistently established that the patient was involved in emotional thinking. Certain sensory stimuli induced it, but only when selective emotional thoughts were stirred.

The change was consistently localized to parts of the old olfactory structures of the brain: the rostral hippocampus, the amygdala, and, on occasions, the septal region. Base-line electroencephalographic recordings from the hippocampal region were characterized by a mixture of slow and fast frequencies and appeared irregular and desynchronous, generally at a fairly high amplitude, but ranging from 5 to 250μv. Amygdala base-line frequencies varied, but were usually rather fast, ranging from 12 to 20 cps.[13] The change in pattern in association with emotional behavior was consistent: Distinct bursts of faster activity, ranging from 12- to 20-per-second frequency from the rostral hippocampus and from 18- to 35-per-second frequency from the amygdala, together with approximate doubling of amplitude, gave the appearance of synchronous activity. The bursts ranged in duration from 0.5 to 20 seconds and persisted intermittently as long as 20 to 30 minutes if the stimulus (in this case, interview) continued to focus upon emotionally charged material. Onset of the response was immediate and dramatic. The change was not recorded from any of the numerous other deep structures from which simultaneous recordings were made, nor did it appear in the cortical recordings. It was not demonstrable in all 54 subjects. Hippocampal and amygdaloid leads were not implanted in some of the early subjects, but when leads were implanted into these regions, exact locations of electrodes varied. Conceivably, therefore, these observations might have been made in a larger percentage of the subjects, or even in all, if the electrodes had been placed in identical positions in all subjects.

The responses could be repeatedly elicited and promptly terminated by the direction of the interview. In Patient No. A-10, for example, high spindling began in the hippocampus when he recalled a television program on juvenile delinquency that he had seen the previous evening and that recalled extremely disturbing boyhood memories. This electrical activity persisted until he was given a simple mathematical problem. As he began to calculate, the spindling stopped. It returned when the interview was again directed to the subject of his childhood delinquency. (These recordings were presented in *Studies in Schizophrenia*,[14] Figs. E-10, E-11, E-12, and E-13, pp. 580–582.)

On another occasion, an interview with the same patient was directed toward pleasurable associations. The subject was asked if at any time in his life he had experienced intensely good feelings. Promptly, high-amplitude 14-per second hippocampal activity reappeared as he recalled a rare sense of well-being and success when "Army stew tasted even better than steaks do now." (This recording appears in the article "Rhinencephalic Activity during Thought,"[18] Fig. 1, p. 434.) Thus, essentially the same recording pattern appeared in this patient in association with recall of pleasurable memories and of painful memories. The pattern was repeatedly elicited for a period of several months in association with certain long-past emotional experiences.

In another intact but paranoid patient, who reported his feelings competently, the pattern shown in Figure 3 (see base-line recording in Figure 2) developed when he became angry as the psychiatrist directed the interview into an area described by the patient as "full of bad memories."

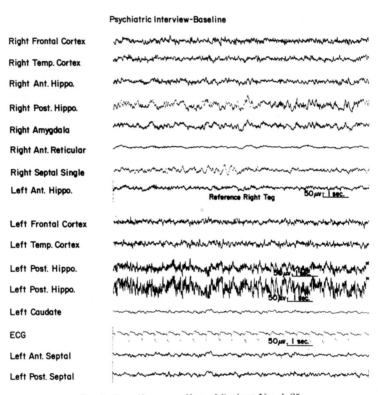

FIG. 2. Base-line recording of Patient No. A-25.

The recording change with recall of memories was not usually associated with observable evidence of intense emotion; patients rarely exhibited agitation or gross vasomotor change. (Extensive peripheral physiologic measurements have not been made to date.) In contrast, patients sometimes experienced severe emotional outbursts concerning current situations without associated changes in the tracings. For example, Patient No. A-10 appropriately made vigorous, angry remarks, punctuated with curses, about an attendant because of an upsetting incident that had occurred on the ward, but no change was reflected in his recording. The deep recordings of Patient No. A-16 did not change when she displayed pronounced disorganization of thought and complained of fear as a result of a current situation involving the administration of *d*-lysergic acid 25, but high-amplitude 16-per-second bursts of hippocampal activity developed when she recalled an earlier course of electroshock therapy. (This recording appears in the article, "Rhinencephalic Activity during Thought,"[18] Fig. 4, p. 438.)

Exceptions were rare to the general observation that current emotionally charged situations did not invoke the recording change. Patient No. B-2, for

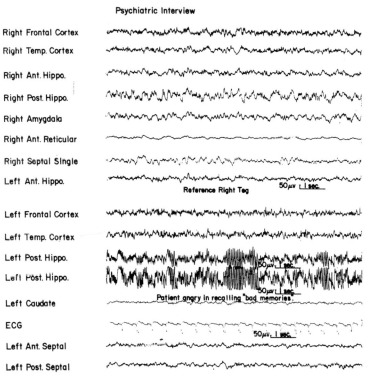

FIG. 3. Recording of Patient No. A-25 when he was angry in recalling "bad memories."

example, was strongly addicted to smoking and became angry if denied a cigarette. While he was under study, he acquired a strong antagonistic attitude toward one of the electroencephalographic technicians. If the technician denied him a cigarette, his angry protests were accompanied by the spindling activity shown in Figure 5. (See Figure 4 for a base-line recording for Patient No. B-2.) Interestingly, he appeared equally angry if denied a cigarette by other staff members, but the spindling did not appear. The patient was a poor reporter, and we were not able to obtain information which might relate the technician to an earlier significant figure in his life, although such a relation was suspected.

Activation of spiking in the septal region repeatedly occurred in association with an expression of intense anger by one patient concerning his de-

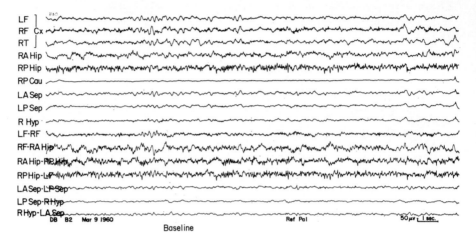

FIG. 4. Base-line recording of Patient No. B-2.

lusional system, as shown in Figure 7. (Fig. 6 is a base-line recording.) The spiking was dramatic when a technician, with whom he had developed a close relation during the period of study, teasingly informed him that he was not God, a statement contrary to the patient's delusion.

In earlier reports, we emphasized the unique effectiveness of olfactory

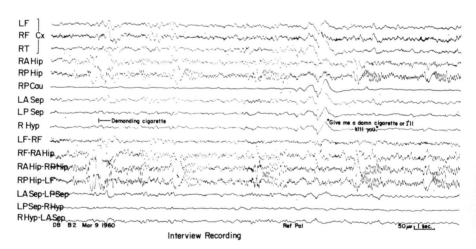

FIG. 5. Recording of Patient No. B-2 during period of agitation.

stimuli in eliciting a spindling electrical response from the hippocampus and amygdala. Olfactory stimuli, if regarded by a subject as strongly pleasant or strongly unpleasant, frequently induced this electrical response. Additionally, the response occurred even in the absence of a direct olfactory stimulus when a subject recalled odors about which he had strong feelings.

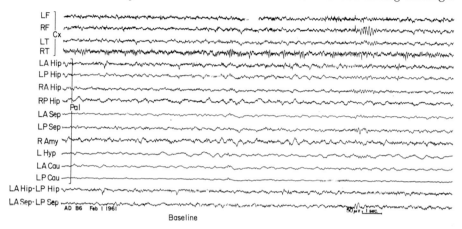

FIG. 6. Base-line recording of Patient No. B-6.

In Patient No. A-16, spindling appeared as she recalled memories of an eccentric elderly woman who had cared for her during childhood. The onset of spindling was associated with memories of odors in a room kept locked by the woman and filled with an assortment of useless objects with distinct odors, such as newspapers and pieces of dried fruit. Spindling also appeared in response to a direct olfactory stimulus and was the same as that elicited

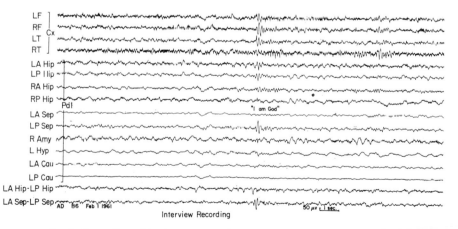

FIG. 7. Recording of Patient No. B-6 during angry expression of delusions.

in this patient by memory recall. Similar recordings were obtained when the patient recalled, without a direct olfactory stimulus, the scent of gardenias, which she associated with a school dance. Spindles also appeared

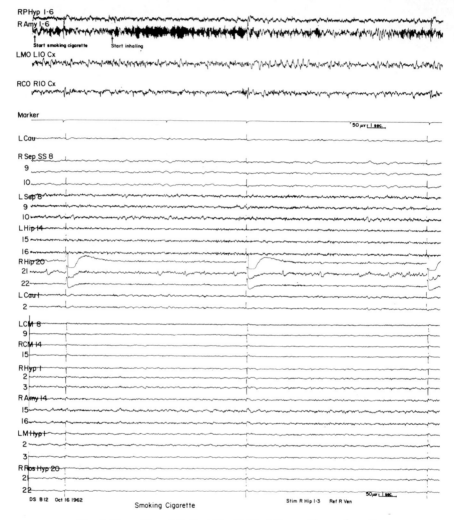

FIG. 8. Recording of Patient No. B-12 while smoking a cigarette.

when she displayed an obvious erotic interest in her interviewer, who made her feel rejected and who reportedly reminded her of a former boy friend. (Recordings appear in the article, "Rhinencephalic Activity during Thought,"[18] Fig. 3a and b, p. 437.)

Recent studies demonstrate that the spindling response in olfactory structures to sensory stimuli is not unique to *olfactory* stimuli, as originally considered, but occurs also with other forms of sensory stimuli which induce strong emotional feelings with memory associations. The recording in Figure 8, obtained when Patient No. B-12, a cigarette addict, was smoking, shows a pronounced increase in amplitude in the amygdaloid lead. Figure

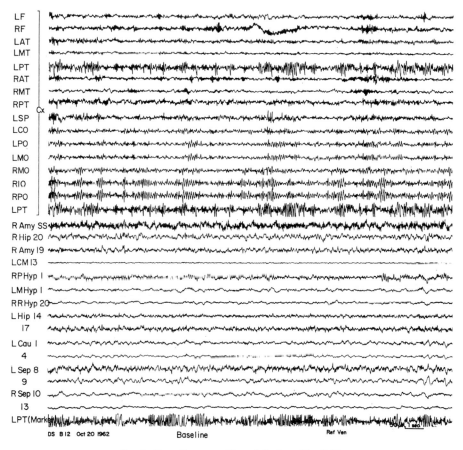

FIG. 9. Base-line recording of Patient No. B 12.

9, which shows a different electrode arrangement in the same patient, is a base-line tracing for Figures 10, 11, and 12. The patient, while not smoking, was asked to recall his feelings when smoking, and the same type of high-amplitude amygdaloid spindling again appeared (Fig. 10). The recording in Figure 11 was obtained when Patient No. B-12 was shown pictures with a strong sexual signification, to which he responded with intense interest; he seemed, in fact, aroused. The same type of high-amplitude spindling activity appeared—this time in association with a developing, highly pleasurable state of sexual motivation. Later, during an interview, the patient recalled memories of pleasurable sexual activity, and the spindles reappeared (Fig. 12). In another experiment with this patient, breakfast and

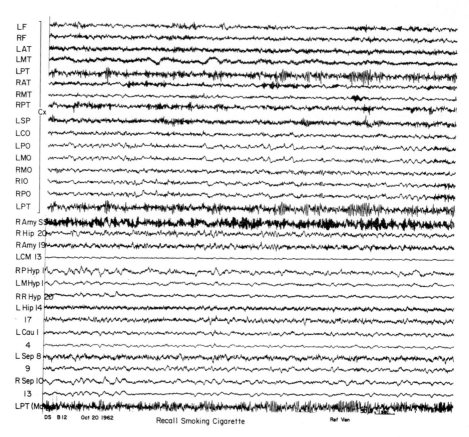

FIG. 10. Recording of Patient No. B-12 when he was asked to recall his feelings when smoking.

lunch were withheld. Recordings obtained as his favorite food was served late in the day demonstrated spindling of the same type. Thus, the changes in the recording appeared in association with a wide variety of pleasurable stimuli which elicited strong feelings about current happenings. In our previous experience, changes occurred only with emotional reactions associated with old, usually childhood, memories. Recent observations in this and other patients suggest that similar changes sometimes occur with emotionally charged current events. In those instances in which emotionally charged current events were accompanied by spindling, they may have been related to old emotional reactions. We were unable, because of the psychiatric disorder, to obtain sufficient reporting data to clarify this point.

Recordings during extremes of emotional behavior associated with the epileptic aura contribute further to an understanding of the behavior-brain

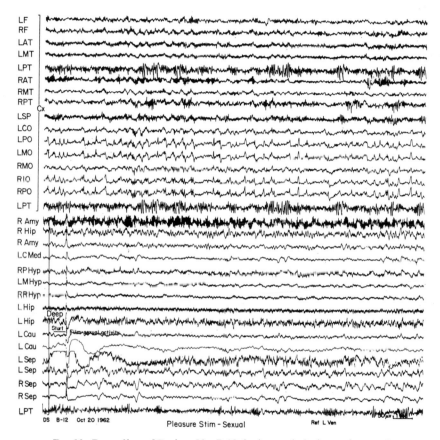

FIG. 11. Recording of Patient No. B-12 during period of sexual arousal.

relation. The epileptic aura is usually characterized by overwhelming, painful emotion, most commonly fear, rage, depression, despair, and anguish. Bizarre sensory phenomena, visual and olfactory, and unusual memory recall (*déjà vu*) have been experienced. Pleasure, alertness, and a general feeling of well-being rarely characterize the aura, although such pleasurable reactions have been described.[4] Figure 13, a recording from an epileptic patient, shows spike, slow wave, and spindling in the hippocampus and amygdala; this activity was recorded from the same structures from which we recorded spindling associated with strong emotional feelings as revealed during interview. The discharge pattern from the hippocampus and amygdala, in association with the intensely painful emotional experiences of the aura, has been consistent in our seven epileptic patients. We have not obtained recordings during pleasurable aura, but, as reported in another paper

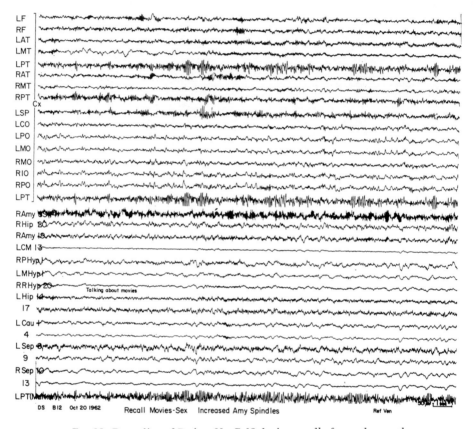

FIG. 12. Recording of Patient No. B-12 during recall of sexual arousal.

in this monograph (page 219), pleasurable feelings were described by epileptic patients when chemical stimulation to the septal region induced high-amplitude spindling in recordings from this region.

RECORDINGS OBTAINED WITH ADMINISTRATION OF PAIN-REDUCING AND EUPHORIA-INDUCING DRUGS

As a means of investigating further the nature of neural mechanisms underlying pain and pleasure, chemicals well known for pain-killing and

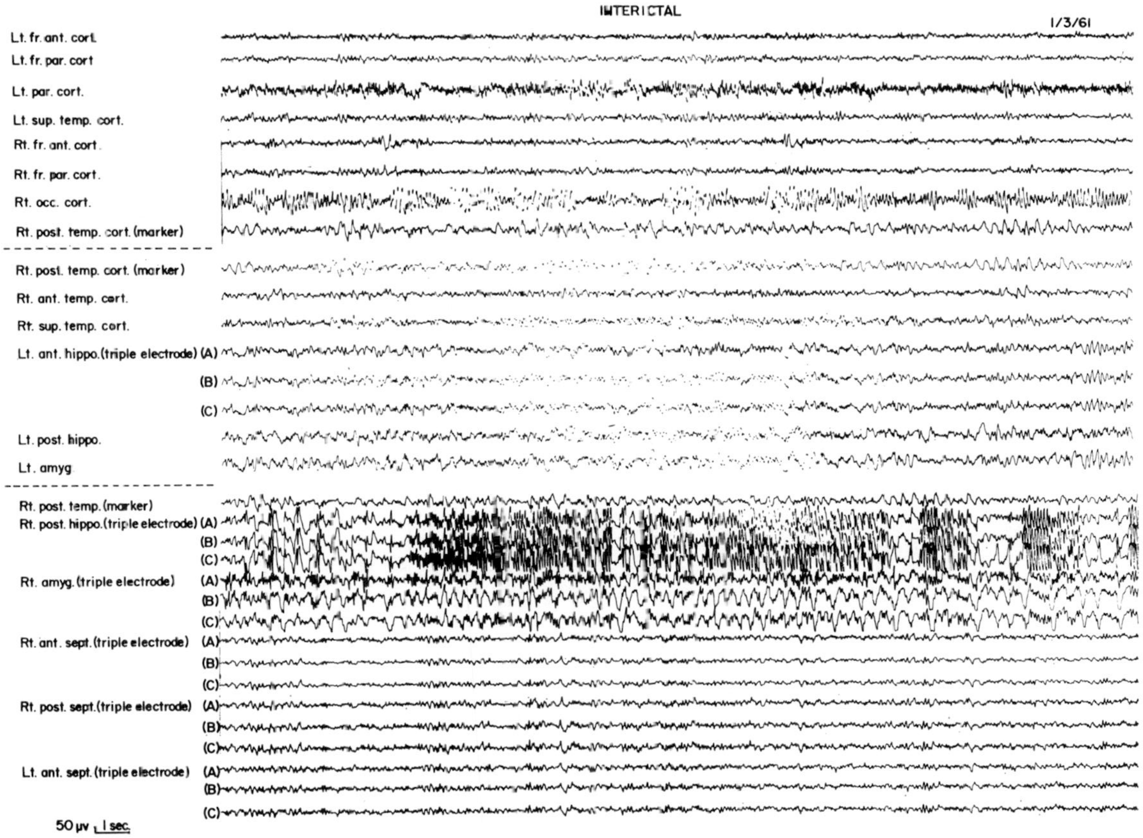

INTERICTAL
1/3/61
Lt. fr. ant. cort.
Lt. fr. par. cort
Lt. par. cort.
Lt. sup. temp. cort.
Rt. fr. ant. cort.
Rt. fr. par. cort.
Rt. occ. cort.
Rt. post. temp. cort. (marker)
Rt. post. temp. cort. (marker)
Rt. ant. temp. cort.
Rt. sup. temp. cort.
Lt. ant. hippo. (triple electrode) (A)
(B)
(C)
Lt. post. hippo.
Lt. amyg
Rt. post. temp. (marker)
Rt. post. hippo. (triple electrode) (A)
(B)
(C)
Rt. amyg. (triple electrode) (A)
(B)
(C)
Rt. ant. sept. (triple electrode) (A)
(B)
(C)
Rt. post. sept. (triple electrode) (A)
(B)
(C)
Lt. ant. sept. (triple electrode) (A)
(B)
(C)
50 µv
1 sec.

FIG. 13. Interictal recording of Patient No. B-5.

euphoria-inducing qualities were administered to three patients prepared with depth electrodes. The compounds administered were morphine sulfate, meperidine hydrochloride (Demerol), and cocaine hydrochloride.

Morphine sulfate, administered intramuscularly in doses ranging from 10 to 20 mg., produced minimal clinical or electroencephalographic changes in

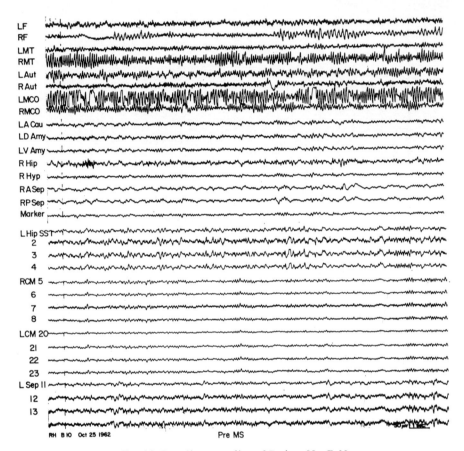

FIG. 14. Base-line recording of Patient No. B-10.

the patients. The tracings shown in Figure 15 (base-line tracing in Fig. 14), obtained from a psychomotor epileptic while he was under the influence of morphine, demonstrate only some relaxation. The only clinical change was relaxation and perhaps increased drowsiness. A patient with chronic schizophrenia also showed no change associated with administration of this compound. Patient No. B-12, also a chronic schizophrenic, and a poor reporter, said that he felt somewhat better, but no obvious behavioral changes were noted—certainly no euphoria. His recording (Fig. 16), when compared with his base-line recording (Fig. 9), shows a decrease in amplitude of the beta activity over the base line. During this experiment in Patient No. B-12, potentials were evoked and recorded from numerous cerebral sites by introduction of a single-pulse stimulus (4 v. of 0.1 millisecond duration) into the hippocampus once every 10 seconds. Under the effects of morphine, the evoked potential in the deep structures decreased in amplitude while the potential evoked from the cortex increased in amplitude by $50\mu v$.

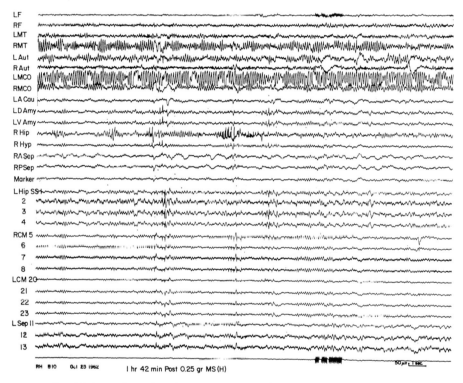

FIG. 15. Recording of Patient No. B-10 while under influence of morphine.

Demerol, administered intramuscularly in a dose of 100 mg. to two patients (No. B-10 and No. B-12), induced some clinical change. The subjects reported that they felt better and exhibited objective evidence of a mild feeling of well-being. The recordings of Patient No. B-10 showed only increased relaxation, which did not differ from that seen during spontaneous relaxation. The recordings of Patient No. B-12 (Fig. 17) showed a significant increase of focal slowing from the septal region. Demerol produced no change in the potential evoked from the occipital cortex by introduction of a single-pulse stimulus to the hippocampus. The third patient did not demonstrate behavioral or electroencephalographic changes.

Cocaine hydrochloride was administered in a 10% solution of intranasal spray (1 to 2 ml.) to the two subjects, No. B-11 and No. B-12. Patient No.

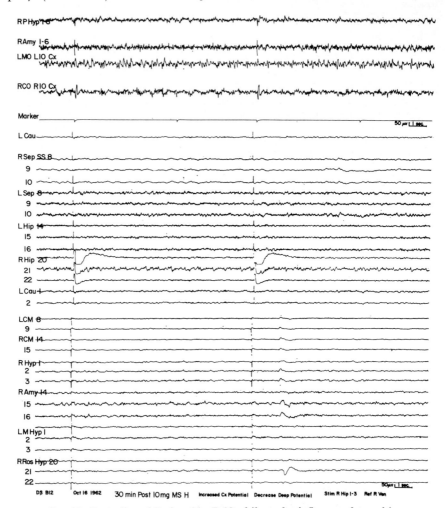

FIG. 16. Recording of Patient No. B-12 while under influence of morphine.

B-11, who failed to respond to morphine or Demerol, did not respond to cocaine either. Increased spindling in the amygdala appeared in the tracing of Patient No. B-12 (Fig. 18), as seen by comparison with the base-line tracing in Figure 9, and he expressed feelings of apprehension. For a time he appeared extremely anxious, manifesting hyperventilation and complaining of tightness in the chest and difficulty in breathing, a sensation he associated with feelings previously experienced with electroshock therapy. This induced a panic reaction. His general response was painful.

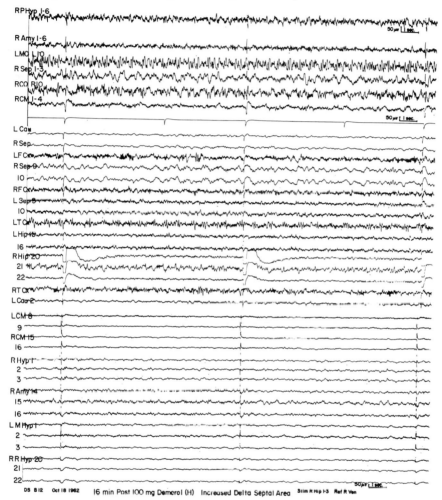

FIG. 17. Recording of Patient No. B-12 while under influence of Demerol.

One patient, No. B-10, a psychomotor epileptic, showed activation of spiking in the hippocampal and amygdaloid recordings with administration of a number of compounds, including sedatives and psychotomimetic agents, such as d-lysergic acid 25, as well as analgesics. The common denominator of this recording change was sleep. The recording could not be correlated with a specific drug, since it also occurred consistently in association with spontaneous sleep. Thus, the electrical activation was attributable not to the compound administered but rather to the sleep induced by the compound. Activation of this type of dysrhythmia in deep structures has occurred consistently in other psychomotor patients in our series.

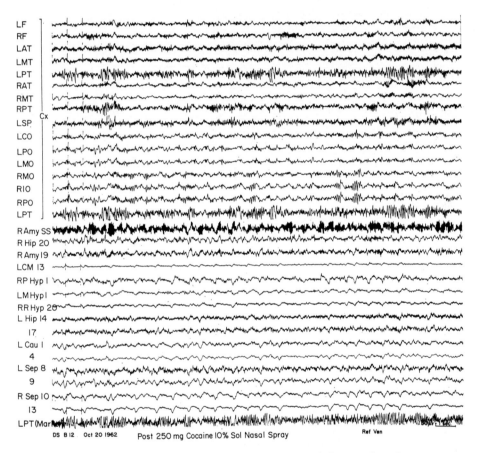

FIG. 18. Recording of Patient No. B-12 while under influence of cocaine.

In summary, the pain-killing, pleasure-inducing compounds used in this study failed to induce a significant pleasurable response in the subjects. Only minimal changes occurred in the recordings of one subject in response to cocaine, and these were restricted to rhinencephalic structures in association with anxiety symptoms.

DISCUSSION

The specially prepared group of patients has provided a unique opportunity to study the relation between emotional behavior and neural activity. Although none of the subjects were "normal," they suffered from a variety of pathologic processes, and we therefore assume that the phenomena observed were not a feature of a particular disease. Emotion is an extremely difficult phenomenon to investigate; it is vague, and satisfactory objective measurement is still not available. Observation of general behavior provides little enlightenment. The most useful data concerning emotional states are obtained through speech; by speaking, people communicate their feelings and thoughts to others. Even the introspective verbal reports of a cooperative subject and general behavioral observations do not, however, furnish complete information concerning emotional responses. In addition to the shortcomings due to deficient methods for measuring emotion, studies of this type have other limitations. With the methods used, including pneumoencephalography, the sites of electrodes and cannulae, particularly those adjacent to the ventricular system, are fairly accurately localized, but less precisely than by the histologic verification possible in animal studies.

Data obtained on the 14 subjects for whom spindles were recorded were distinct and reproducible. The change was focal in specific rhinencephalic structures. The spindling could be evoked and terminated by manipulating the stimulus (the interpersonal interview or a specific sensory stimulus) or by spontaneous shifting of the patient's thoughts. The phenomenon did not accompany all emotional reactions. Strong emotion generated by current situations did not consistently evoke spindling unless the current situation was rooted to older, highly charged memories. Neither recall of unemotional experiences nor simple sensory stimuli, detached from emotional significance, evoked the discharge. During abstract thought, e.g., during mathematical calculation, the spindling stopped. We are not able to explain the observation that the recording response was the same during a pleasurable emotional response as during a painful emotional response.

Forty of our subjects with implanted depth electrodes did not exhibit the phenomenon, although they, too, were repeatedly interviewed. Animal experiments devised by Lesse[17] as an extension of preliminary observations in human subjects demonstrated that the area from which the spindling occurred in animals was focal within the nuclei of the amygdala. The spindling occurred in cats only in the lateral nucleus of the amygdala and subjacent pyriform cortex in response to a stimulus to which the animal had been conditioned to give an aversive response. Although we are certain that electrodes were in the structures indicated, it is possible that the region in human subjects from which the spindles are recorded is also discrete.

The extremely focal recordings cannot be interpreted as evidence that changes in electrical activity take place only in these precise parts of the olfactory system within the brain. These regions are richly interconnected with other regions of the brain, especially the mesencephalic tegmentum and the cortex. A change of this magnitude taking place in the olfactory system unquestionably affects the more distal regions, and, conversely, the rhinencephalic spindling could be initiated by activity indicated at a more distal site. With development of instrumentation for more precise record-ings, it is likely that recording changes in association with emotional be-havior will also be detected elsewhere in the brain. From our observations we can conclude only that these particular anatomic sites actively partici-pate in certain types of emotional expression, particularly expression of emotions rooted in old, highly charged memory experiences.

The recording and behavioral data obtained from subjects administered pain-killing and euphoria-inducing drugs contribute little additional infor-mation to our understanding of the relation between cerebral activity and emotion. In the subjects used, two chronic schizophrenics and one epileptic, a distinct response was not induced. The only significant change occurred in one subject in response to cocaine, and even this was less than some responses that he exhibited during stimulation by interpersonal interview. When the change occurred with a narcotic drug, however, it was in the same structures, possibly in the same circuitry in which changes occurred during spontaneous fluctuations in emotion. Cocaine is probably the com-pound which most consistently, but temporarily, produces a nearly ideal clinical effect in modifying behavior. But the undesirable side effects which become manifest with repeated usage are so pronounced that the compound cannot be used. In addition to a feeling of well-being, cocaine temporarily induces a degree of alertness. These features aroused the interest of Freud, who experimented with it for treatment of neuroses.[16] In animal studies the compound has been shown to induce high-amplitude spindling, particularly through the region of the amygdala,[5] which resembles electroencephalo-graphic changes obtained in human subjects during intensely emotional episodes.

The outstanding feature of the data obtained with our methods is a cor-relation between physical activity in specific parts of the old olfactory struc-tures of the brain and emotional behavior. The evidence suggests that these regions of the brain represent important links in the neural substrate for expression of emotion.

REFERENCES

1. BECKER, H. C., FOUNDS, W. L., PEACOCK, S. M. HEATH, R. G., and LLEWELLYN, R. C. "Improvements in the Technique for Implanting Subcortical Electrodes in Man by a Stereotaxic Method," in *Studies in Schizophrenia,* by Heath, R. G., and the Department of Psychiatry and Neurology, Tulane University. Cambridge, Mass., Harvard, 1954, pp. 565–570.

2. BECKER, H. C., FOUNDS, W. L., PEACOCK, S. M., HEATH, R. G., LLEWELLYN, R. C., and MICKLE, W. A. A roentgenographic stereotaxic technique for implanting and maintaining electrodes in the brain of man. *Electroenceph. Clin. Neurophysiol. 9*:533, 1957.

3. BRADY, J. V. "Emotional Behavior," in *Handbook of Physiology,* Section I, *Neurophysiology,* Vol. 3, ed. by Field, J. Washington, D.C., American Physiological Society, 1960, pp. 1529–1552.

4. DOSTOYEVSKY, F. M. *The Idiot.* London, Dent, 1914, pp. 215–216.

5. EIDELBERG, E., LESSE, H., and GAULT, F. P. "An Experimental Model of Temporal Lobe Epilepsy: Studies of the Convulsant Properties of Cocaine," in *EEG & Behavior,* ed. by Glaser, G. H. New York, Basic Books, 1963, pp. 272–283.

6. HEATH, R. G., and the Department of Psychiatry and Neurology, Tulane University. *Studies in Schizophrenia,* Cambridge, Mass., Harvard, 1954.

7. HEATH, R. G. Correlations between levels of psychological awareness and physiological activity in the central nervous system. *Psychosom. Med. 17*:383, 1955.

8. HEATH, R. G. Correlation of electrical recordings from cortical and subcortical regions of the brain with abnormal behavior in human subjects. *Confin. Neurol. 18*:305, 1958.

9. HEATH, R. G. Physiological and biochemical studies in schizophrenia with particular emphasis on mind-brain relationships. *Int. Rev. Neurobiol. 1*:299, 1959.

10. HEATH, R. G., and FOUNDS, W. L. A perfusion cannula for intracerebral microinjections. *Electroenceph. Clin. Neurophysiol. 12*:930, 1960.

11. HEATH, R. G., JOHN, S., and FOSS, O. Stereotaxic biopsy. *Arch. Neurol. 4*:291, 1961.

12. HEATH, R. G., and MICKLE, W. A. "Evaluation of Seven Years' Experience with Depth Electrode Studies in Human Patients," in *Electrical Studies on the Unanesthetized Brain,* ed. by Ramey, E. R., and O'Doherty, D. S. New York, Hoeber-Harper, 1960, pp. 214–247.

13. HEATH, R. G., MICKLE, W. A., and MONROE, R. R. Characteristics of recordings from various specific subcortical nuclear masses in the brain of psychotic and nonpsychotic patients. *Trans. Amer. Neurol. Ass. 81*:17, 1956.

14. HEATH, R. G., PEACOCK, S. M., MONROE, R. R., and MILLER, W. H. "Electroencephalograms and Subcorticograms Recorded Since the June 1952 Meetings," in *Studies in Schizophrenia,* by Heath, R. G., and the Department of Psychiatry and Neurology, Tulane University. Cambridge, Mass., Harvard, 1954, pp. 573–608.

15. HODES, R. HEATH, R. G., FOUNDS, W. L., LLEWELLYN, R. C., and HENDLEY, C. D. Implantation of subcortical electrodes in man by stereotaxic method. *Amer. J. Physiol. 171*:736, 1952.

16. JONES, E. "The Cocaine Episode, in *The Life and Work of Sigmund Freud,* Vol. I. New York, Basic Books, 1953, pp. 78–97.

17. LESSE, H. Electrographic recordings of amygdaloid activity during a conditioned response. *Fed. Proc. 16*:79, 1957.

18. LESSE, H., HEATH, R. G., MICKLE, W. A., MONROE, R. R., and MILLER, W. H. Rhinencephalic activity during thought. *J. Nerv. Ment. Dis. 112*:433, 1955.

19. LINDSLEY, D. B. *Handbook of Experimental Psychology,* ed. by Stevens, S. S. New York, Wiley, 1950, p. 473.

IRWIN A. BERG, PH.D.
Louisiana State University

Discussion

LINDSLEY HAS FOCUSED HIS ATTENTION on the problem of the origin of pleasure and the evidence for its appearance in the course of neural and behavioral development. He has noted that newborn animals and infants appear to seek or, as the Russian physiologist Sechenov expressed it, to *strive* for sensory stimulation. The developing organism indeed appears to require sensory stimulation, for a variety of studies indicate that when immature animals or infants are placed under conditions of sensory deprivation, they become extremely restless and hyperactive, as if the organism were seeking increased stimulation through its own activity.

Infancy is a period of considerable mobility, and achievement of the sensory stimulation sought by the infant will perforce sometimes be satisfying and thus pleasurable, whereas at other times it will be painful and hence aversive. Moreover, reactions to particular stimuli are not fixed, for, as Harlow has observed, the same stimulus which at one stage of development produces avoidance responses may at a later stage elicit approach behavior. Lindsley has noted that such differential reactions to the same stimulus at different periods of development are probably related to the maturation of the cerebral cortex which, at the time of birth, plays but a small part in mediating responses to sensory stimulation. Such behavioral integration during the first few months of life is mainly at a brain-stem level. The active infant, striving for sensory stimulation, will regularly disrupt the homeostatic condition, and the ensuing restoration of physiologic equilibrium will probably be satisfying and pleasurable. If the safe-tolerance limits of homeostatic disruption are exceeded as a result of the infant's activity, distress or pain will ensue. Moderate activity, by contrast, will probably be pleasurable and will be gradually conditioned to various sensory stimuli such as those, for example, which accompany ingestion of food.

Thus it seems probable that in the maturing human organism sensory stimulation is actively sought and, under certain conditions, relates to the experience of pleasure. Olds and Olds, working with animals, have been concerned with the neural mechanisms of voluntary behavior as opposed to the maturational factors which may be involved in such mechanisms. Their technic, involving use of electrodes implanted in various areas of animals' brains, provided a means of direct electrical stimulation of the brain. With electrodes inserted in the lateral hypothalamus, rats learned to press a lever which provided mild electrical stimulation of the brain, and they pressed it at the incredible rate of 10,000 times an hour. The rats probably experienced intense pleasure from the stimulation. With electrodes inserted in certain areas of the brain, the rats demonstrated aversive responses when stimulated; and with electrodes in still other areas, they exhibited a positive-negative reaction. Upon reviewing anatomic and physiologic factors involved in these three effects, Olds and Olds speculated that there may be circuits of neural fibers with alternate members which produce positive or negative reinforcement under stimulation. They postulated that the nuclei for such circuits contain synapses between fibers of positive and negative effect and thus produce the mixed or positive-negative effects.

Bishop, Elder, and Heath used intracranial self-stimulation differently. These pioneers in the use of intracranial self-stimulation by human subjects attempted to control operant behavior by electrical stimulation of the brain in two patients. However, both patients demonstrated clear evidence of pronounced behavioral abnormalities, and one was extremely uncooperative; no data are available from other human subjects under similar conditions for comparative purposes. Nevertheless, certain observations made by these investigators are provocative, if inconclusive. Olds and Olds, for example, found regions of the brain which had mixed positive-negative effects in the rat; Bishop, Elder, and Heath found similar reward-aversion effects in a human subject but in apparently more divergent cerebral sites. The methodology used in the study by Bishop and his associates appears to be sound, and consistently positive results in controlling human operant behavior would have been expected from their experiments. Interesting positive results were obtained. The puzzling instances of failure to control self-stimulation behavior by changes in experimental conditions may be attributable to the psychiatric illnesses of their subjects or to numerous other factors. Further studies with a larger series of subjects and a greater variety of sites of electrode implantation may provide the necessary clues.

The study by Heath and Gallant of brain activity during emotional thought in human subjects, like the investigation by Bishop and associates, is also a pioneering research venture. Each of 54 human subjects with electrodes deeply implanted into the brain was interviewed over a period of time. The Tulane investigators found that emotional thought was associated with pronounced changes in electrical activity in deep, specific regions of the olfactory system of the brain, as measured by electroencephalographic amplitude and frequency. Curiously and significantly, these electrical changes in deeper-lying structures of the brain occurred only with *old* emotion-laden memories. Current emotionally charged situations, such as anger directed at a ward attendant, produced loud curses and similar overt expressions of emotion but no remarkable changes in electrical activity recorded from the deep olfactory structures of the brain. Furthermore, the revival of old emotional memories during the interviews was not necessarily accompanied by overt displays of emotion, as was the case with recent emotional experiences. Since changes in electrical activity associated with recollection of old emotional experiences halted rather abruptly when the subjects were given simple mathematical problems to solve, the electrical changes in the deeper-lying structures of the brain are apparently readily suppressed by other thought processes. Some sensory stimuli produced electrical changes of the type described here, but only when emotion was involved. Pain-killing and pleasure-inducing drugs did not produce significant electrical changes in the areas of electrode implantation. The data obtained in the study by Heath and Gallant indicate that changes in electrical activity in particular regions of the phylogenetically old olfactory structures of the brain are correlated with the recall of old emotional experiences but not with current or extremely recent emotional situations. This observation raises more questions than it answers, and that is what pioneering investigations should do.

PART II

Pharmacologic Studies

LARRY STEIN, PH.D.
Wyeth Laboratories, Inc.

Reciprocal Action of Reward and Punishment Mechanisms

A s an initial step in the analysis of behavior, it is convenient to distinguish between reflex and operant behaviors.[26] The distinction does not refer to the form of the response; a reflex eyelid closure elicited by a cinder may appear identical with a voluntary blink. From the viewpoint of a psychologist, the distinction refers to the control exerted by environmental stimuli. The important stimuli in the case of a reflex *precede* the response and specifically *elicit* it. An operant is thought to be generated, at least to some extent, intrinsically because often it is difficult or impossible to specify an environmental stimulus that could have elicited it.* In Skinner's terminology, operants are emitted, not elicited.

The important stimuli in the operant case *follow* the response and, through a process known as reinforcement, modify its rate of emission. Some stimuli, called rewards, make the behaviors they follow more likely to be repeated; other stimuli, called punishments, make them less likely. If reinforcement is withheld or terminated, symmetrically opposite effects are obtained. Behavior that leads to a loss of reward is inhibited or "extinguished," whereas behavior that avoids or terminates punishment is facilitated or "negatively reinforced."†

These long-recognized actions of reinforcing stimuli have been the subject of a great deal of speculation. My purpose here is to try to relate some of these speculations to recent behavioral and physiologic observations. To keep the account as uncomplicated as reasonably possible, I have tended to emphasize consistencies, despite the risk of appearing unmindful of difficul-

---

* Hence, for example, the designation of free movement as "spontaneous motor activity."
† Terminology in this field has not been standardized. "Negative reinforcement," which refers in this paper to the *facilitation* of behavior by the termination of a punishing stimulus, should not be confused with "punishment," which refers to the *inhibition* of behavior by the presentation of a punishing stimulus.

ties. In any event, I am ready to admit that speculative endeavors of this sort should, at best, be regarded merely as guides for research.

THEORIES OF REINFORCEMENT

A satisfactory theory of reinforcement must explain not only how behavior is strengthened or weakened by rewards and punishments but also how a response can be influenced by a stimulus which occurs after the response is completed. Future events obviously cannot be governed by present occurrences; hence, it must be that the behavior is modified by the persisting effects of prior reinforcement. Because these effects may persist for long periods (years), it is generally assumed that some sort of permanent change occurs in the brain when behavior is reinforced.

Two important types of mechanisms have been proposed to explain the actions of reinforcers. One type has been referred to as a "confirming" mechanism and the other as an "expectancy" mechanism. The idea that reinforcement acts as a confirming mechanism was first proposed by Thorndike[34] and later developed by Hull.[11] These theorists assumed, contrary to Skinner, that all responses in an organism's repertoire (including operants) are attached to specific eliciting stimuli by hypothetical associative connections. Reinforcers act by modifying the strength of these associative connections. If a particular stimulus-response pair is followed by reward, the associative connection between that stimulus and response is strengthened. Punishments have the opposite effect, at least in an early version of Thorndike's theory, and weaken connections. This theory, then, accounts for the persistent action of reinforcers on the basis of the relatively permanent changes they produce in the eliciting tendencies of stimuli.

I find this idea unattractive physiologically. A substrate for all possible stimulus-response connections, as well as a mechanism for their continual modification by reinforcement, it seems to me, calls for a brain of unreasonable complexity. The Thorndikian view of reinforcement also has been criticized on purely behavioral grounds.[15]

The idea that reinforcement acts by an expectancy mechanism was suggested originally by Tolman[35] and later, in one form or another, by many psychologists.[4, 23, 24, 27] Mowrer's[15] treatment is best developed, and my version presented hereafter closely follows it.

Loosely, it is the anticipation or expectation of reinforcement, and not its actual occurrence, that directly engages or motivates operant behavior. Obviously, operant (pursuit) behavior is unnecessary if reward already has been obtained; similarly, operant (avoidance) behavior is superfluous if punishment already has been delivered. Subjectively, it seems as though pursuit were motivated by the expectation of reward and avoidance by the expectation of averting punishment. According to this view, the reinforcing stimulus itself (or its termination) plays a critical but indirect part, i.e., to establish and maintain the expectation.

To be of scientific value, the concept of expectation must be stripped of its teleologic connotations and placed on a mechanical or physiologic basis. This may be done by assuming that the expectation of reinforcement is a Pavlovian conditioned reflex.[22] It is also necessary to show how expectations can make contact with operant behavior. These arguments will be presented in detail after a brief discussion of work on the identification of reinforcement systems in the brain.

SUBSTRATES OF REINFORCEMENT

In 1954 Delgado, Roberts, and Miller[5] (following early work of Hess[10]) reported the first experimental proof that electrical stimulation of the brain could serve as a punishment. Coincidentally, in the same year, Olds and Milner[18] described for the first time the unexpected finding that electrical stimulation of the brain could serve as a reward. Later work confirmed and extended both observations and permitted some limited appreciation of the organization of the reinforcement systems in the brain. Largely as a result of the efforts of Olds,[16] it now seems highly probable (although direct evidence is lacking) that the hypothalamic medial forebrain bundle and its connections play a central role in the mediation of reward and that the periventricular system of the diencephalon and midbrain has a critical part in the mediation of punishment. Le Gros Clark[12] published excellent diagrams of both systems in 1938, long before we had any idea of their behavioral significance (Fig. 1). Obviously, each of these structures composes only one part of a more complex system. Nevertheless, for convenience, I shall refer henceforth to a medial forebrain bundle reward or incentive system and a periventricular punishment system. The medial forebrain bundle may be thought of as part of a "go" mechanism that facilitates ongoing operant behavior, and the periventricular system as part of a "stop" mechanism that inhibits ongoing operant behavior. Furthermore, there is reason to believe that the go and stop mechanisms are mutually inhibitory, like antagonistic spinal reflexes. Hence activation of one mechanism can depress the other. Similarly, sudden deactivation of one mechanism can release the other from inhibition and cause a brief period of heightened activity by a rebound effect.

REINFORCEMENT OF OPERANT BEHAVIOR

With this background, it is possible to speculate about the reinforcement of operants. Assume first that operant responses are composed of a chain of components. For example, the act of pressing a lever involves approach-

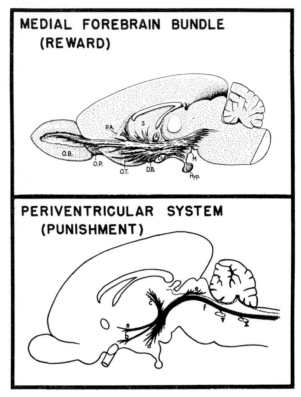

Fig. 1. Upper: Diagram representing medial forebrain bundle—presumed substrate of reward mechanism—in a generalized and primitive mammalian brain. Some abbreviations are: A, anterior commissure; D.B., nucleus of the diagonal band; M, mammillary body; S, septum. Lower: Similar diagram representing periventricular system of fibers—presumed substrate of punishment mechanism. Some abbreviations are: b, anterior hypothalamus; c, thalamus; d, posterior hypothalamus; e, tectum. (From Le Gros Clark.[12])

ing, pressing, and releasing components. Next, assume that each response component is accompanied by distinctive cues or stimuli. These response-related stimuli may be environmental (e.g., sight of lever, smells of chamber) or intrinsic (especially proprioception of movements), and their relative importance will vary in different situations.

Pairing an operant response with reward may be viewed as an instance of Pavlovian conditioning. Response-related stimuli are the conditioned stimulus, and the reward is the unconditioned stimulus. By virtue of the pairing, the medial forebrain bundle go mechanism or some structure (reflexly activated by the reward) that activates the go mechanism is conditioned to response-related stimuli. Thus, on future occasions, any tendency to engage in the previously rewarded behavior initiates facilitory feedback by an activation of the go mechanism and thereby increases the probability that the response will run off to completion. In the case of punishment, periventricular activity is conditioned to stimuli associated with the punished operant. This decreases the probability that the operant will be emitted in the future, because feedback from the stop mechanism will tend to inhibit the behavior.

Two features of this Pavlovian conditioning process should be made explicit. First, it provides for activation of reinforcement systems of the brain before the occurrence of the reinforcing stimulus and is therefore a mechanism for anticipation or expectation. Second, it limits activation of reinforcement mechanisms to stimuli of previously reinforced behavior, as it obviously should.

A critical and somewhat novel feature of the theory, the role of reward-punishment interactions, remains to be discussed. From our own experiences we know (1) that rewards may lose their effectiveness under the threat of punishment and, conversely, (2) that punishment may be ineffective if accompanied by strong reward. Experimental data support these observations. An example of (1) is provided by work of Estes and Skinner[7] on the conditioning of fear. These investigators showed that operant behavior maintained by food reward is disrupted in the presence of a tone that signals an impending painful shock. An example of (2) is furnished by Masserman's[13] demonstration that cats will learn to accept a punishing air blast in the face to obtain milk. These observations support the idea that reward and punishment mechanisms are reciprocally inhibitory.

Another kind of interaction also is implied by the theory. This stems from the conception that the go and stop systems feed continuously into motor mechanisms and jointly determine the net effect, facilitation or inhibition, on operant behavior. I cannot exaggerate the importance of this assumption of continuous and joint action. It implies, for example, an involvement of the punishment mechanism even in "pure" reward situations. For example, suppose that a hungry rat is trained to traverse an alley to obtain food at the far end. Early in training, progress down the alley is slow, and various behaviors are observed which interfere with running. After a number of rewarded trials, however, the rat races directly down the alley each time it is tested. How does the theory explain this?

Placing the rat at the starting point activates the hypothalamic incentive mechanism because, on previous trials, stimuli of the alley have been associated with reward. If the animal starts down the alley, the incentive mechanism will increase its output, since cues of running and alley stimuli past the starting point are closely associated with reward. The increase in hypothalamic output facilitates the ongoing behavior and thus augments the tendency of the rat to continue going down the alley.

What if, instead of proceeding down the alley at the start, the rat turns around and explores the back wall? Since cues of turning around and looking at the back wall always have been extremely remote from reinforcement, they have less tendency to activate the hypothalamic incentive mechanism than the initial stimuli. Incentive will drop and, by reciprocal inhibition, periventricular activity will rise. These changes will tend to cut the behavior short and, by conditioning, will tend to inhibit it on future occasions.

If the theory is correct, one must conclude that positive reinforcement of an operant acts in at least two ways to increase the likelihood that the behavior will be repeated. First, the operant chain itself will be facilitated by positive feedback from the incentive system; and second, competing behavior chains will be inhibited, at least to some extent, by punishing feedback.

It can be shown by analogous argument that punishment of an operant similarly acts in two ways to decrease the probability that the response will be repeated. The punished operant itself will be inhibited by periventricular feedback, whereas competing behavior will enjoy at least some degree of (rebound) hypothalamic facilitation.

To summarize the argument:

1. Operant behavior is motivated by the expectation, rather than the occurrence, of reward and punishment.

2. The mechanism for expectation is a Pavlovian conditioned (neural) reflex, resulting in activation of the medial forebrain bundle region of the hypothalamus in the case of reward and the periventricular region of the diencephalon and midbrain in the case of punishment.

3. Activation of the hypothalamic reward mechanism provides facilitory feedback to ongoing operant behavior, whereas activation of the periventricular punishment mechanism provides inhibitory feedback to ongoing operant behavior.

4. Response-related cues (environmental as well as proprioceptive) are largely responsible for activation of reinforcement mechanisms.

5. Reward and punishment mechanisms are mutually inhibitory and continuously and jointly determine the net effect on operant behavior.

WEAKNESSES OF THE THEORY

Some difficulties and omissions of the theory may be briefly noted. First, no mention is made of the part played by biologic needs or deprivation states, although it is clear that needs critically influence the effectiveness of rewards. (For example, hunger determines the reward value of food.) My unelaborated guess would be that needs act principally to produce shifts in the reactivity of the brain to the different reinforcing stimuli.

Second, the question of response initiation has been passed over. Although there is undoubtedly much truth in Skinner's idea that operant behavior is emitted and not elicited, still it is also true, as sensory deprivation studies indicate, that brain activity and behavior are heavily dependent on input from the environment.

Feedback theories of reinforcement are commonly criticized on the ground that the correct response chain (or its underlying neural process) must somehow first get started in order to engage the feedback mechanism. If response initiation is random, a number of incorrect behaviors might have to be executed before the correct one turns up and is locked in by positive feedback. In such a case, it is difficult to explain, by a feedback theory, the well-established fact that the latency of a rewarded response decreases sharply with training. Perhaps the idea that all nonreinforced behaviors are punished in a reward situation (by rebound activation of the punishment mechanism) increases the plausibility of a random initiation process. Because incorrect responses may then be inhibited almost as soon as they occur, the correct response can have a short latency, even if several incorrect responses happen to turn up first.

Finally, no provision has been made to control the positive feedback process assumed to be the basis of reward. What prevents the behavior from "running away" once positive feedback has started? Reciprocal inhibition of the punishment mechanism further increases the likelihood of runaway behavior. Clearly, the go mechanism requires a governor, but this has not yet been worked out.

EXPERIMENTAL DATA

Four experimental situations of major importance (reward, punishment, extinction, and avoidance) are derived by presenting or withholding either reward or punishment after an operant response (Table 1). The behavioral effects of these manipulations also are indicated in Table 1: Presenting reward or withholding punishment facilitates responding, whereas withholding reward or presenting punishment inhibits responding. Cases involving presentation of reinforcement—reward and punishment—will be given only cursory documentation here. The more refractory cases (from the viewpoint of theory) in which reinforcement is withheld—extinction and avoidance—are treated more extensively hereafter.

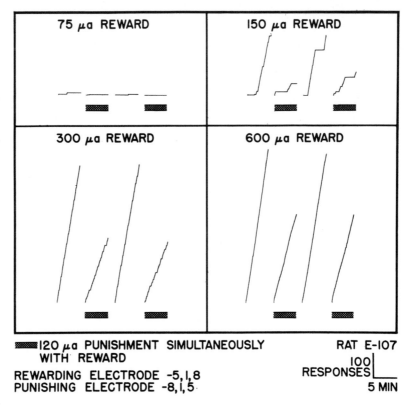

FIG. 2. Cumulative records of self-stimulation for reward alone (first and third segments in each quadrant) and for both reward and punishment (second and fourth segments). Height of each segment indicates total self-stimulation output in a 5-minute period. Electrode coordinates are in millimeters as follows: anterior (+) or posterior (−) from bregma; lateral from midline; depth from surface of brain.

Figure 2 consists of records of self-stimulation of a rat with both a rewarding electrode in the posterior hypothalamus and a punishing electrode in the periventricular system of the midbrain. The experiment is programmed in alternating 5-minute periods. In odd-numbered periods, each lever press delivers a rewarding hypothalamic stimulus; in even-numbered periods, responses are rewarded in the hypothalamus and punished in the midbrain simultaneously. The punishing periventricular current is fixed throughout at 120μa., but the rewarding current is systematically varied.

Comparison of the "unpunished" curves in each quadrant shows that operant output varies directly with rewarding current and hence presumably with the degree of hypothalamic activation. Comparing "punished" and "unpunished" records shows that activation of a periventricular punishing system inhibits operant behavior. Note that the inhibitory effect of punishment is smaller under high-intensity reward. Clearly, incentive and punishment systems jointly influence the tendency to engage in operant behavior.

TABLE 1. EXPERIMENTAL SITUATIONS RESULTING FROM PRESENTATION OR WITHHOLDING OF EITHER REWARD OR PUNISHMENT AFTER A DESIGNATED RESPONSE[a]

Type of stimulus	Presented	Withheld
Rewarding	Reward (facilitation)	Extinction[b] (inhibition)
Punishing	Punishment (inhibition)	Avoidance (facilitation)

[a] Effect on the behavior is given in parentheses.

[b] Strictly speaking, this refers to an experimental situation in which the regular presentation of reward is interrupted each time the response occurs. In the usual extinction situation, reward is withheld altogether.

AVOIDANCE BEHAVIOR

Operant behavior is facilitated if it decreases or terminates punishment (escape) or the threat of punishment (avoidance). For example, most rats can be trained to press frequently on a lever if doing so avoids painful shocks.[25] Such examples of negative reinforcement pose difficulties for a theory which assumes that behavioral facilitation is mediated by a reward mechanism. However, by the assumption of reciprocal inhibition, it is possible to show that the hypothalamic incentive mechanism can play a key role in the motivation of operant avoidance behavior.

To my knowledge, the idea that avoidance is maintained by a positive incentive was suggested first by Woodworth and Schlosberg.[36] * These writers, noting that "behavioral evidence of fear is absent" in late stages of avoidance training, asked "whether safety is not a sufficient positive incentive to maintain the avoidance response" (p. 675). Mowrer[15] has expressed

---

* I am indebted to Dr. Richard L. Solomon for bringing this citation to my attention.

a similar view, substituting the term "relief" (to him a form of reward) for "safety." The most detailed statement of the idea, however, has been made by Olds.[17] My scheme is based on his idea, which may be paraphrased as follows: during exposure to a threatening stimulus, brain mechanisms for punishment are activated and mechanisms for reward are therefore

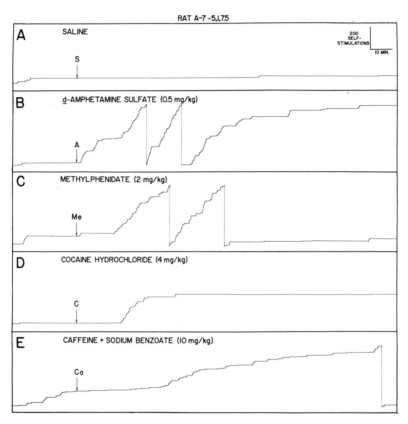

FIG. 3. Facilitation of self-stimulation by four psychostimulants at matched doses of antireserpine potency. Setting current level just below threshold (note low control rate in panel *A*) increases sensitivity of test.

suppressed. If an operant response terminates the threat, the reward mechanisms suddenly are released from inhibition and, by a rebound effect, go through a brief period of increased activity. This burst of reward activity serves to reinforce the avoidance response. In the language of the present theory, the burst of reward activity is conditioned to cues of the avoidance response and increases its likelihood on future occasions by providing facilitory feedback.

This idea was suggested to Olds by the observation that two variables—cortical spreading depression and the tranquilizing drug chlorpromazine—had identical (inhibitory) effects on operant behavior in tests of self-stimulation and avoidance. Additionally, he noted that a continuous background of rewarding hypothalamic stimulation augmented escape from punishing tegmental stimulation.[21] This surprising finding of synergism also coincided with the idea that avoidance behavior is dependent on hypothalamic facilitation.

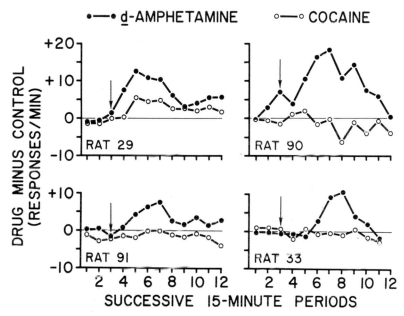

Fig. 4. Comparisons in four rats of stimulating effects of d-amphetamine sulfate (0.5 mg. per kilogram) and cocaine hydrochloride (4 mg. per kilogram) on rate of avoidance in Sidman test. Plots show deviations from control response rates in successive 15-minute periods; deviations above zero line indicate stimulation. Arrows indicate time of injection.

My data lend additional support to this view. First I shall show that stimulant drugs augment both self-stimulation and avoidance behavior in nearly identical fashion. Then I shall present evidence of a remarkable potentiation of avoidance-responding in a shuttlebox by brief priming bursts of rewarding stimulation of the brain.

DRUG STUDIES

My interest in stimulant drugs grew out of early work on reserpine.[31, 33] These studies showed that the behavioral depression induced by reserpine is reversed by psychostimulants like amphetamine, cocaine, and caffeine, but not by other so-called stimulant drugs, such as picrotoxin, Metrazol, strychnine, or nicotine.

Besides this antireserpine effect, the psychostimulants, but not the other drugs, augment self-stimulation and other operant behavior.[28, 29] This apparent correlation between antireserpine activity and operant facilitation was subjected to a rigorous test by matching doses of four psychostimulants for antireserpine potency and then comparing the matched doses in the self-stimulation test. Results obtained from seven rats are exemplified by data from one rat shown in Figure 3. Despite equal effects against reserpine, the activity of the drugs varied widely in self-stimulation, amphetamine

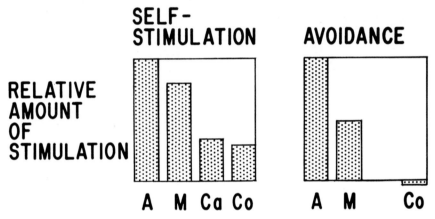

FIG. 5. Relative stimulating effects of d-amphetamine (A), methylphenidate (M), caffeine (Ca), and cocaine (Co) in self-stimulation and Sidman avoidance. Doses of the four drugs are matched for antireserpine potency.

being the most active and cocaine the least. These differences were surprising and still are unexplained, but the large discrepancy between amphetamine and cocaine recalled a similar observation in the Sidman avoidance test. Amphetamine was much more active; in fact, cocaine seemed to have no stimulating effect at this relatively low dose (Fig. 4).

Figure 5 summarizes the pharmacologic observations. Although the avoidance data are not complete, stimulant drugs clearly have similar actions in both tests, just as do phenothiazine tranquilizers. This observation may be explained by the assumption that a brain mechanism common to both situations is an important site of drug action. If, as suggested earlier, this common mechanism involves hypothalamic activation, it would be reasonable to speculate that amphetamine augments both self-stimulation and avoidance by lowering thresholds in the hypothalamic incentive system.

This idea parallels the speculation of Olds[16] that chlorpromazine inhibits self-stimulation and avoidance by raising reward thresholds. Direct evidence of effects of both drugs on hypothalamic self-stimulation thresholds already has been reported.[32]

EXPERIMENTS IN BRAIN STIMULATION

Figure 6 contains a diagram of the classic avoidance procedure that was used for stimulation experiments. Warning lights at both ends of the shuttlebox signal to the rat that it must cross to the opposite side within 7.5 seconds or receive a punishing periventricular brain shock. A successful

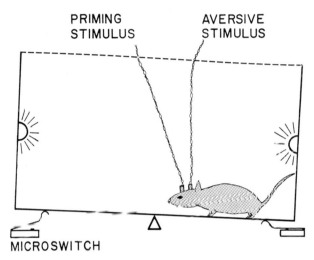

FIG. 6. Diagram of shuttlebox. Light onset indicates aversive shock in 7.5 seconds unless rat crosses over.

avoidance response averts the shock and turns the lights out for a 15-second period of safety before the next trial. Otherwise, the lights stay on, and a brief train of aversive stimulation is delivered every 7.5 seconds. Typically, delivery of the first aversive brain shock elicits a leap to the other side of the box, which terminates the trial.

Avoidance learning is slow in this situation, and performance levels tend to stabilize at a low value even after extensive training. One important retarding factor here is "freezing;" rats understandably are reluctant to approach the opposite warning light or to return to a place where punishment was received. In any case, the low base-line levels are desirable, since the aim is to potentiate avoidance behavior.

After base lines of avoidance are established, the effects of stimulating various points in the brain are studied. A brief priming stimulus is delivered simultaneously with the onset of the warning lights. The priming stimulus terminates automatically after 0.2 second and hence is independent

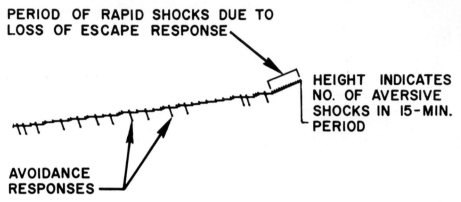

FIG. 7. Sample record of shuttlebox performance. Curve is drawn by cumulating aversive shocks over time and hence represents failures to avoid or escape.

of the rat's behavior. In a typical experiment, 15-minute control periods (no stimulation) are alternated between test periods of equal duration. After avoidance data are collected, each priming electrode is analyzed for positive motivational effects by a self-stimulation test.

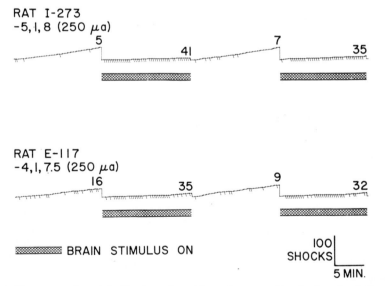

FIG. 8. Two examples of facilitation of avoidance by rewarding brain stimulation. Top record shows that rat I-273 had 41 and 35 avoidances when rewarding electrode was primed, but only 5 and 7 avoidances in control test. See Figure 7 for further explanation.

A sample record of shuttlebox performance in Figure 7 demonstrates the recording procedure. Diagonal pips of the curve indicate avoidance responses, which constitute the most important datum for present purposes. Figures 8 and 9 illustrate the major results. If the priming stimulus activated a rewarding point in the brain, the number of avoidance responses usually was increased strikingly (Fig. 8). If the priming stimulus was nonrewarding, no such increase in avoidance ensued (Fig. 9). Data for 11 rewarding electrodes (more than 1,000 self-stimulations per hour) and 13 nonreward-

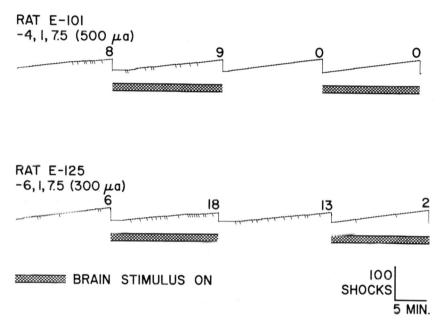

FIG. 9. Two examples of negligible effects on avoidance if priming stimulus is non rewarding. See Figure 7 for further explanation.

ing electrodes (less than 150 self-stimulations per hour) are summarized in Figure 10.

It may be thought that the rewarding stimulus facilitates avoidance merely by providing an additional warning cue. However, when a brief, but clearly audible, buzzing noise was substituted for rewarding stimulation of the brain, no appreciable facilitation of avoidance was obtained. Moreover, the negative findings with nonrewarding priming stimuli, which should provide extra cues too, militate against this idea.

Some other explanations also may be excluded. Observation of animals and latency data indicate that rewarding priming stimuli do not evoke reflex (short-latency) responses. Positive results in later experiments, where the interval between trials was independent of the rat's behavior, proved that avoidance responses were not reinforced by shortening of the interval between priming stimuli. Spontaneous, intertrial crossings were often, but not always, increased by rewarding stimulation; this effect is expected if it is correct to view spontaneous crossings as generalized avoidance responses.

My idea is that the rewarding priming stimulus acts in two ways to facilitate avoidance. First, by antagonizing the freezing effect of periventricular activation, it allows the avoidance response to become initiated. Second, by lowering thresholds or directly activating the hypothalamic go mecha-

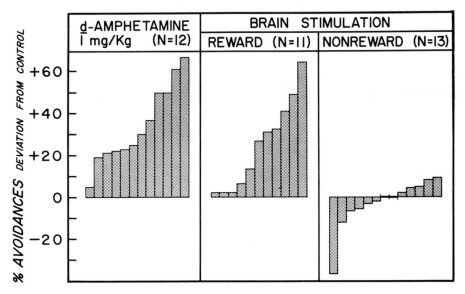

Fig. 10. Summary data showing effects of brain stimulation or amphetamine on shuttlebox avoidance. Each bar stands for one case and shows the absolute deviation from control performance induced by brain stimulation or the drug. (Each animal served as its own control.)

nism, it increases the probability that the avoidance response, once started, will continue to completion.

Intensity studies also emphasize the motivational significance of the priming stimulus. If the power of a brain stimulus to facilitate avoidance depends in part on its reward value, then variations of current will produce correlated changes in avoidance performance and self-stimulation (Fig. 11).

EXTINCTION

Operant behavior is inhibited when reward is omitted, decreased, or even delayed. Presumably, this makes it possible not only to suppress unsuccessful behaviors but also, by elimination of inefficient components, to refine complex operant chains into skills that maximize reinforcement. Extinction poses difficulties for a theory which assumes that behavioral inhibition is mediated by a punishment mechanism, since responding in these situations is inhibited in the absence of punishing stimulation from environment. Nevertheless, and again by the assumption of reciprocal inhibition,

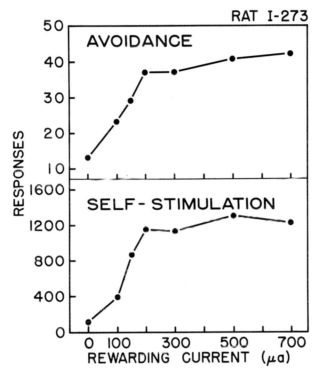

FIG. 11. Intensity functions obtained from same rewarding electrode in avoidance and self-stimulation tests. High degree of correspondence is evidence of a mechanism common to both situations.

it is possible to show that a mechanism of the brain for punishment can be activated in extinction to effect inhibition of operant behavior.

The argument is as follows. During the execution of a previously rewarded operant chain, a mechanism of the brain for reward is activated and a mechanism for punishment is therefore suppressed. If, after the chain is completed, reinforcement is not delivered, the punishment mechanism suddenly will be released from inhibition and, by a rebound effect, will go through a period of increased activity. This burst of periventricular activity punishes the unrewarded operant and, by conditioning, tends to inhibit it on future occasions.

The suggestion that extinction has an aversive aspect has been made by a number of psychologists, and evidence supporting this idea has been reviewed recently by Amsel.[1] In the final section of this paper is presented some new experimental material involving stimulation of the brain which is pertinent to this question. First, however, I wish to use this idea to explain some unusual effects of rewarding stimulation of the brain on discrimination learning.[19, 30]

DISCRIMINATION LEARNING AND STIMULATION OF THE BRAIN

Stein and Hearst[30] found that discrimination learning is severely retarded if rewarding brain stimulation is given before, rather than after, the occurrence of the response. In this experiment, thirsty rats were trained to discriminate between a pure tone and a clicking sound to obtain a small reward of water. The rats worked in a two-lever box. If the tone sounded, a press on the left-hand lever delivered water; if the clicker sounded, the lever on the right was the correct one. One of the auditory stimuli always was accompanied by a brief, positively rewarding brain stimulus which terminated automatically after 0.5 second. The other stimulus always was presented alone.

In each of four cases, the rat learned far more slowly to respond correctly to the stimulus paired with brain shock (Fig. 12). Control experiments, with blinking lights and foot shocks substituted for the rewarding brain stimulation, made it possible to eliminate simple distraction as an explanation. The rewarding properties of the stimulation were implicated by showing that a food pellet had a similar, but much smaller, retarding effect.* To explain these results, it was speculated that electrical stimulation of the reward system jams delicate associative networks that mediate learning.

In a related study, Olds and Olds[20] had rats learn anew each day whether a right-hand or a left-hand lever at the end of a runway delivered food. With practice, the animals came to respond perfectly throughout the daily session after a brief initial period of trial and error. After daily errors stabilized, brain stimulation was given on an uncontingent (response-independent) basis in 0.5-second trains every 3 seconds all during the test. Rewarding stimulation severely disrupted performance; although the rats continued

---

*The significance of this result is bolstered by the fact that rats have a powerful urge to drink immediately after eating. Hence, learning was retarded despite the possibility of a substantial increase in the reinforcing value of the water reward.

to work, errors were no longer eliminated. Other brain stimuli, including punishing ones in the tegmentum, usually had no retarding effect.

The authors offered several interpretations of these observations. One was identical with the early view of Stein and Hearst that electrical stimulation of reward areas causes confusion of associative processes. Another held that the background of rewarding stimulation impairs learning by par-

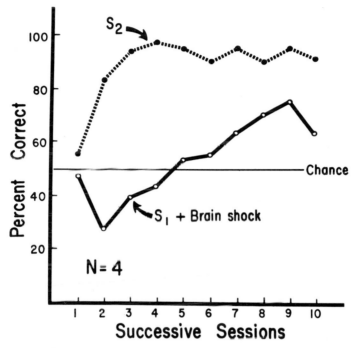

FIG. 12. Averaged learning curves in discrimination experiment, showing rapid acquisition of correct response to unpaired auditory stimulus (S_2) and retarded learning to stimulus (S_1) paired with rewarding brain shock. Note that S_1 curve dips below chance level in initial sessions. Twenty-five presentations of each stimulus given per session.

tial reinforcement of the wrong response, although it was recognized that this argument could not be applied to the Stein and Hearst experiment.*

Although the "confusion of learning mechanisms" explanation is plausible, I now prefer another based on the present conception of response inhibition. The substance of this idea is that a background of rewarding

---

* I believe that this idea can be ruled out because the rewarding stimulation in the Olds and Olds[20] study was uncontingent. In partial reinforcement, reward is always applied on a contingent basis but merely omitted on some occasions. Advocates of adventitious reinforcement explanations will disagree that this idea is easily ruled out.

stimulation impairs choice behavior by suppressing aversive reactions elicited by nonreinforcement. This may become clearer if we re-examine the base-line behavior in the study by Olds and Olds.

What do the animals learn every day in this situation? The possibilities are: (1) to approach the correct lever, (2) to avoid the incorrect lever, or (3) both of these. Published reports of experimental work suggest that (3)

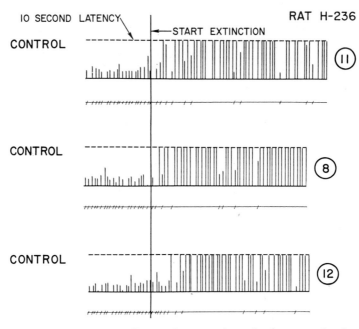

FIG. 13. Three records of base-line performance in extinction test, showing latencies of each response in sequence. Each vertical line indicates a trial. Short lines to left of vertical extinction marker give latencies of initial 20 reinforced responses. Longer lines to right of vertical marker show extinction latencies. Average intertrial interval is 30 seconds. Line with diagonal pips below each latency record also indicates responses. Circled number at right indicates total number of responses in extinction.

is probably correct but that learning to avoid the incorrect lever is the more critical process.[1, 6, 9] Thus, in large part, animals in the experiments by Olds and Olds learn to eliminate errors, and they do so because punishment follows errors.

How does a background of rewarding brain stimulation prevent the elimination of errors? Loosely, rewarding stimulation may be said to take the sting out of errors. Continual activation of the reward mechanism constantly suppresses the punishment mechanism; hence, in the language of the present theory, no inhibitory feedback is generated if the rat starts to make an incorrect (nonreinforced) response. This idea also explains why moderate (nonfreezing) levels of aversive stimulation do not impair performance and even predicts that such stimulation might improve performance by making it easier to inhibit errors.

Olds and Olds[19] reported a second phase of their experiment which bears on the rival interpretations, i.e., the confusion idea versus the aversiveness-of-errors idea. Only after animals achieved errorless performance was the

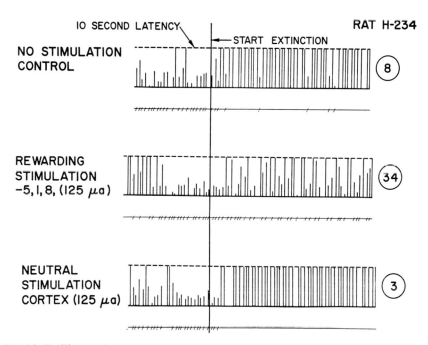

FIG. 14. Facilitory effect of rewarding background stimulation on extinction responding (middle record). Control stimulation in cortex does not facilitate and probably reduces extinction responding (bottom record). Note also brief disrupting effect of rewarding stimulation on initial reinforced trials. See Figure 13 for further explanation.

rewarding stimulation introduced. If rewarding stimulation acts by confusing learning, it should have had no effect, since learning already was complete. But if it acts by reducing the aversiveness of errors, the stimulation still should have been disruptive, since the maintenance of error-free performance depends on aversive feedback from nonreinforcement. In 15 out of 17 cases, the stimulus caused a complete relapse to errors. In the 2 remaining cases, a moderate relapse was observed. Clearly, this experiment supports the aversiveness-of-errors idea and does not substantiate the confusion-of-learning idea.

EXTINCTION AND STIMULATION OF THE BRAIN

If activation of the hypothalamic reward mechanism diminishes aversive reactions to nonreinforcement, it should be possible to demonstrate that a background of rewarding stimulation will interfere with simple extinction. Conventional extinction designs require comparisons between groups of animals. As a means of facilitating study of this problem, a daily extinction test was devised that allows the animal to act as his own control.

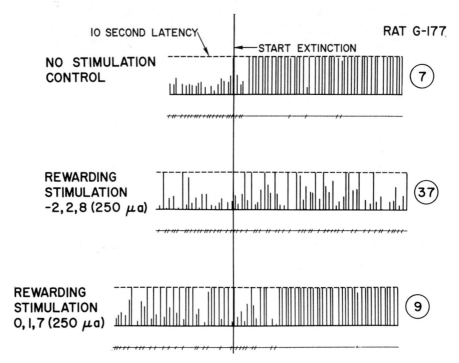

FIG. 15. Example of a rewarding electrode that did not facilitate extinction responding (bottom record). In the same rat, another rewarding electrode had a profound effect (middle record). See Figure 13 for further explanation.

Hungry rats are trained to press a lever to obtain food only in the presence of a tone. If they respond within 10 seconds, food is delivered; otherwise, the tone terminates automatically. Intertrial responses are never reinforced (and if necessary the presentation of tones is postponed to ensure that at least 3 seconds elapse between a response and a tone). Tones are presented about every 30 seconds, but without predictable regularity. After performance is perfect, the extinction procedure is introduced. At the beginning of each daily session, rats are given 20 reinforced trials, followed immediately by 50 extinction trials. This procedure is repeated daily until the number of responses in extinction stabilizes.

Control records shown in Figure 13 exemplify the base line. Important features are (1) the rapid cessation of responding in extinction and the stability of total extinction output and (2) the overnight recovery of perfect responding in the initial 20 reinforced trials. The most important datum

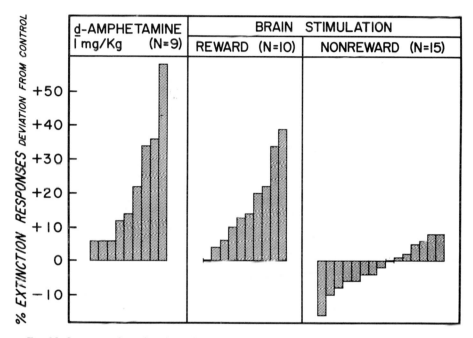

Fig. 16. Summary data showing effects of brain stimulation or amphetamine on tendency to respond in daily extinction test. Each bar stands for one case and shows absolute deviation from previous day's control performance induced by brain stimulation or drug. (Each animal served as its own control.)

for present purposes is the total number of responses in the 50 extinction trials.

Brain stimulation was given on an uncontingent basis in 0.15-second trains every 1.5 or 3 seconds all during the test. After extinction data were collected, each electrode was evaluated for positive reinforcement in a self-stimulation test. Ten electrodes yielded more than 1,000 responses per hour (reward) and 15 electrodes less than 150 responses per hour (nonreward).

Extinction responding was increased significantly by most rewarding electrodes (Figs. 14, 15, and 16), although often parameters had to be juggled to find optimal levels. Nonrewarding electrodes, on the other hand, had no definite effect or perhaps a slight tendency to reduce extinction responding (Figs. 14 and 16). Intertrial responding (which also was extinguished) was increased by rewarding background stimulation but not by nonrewarding stimulation.

PHARMACOLOGIC STUDIES

Pharmacologic studies were carried out to provide additional tests of the idea that a mechanism of the brain for punishment is activated in extinc-

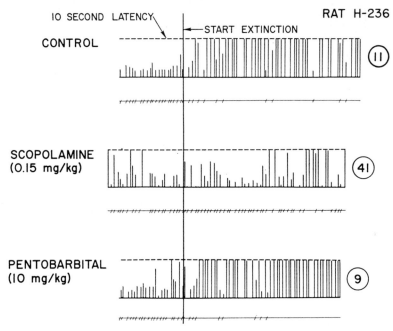

FIG. 17. Effects of drugs on well-practiced extinction. Pentobarbital has no effect on extinction output (bottom), but scopolamine often gives striking increases (middle). See Carlton[3] for a discussion of effects of scopolamine on extinction.

tion. Work of Miller[14] and of Geller and Seifter[8] indicates that the inhibitory effect of punishing electric shock on operant behavior is largely antagonized by barbiturates. If nonreward had a punishing action, then barbiturates will retard the course of extinction. Such a result has been reported recently by Barry and coworkers.[2]

Surprisingly, pentobarbital had no extinction-retarding effect in the daily extinction test (Fig. 17). The explanation does not lie in the insensitivity of the test to pharmaceuticals, since extensive effects have been obtained with amphetamine and scopolamine (Figs. 16 and 17).

Can these apparently conflicting observations be reconciled? One appealing possibility is to assume with Amsel[1] that nonreinforcement is aversive *only if reward is anticipated*. Indeed, the assumption of reciprocal inhibition implies exactly this, since the degree to which the punishment mechanism rebounds after nonreinforcement must depend, at least in part, on the extent of its previous suppression by the reward mechanism.

If this idea is correct, aversive reactions will be important only early in extinction while reward still is anticipated. Their importance will be diminished later in extinction, or in well-practiced extinction (daily extinction experiment), as a result of deconditioning or counterconditioning of the incentive mechanism by frequent omissions of the reinforcing stimulus (Pavlovian extinction). This view, then, attributes the performance deficit in late or well-practiced extinction more directly to a low level of incentive than to a high level of inhibition.

Results with barbiturates are consistent with this analysis. The positive result of Barry and associates[2] was observed in early extinction, and my negative result was observed in well-practiced extinction. Also consistent here is the observation of a strong positive effect with amphetamine, as this drug has been assumed to increase incentive. Finally, this analysis suggests that the response facilitation produced by a background of rewarding stimulation of the brain in the daily extinction test is better interpreted in terms of increased incentive than it is in terms of decreased inhibition.

SUMMARY

A theory of reward and punishment, described herein, permits an integrated understanding of operant behavior in the four basic experimental situations: reward, punishment, extinction, and avoidance. Behavioral facilitation produced by reward or avoidance of punishment results from direct or rebound activation of a hypothalamic reward mechanism; behavioral inhibition produced by punishment or loss of reward results from direct or rebound activation of a periventricular punishment mechanism. New data are presented, including effects of stimulation of the brain and drugs on avoidance and extinction, to document the analysis.

REFERENCES

1. AMSEL, A. Frustrative nonreward in partial reinforcement and discrimination learning: Some recent history and a theoretical extension. *Psychol. Rev. 69*: 306, 1962.

2. BARRY, H., III, WAGNER, A. R., and MILLER, N. E. Effects of alcohol and amobarbital on performance inhibited by experimental extinction. *J. Comp. Physiol. Psychol. 55*:464, 1962.

3. CARLTON, P. L. Cholinergic mechanisms in the control of behavior by the brain. *Psychol. Rev. 70*:19, 1963.

4. CRESPI, L. P. Amount of reinforcement and level of performance. *Psychol. Rev. 51*:341, 1944.

5. DELGADO, J. M. R., ROBERTS, W. W., and MILLER, N. E. Learning motivated by electrical stimulation of the brain. *Amer. J. Physiol. 179*:587, 1954.

6. DENNY, M. R., and DUNHAM, M. D. The effect of differential nonreinforcement of the incorrect response on the learning of the correct response in the simple T-maze. *J. Exp. Psychol. 41*:382, 1951.

7. ESTES, W. K., and SKINNER, B. F. Some quantitative properties of anxiety. *J. Exp. Psychol. 29*:390, 1941.

8. GELLER, I., and SEIFTER, J. The effects of meprobamate, barbiturates, *d*-amphetamine and promazine on experimentally induced conflict in the rat. *Psychopharmacologia (Berlin) 1*:482, 1960.

9. HARLOW, H. F., and HICKS, L. H. Discrimination learning theory: Uniprocess vs. duoprocess. *Psychol. Rev. 64*:104, 1957.

10. HESS, W. R. *Das Zwischenhirn: Syndrome, Lokalisationen, Funktionen.* Basel, Schwabe, 1949.

11. HULL, C. L. *Principles of Behavior.* New York, Appleton, 1943.

12. LE GROS CLARK, W. E., BEATTIE, J., RIDDOCH, G., and DOTT, N. M. *The Hypothalamus.* Edinburgh, Oliver & Boyd, 1938.

13. MASSERMAN, J. H. *Behavior and Neurosis.* Chicago, University of Chicago Press, 1943.

14. MILLER, N. E. Some recent studies of conflict behavior and drugs. *Amer. Psychologist 16*:12, 1961.

15. MOWRER, O. H. *Learning Theory and Behavior.* New York, Wiley, 1960.

16. OLDS, J. Hypothalamic substrates of reward. *Physiol. Rev. 42*:554, 1962.

17. OLDS, J. Mechanisms of instrumental conditioning. *Electroenceph. Clin. Neurophysiol., Suppl. 24,* 1963.

18. OLDS, J., and MILNER, P. Positive reinforcement produced by electrical stimulation of septal area and other regions of the rat brain. *J. Comp. Physiol. Psychol. 47*:419, 1954.

19. OLDS, J., and OLDS, M. E. "Interference and Learning in Paleocortical Systems," in *Brain Mechanisms and Learning,* ed. by Delafresnaye, J. E. Oxford, Blackwell, 1961.

20. OLDS, M. E., and OLDS, J. Emotional and associative mechanisms in rat brain. *J. Comp. Physiol. Psychol. 54*:120, 1961.

21. Olds, M. E., and Olds, J. Approach-escape interactions in rat brain. *Amer. J. Physiol. 203*:803, 1962.

22. Pavlov, I. P. *Conditioned Reflexes,* tr. by Anrep, G. V. London, Oxford, 1927.

23. Seward, J. P. Secondary reinforcement as tertiary motivation: A revision of Hull's revision. *Psychol. Rev. 48*:130, 1950.

24. Sheffield, F. D., Roby, T. B., and Campbell, B. A. Drive reduction versus consummatory behavior as determinants of performance. *J. Comp. Physiol. Psychol. 47*:349, 1954.

25. Sidman, M. Two temporal parameters of the maintenance of avoidance behavior by the white rat. *J. Comp. Physiol. Psychol. 46*:253, 1953.

26. Skinner, B. F. *The Behavior of Organisms.* New York, Appleton, 1938.

27. Spence, K. W. *Behavior Theory and Conditioning.* New Haven, Yale, 1956.

28. Stein, L. "New Methods for Evaluating Stimulants and Antidepressants," in *Psychosomatic Medicine,* ed. by Nodine, J. H., and Moyer, J. H. Philadelphia, Lea & Febiger, 1962.

29. Stein, L. "Amphetamine and Neural Reward Mechanisms," in *Animal Behaviour and Drug Action,* ed. by Steinberg, H. London, Churchill, 1964.

30. Stein, L., and Hearst, E. Inhibitory effect of positively reinforcing brain stimulation on learning. *Amer. Psychologist 13*:408, 1958. (Abst.)

31. Stein, L., and Ray, O. S. Accelerated recovery from reserpine depression by monoamine oxidase inhibitors. *Nature (London) 188*:1199, 1960.

32. Stein, L., and Ray, O. S. Brain stimulation reward "thresholds" self-determined in rat. *Psychopharmacologia (Berlin) 1*:251, 1960.

33. Stein, L., and Seifter, J. Indexing of centrally stimulating drugs by restoration of reserpine depressed operant behavior *Pharmacologist 2*:70, 1960. (Abst.)

34. Thorndike, E. L. *Educational Psychology: The Psychology of Learning,* Vol. 2. New York, Teachers College, 1913.

35. Tolman, E. C. *Purposive Behavior in Animals and Man.* New York, Appleton, 1932.

36. Woodworth, R. S., and Schlosberg, H. *Experimental Psychology.* New York, Holt, 1954.

G. A. DENEAU, PH.D.

T. YANAGITA, M.D.

M. H. SEEVERS, M.D., PH.D.

University of Michigan Medical School

Drug Dependence in the Monkey

THROUGH THE AGES MANKIND has used drugs for two purposes: (1) to treat disease or relieve symptoms and (2) to modify perception and mentation in an effort to make life more pleasant or tolerable. Many people who use drugs for this latter purpose acquire one or more forms of drug dependence and are considered to be abusing the drugs. Whereas most pharmacologists study the mechanisms underlying the therapeutic aspects of drugs, our own efforts have been directed primarily toward the study of drug abuse.

Figure 1 outlines the elements involved in drug abuse in man and serves as a basis for the definitions of terms to be used in this paper as well as an indication of those aspects of the entire problem which we are studying in the laboratory. Drug abuse may be classified into two types, depending on the pattern of ingestion by the user: (1) the single dose or spree type and (2) the chronic type. All abusers of drugs begin by taking single doses or going on periodic sprees. The drug may be any one which alters function of the central nervous system, but a few, such as the volatile solvents and the hallucinogens, are not likely to be abused continually. With most drugs, the initial spree type of ingestion eventually develops into chronic or continual abuse.

The abuse of drugs is not inevitable in all people who have experienced the effects of single doses. In fact, only a small portion of such people, the "susceptible ones," acquire a strong preference for the drugged state over their normal condition. These susceptible persons acquire a "psychogenic dependence" on the drug, either because it creates a highly desirable effect or because it negates an extremely undesirable aspect of life. Such people abuse the drug compulsively.

Repeated use of all central nervous system depressants and the amphetamine-like stimulants leads to the development of "tolerance," with the

Supported by grants from the Committee on Drug Addiction, National Academy of Sciences-National Research Council, and the U.S.P.H.S. (MY-2814 and MY-5320).

result that larger doses of the drug are required to produce the desired effects. Prolonged and continual use of the depressant drugs also induces gradual physiologic adaptations to their effects, so that a state of physiologic imbalance results when the drug is removed, and serious and distressing signs and symptoms of abstinence appear. This is the phenomenon of "physical dependence." The dread of an impending abstinence syndrome strongly reinforces the element of compulsive abuse. Ingestion of large doses of some drugs or withdrawal of others results in disturbances of

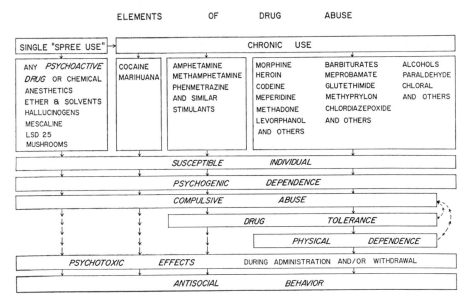

FIG. 1. Schema of various pharmacologic, psychiatric, sociologic, and legal elements of drug abuse. (From Seavers and Deneau.[8])

behavior or "psychotoxicity," which, in turn, may lead to "antisocial behavior" in the form of aggressive acts upon persons and property.

Of these various elements of drug abuse, physical dependence and tolerance have been most extensively studied in the laboratory. Recently, technics have been devised to permit investigation of psychogenic dependence.

PHYSICAL DEPENDENCE

Physical dependence on morphine was demonstrated in the monkey by Seevers[6] and by Kolb and DuMez[2] and in the dog by Plant and Pierce[5] in the 1920s. The morphine abstinence syndrome in the monkey was observed to be nearly identical to that in man, whereas the syndrome in the dog differed in several respects. Seevers' classification of signs of morphine abstinence in the monkey illustrates this parallelism with man:[7]

"*Mild* (may be considered as of no significance by the untrained observer): Apprehension, continual yawning, rhinorrhea, lacrimation, hiccup, shivering, perspiration on face, chattering, quarreling, and fighting.

"*Moderate*: Intention tremor, anorexia, pilomotor activity, muscular twitchings and rigidity, holding the abdomen (cramps).

"*Severe*: Extreme restlessness, assumption of peculiar attitudes, vomiting, severe diarrhea, erection and continued masturbation, inflammation of the eyelids and conjunctiva (insomnia), continual calling and crying, lying on the side with eyes closed, severe spasticity.

"*Very severe* (danger of death): Docility in the normally excitable animal, dyspnea, pallor, strabismus, dehydration, loss of weight, prostration, circulatory collapse, and, occasionally, death."

These signs indicate that the morphine abstinence syndrome represents hyperirritability of behavioral and somatic functions as well as of all autonomic activity, including both sympathetic and parasympathetic functions. In these studies, the severity of the abstinence syndrome which followed chronic treatment with the opium derivatives in monkeys paralleled the addiction liabilities of these drugs in man. Capacity to induce physical dependence appeared to be an excellent index for predicting addiction liability in man.

Interest was renewed in this general problem when it became necessary to evaluate the potential abuse liability of the many new synthetic analgesics which were inspired by the German discoveries of meperidine and methadone just before and during World War II. The first step was to determine whether physical dependence on these new agents could be produced in the monkey and whether such physical dependence was related to addiction liability in man. Starting with drugs which had already been studied in man, we analyzed the factors involved in the development of physical dependence in the monkey. Our observations may be summarized as factors related (1) to the properties of the drug and (2) to the administration of the drug.

Factors inherent in the drug may be described as follows:

1. The drug possesses a morphine-like spectrum of pharmacologic actions affecting both somatic and autonomic divisions of the central nervous system. In direct determinations of physical dependence, the type of abstinence signs observed is generally a mirror image of those seen with single administration, and such a compound also has the capacity to suppress the identical specific signs in morphine-dependent animals.

2. The drug has a flat dose-response curve, which permits tissues to be

exposed to large quantities of the drug without inducing dangerous depression.

3. Development of tolerance is rapid and fairly complete, also permitting maximal exposure of tissue as the dose is increased.

4. The capacity of any drug to induce physical dependence is limited by a low convulsant threshold.

5. The capacity to induce physical dependence cannot be correlated quantitatively with the absolute "narcotic" properties of a compound, even in agents with a typical morphine-like spectrum of actions.

6. Whereas liability to physical dependence commonly increases with drug potency for sedation, exceptions are so numerous as to preclude any general rule.

Factors related to administration may be described as follows:

1. Physical dependence cannot be established unless a finite quantity, specific for each compound, is administered under proper circumstances, as characterized below. The minimal quantity for morphine is 400 μg. per day (100 μg. every 6 hours) for 4 weeks. Animals subjected to this regimen can be selected correctly by a trained observer (with no previous knowledge of either the monkeys or the treatment) from a group of normal monkeys after all the dependent and normal animals have received 2 mg. per kilogram of nalorphine. Such a differentiation cannot be made under similar circumstances after abrupt withdrawal or even after morphine has been administered in a dose of 200 μg. per kilogram daily.

2. The frequency of administration must exceed the time course of major detoxication of a unit dose of the drug.

3. The drug must be administered for 1 month without interruption. The total quantity in 24 hours (unit dose times administration interval) shall be of sufficient size to support completely dependence on 12 mg. per kilogram daily of morphine sulfate. Whereas longer administration of increasing doses will enhance the intensity of physical dependence, the level attained with the regimen outlined is adequate for correct classification of liability to physical dependence.

The monkey proved to be valuable for prediction of the qualitative nature of the abstinence syndrome which would result if the synthetic analgesics were administered to and then withdrawn from man. The technic of producing primary physical dependence on each drug was time-consuming and expensive, however. It was well known that when morphine had induced the disordered physiologic state of physical dependence, an adequate additional dose would maintain this state in a masked condition for a period corresponding to the drug's sojourn in the body. Moreover, once signs of morphine abstinence had begun to appear, they could be relieved or suppressed by morphine or any other drug which produced morphine-like physical dependence. A technic to evaluate the phyiscal dependence properties of new drugs has been developed in which the ability of single doses of the test drugs to suppress signs of morphine abstinence is determined both qualitatively and quantitatively. This technic has enabled us to evaluate many new drugs in a relatively small group of stabilized, morphine-dependent monkeys. To date, approximately 500 new, potential analgesic drugs have been evaluated in this manner.

Many hypotheses have been offered in attempts to explain the mechanism of the development of physical dependence. These have been reviewed by

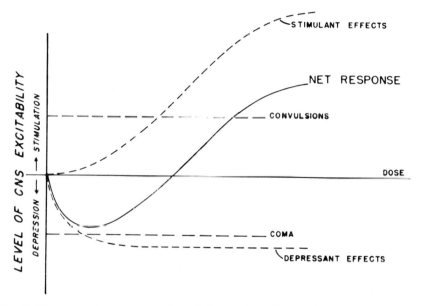

FIG. 2. Diagrammatic representation of integration of opposing actions of narcotic analgesics.

Tatum, Seevers, and Collins[10] and by Kreuger, Eddy, and Sumwalt.[3] Most of these have been based on fragmentary evidence and can be dismissed in the light of more recent observations. Seevers and Woods[9] revised the earlier hypothesis of Tatum and associates, which was based on Bernard's[1] well known observation that morphine possesses both depressant and stimulant properties. Tatum and associates believed that the stimulant effects of morphine, although temporarily recessive, outlasted the depressant effects. As dose after dose of morphine was administered, larger and larger amounts were required to oppose the remaining stimulant effects of previous doses, and when administration was finally halted, the accumulated stimulant actions were manifest in the form of the abstinence syndrome. Seevers and Woods believed that morphine acted at two sites, one depressant and one stimulant. Access to the depressant site was easier than to the stimulant site. After a period of chronic administration of morphine, both sites became almost completely occupied and when dosage was stopped, the drug left the depressant sites of action more quickly than the stimulant sites. During the period when the drug occupied the stimulant sites only, signs of abstinence appeared.

Recent observations in our laboratory have led to revision of our earlier interpretations of the development of physical dependence. In brief, the

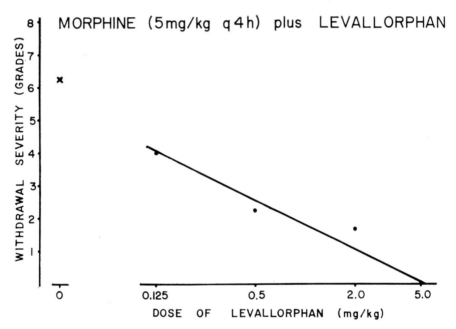

Fig. 3. Effects of chronic administration of levallorphan on development of physical dependence to morphine in rhesus monkey.

observation that morphine produces a mixture of depressant and stimulant effects has been extended. With small doses the depressant action is dominant, and with large doses the stimulant action is dominant (Fig. 2). The narcotic antagonist nalorphine antagonizes the depressant but not the stimulant actions of single doses of morphine. When monkeys are pretreated with nalorphine, signs of stimulation, ranging from mild hyperactivity to convulsions, appear when subsequent doses of narcotics are administered (Table 1).

When mixtures of morphine and an antagonist (levallorphan) are administered together chronically, development of physical dependence is reduced or prevented entirely depending upon the dose of the antagonist (Fig. 3). Because the narcotic antagonists do not interfere with the stimulant actions of morphine and because they can prevent development of physical dependence, this phenomenon must be the result of adaptations to the prolonged depressant action of chronic administration of morphine. The precise mechanism of these adaptations is still unknown.

TABLE 1. EFFECTS OF NARCOTICS AFTER PRETREATMENT WITH NALORPHINE

Dose (mg/kg)		
Pretreatment with nalorphine	Subsequent medication	Effects
	Morphine	
0.5	5.0	Piloerection, tremors
1.0	10.0	Salivation, piloerection, tremors
2.0	20.0	Retching, piloerection, apprehension
	Levorphanol	
0.5	5.0	Slight sedation, salivation, tremors
1.0	10.0	Salivation, tremors, piloerection
2.0	20.0	Piloerection, apprehension, tremors
	Meperidine	
0.5	5.0	Slight sedation, piloerection, salivation
1.0	10.0	Retching, apprehension, tremors
2.0	20.0	Convulsions
	Ketobemidone	
0.5	5.0	Slight sedation, tremors
1.0	10.0	Retching, apprehension, tremors
2.0	20.0	Convulsions
	Methadone	
0.5	5.0	Slight sedation, salivation, piloerection
1.0	10.0	Retching, apprehension, tremors
2.0	20.0	Convulsions

TOLERANCE

Many investigators have observed development of tolerance to morphine-like drugs. It occurs only in relation to the depressant actions of morphine and not to the stimulant actions. Its mechanism has been extensively studied, and although it is still not understood, some possibilities have been excluded. The extensive work of Woods[11] and of Mellett[4] has demonstrated that changes in the distribution or fate of morphine are not sufficient to explain development of tolerance.

PSYCHOGENIC DEPENDENCE

Obviously, the most important question in the entire problem of drug abuse concerns the characteristics which lead to individual susceptibility and the development of psychogenic dependence. Psychogenic dependence is difficult to study in the laboratory and has received much less attention than the other elements previously mentioned.

During the past year we have studied a group of monkeys who had a choice of drinking tap water or a solution of morphine. About one-third of

FIG. 4. Flexible arm and harness used for chronic intravenous injection of drugs into monkeys. See text for full description.

these monkeys acquired a distinct preference for the morphine solution and drank enough of it to become physically dependent. The remaining monkeys were deprived of water for several days and were forced to drink the morphine solution, after which they were again given a choice of water or morphine solution to drink. Approximately half of this group (one-third of the total) displayed a distinct preference for morphine.

Individual susceptibility can be demonstrated in the laboratory. Monkeys which displayed a strong psychogenic dependence on morphine were given the choice of drinking water or solutions of other analgesics such as codeine, meperidine, levorphanol, and methadone. Codeine was the only one of these drugs for which they showed a preference; in fact, they completely rejected the others. Since human opiate addicts do not reject these other drugs, our observations in monkeys obviously do not parallel the situation in man.

As a means of obviating the defects in these experiments resulting from

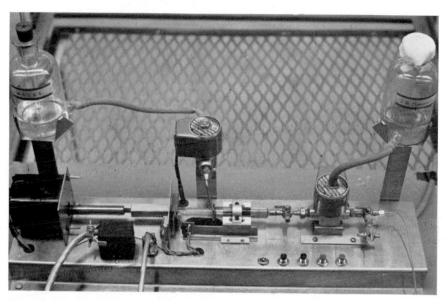

Fig. 5. Automatic injector used for chronic intravenous administration of drugs into monkeys. See text for full description.

the bitter and perhaps repelling taste of these drugs and the slow onset of pharmacologic action after oral administration, a technic for chronic intravenous self-administration in the relatively unrestrained monkey has been developed. The monkey wears a light harness of stainless steel tubing, to which is attached a flexible arm of the same material. The arm, which is anchored to one corner of the cage, allows free movement of the monkey within the cage and also protects the catheter (Fig. 4). An indwelling catheter is introduced through the jugular vein into the right side of the heart and is then led subcutaneously to the monkey's back. It leaves the monkey's body at this point through a stab wound in the skin and enters the flexible arm, through which it is led to the outside of the cage and thence is attached to an injecting apparatus (Fig. 5). The injector consists of a motor-driven syringe which fills from a reservoir of the drug solution and discharges a predetermined volume of the solution. This volume can be varied by changing the placement of a microswitch which, when activated, reverses the motor and causes the syringe to be refilled. A three-way solenoid valve, which is activated at the same time as the motor, connects the syringe with the reservoir or with the monkey's catheter, as required. The motor is set in operation by pressing a lever, or it can be governed by an electric timer. Injections are recorded on an event recorder.

This system permits us to duplicate the human situation, in which intravenous injections are administered as desired. One monkey has now been administering morphine to himself in this manner for 1 year. This monkey also administers synthetic analgesics to himself when they are substituted for morphine. Although we have not yet accumulated a large body of data on psychogenic dependence, we have now developed technics which will permit us to investigate this aspect of drug abuse.

REFERENCES

1. BERNARD, C. Médecine expérimentale: Recherches expérimentales sur l'opium et ses alcaloïdes. Compt. rend. de Sci. 59:406, 1864.
2. KOLB, L., and DUMEZ, A. G. Experimental addiction of animals to opiates. Public Health Rep. 46:698, 1931.
3. KREUGER, H., EDDY, N. B., and SUMWALT, M. The pharmacology of the opium alkaloids. Public Health Rep., Suppl. No. 165, 1941.
4. MELLETT, L. B., and WOODS, L. A. The distribution and fate of morphine in the non-tolerant and tolerant monkey. J. Pharmacol. Exp. Ther. 116:77, 1956.
5. PLANT, O. H., and PIERCE, I. H. Studies of chronic morphine poisoning in dogs: I. General symptoms and behavior during addiction and withdrawal. J. Pharmacol. Exp. Ther. 33:329, 1928.
6. SEEVERS, M. H. Addiction potentialities of morphine, codeine, heroin and dilaudid in the monkey. J. Pharmacol. Exp. Ther. 51:141, 1934.
7. SEEVERS, M. H. Opiate addiction in the monkey. J. Pharmacol. Exp. Ther. 56:147, 1936.
8. SEEVERS, M. H., and DENEAU, G. A. Morphine physical dependence in the monkey (film). Audio-Visual Education Center. The University of Michigan, Ann Arbor, 1963.
9. SEEVERS, M. H., and WOODS, L. A. The phenomena of tolerance. Amer. J. Med. 14:546, 1953.
10. TATUM, A. L., SEEVERS, M. H., and COLLINS, C. K. Morphine addiction and its physiological interpretation based on experimental evidences. J. Pharmacol. Exp. Ther. 36:447, 1929.
11. WOODS, L. A. Comparative distribution of morphine and nalorphine in dog brain. J. Pharmacol. Exp. Ther. 120:58, 1957.

HENRY B. MURPHREE, M.D.
Bureau of Research in Neurology and Psychiatry

Addiction and the Pleasure Principle: Pharmacodynamics versus Psychodynamics

M UCH OF OUR KNOWLEDGE of normal physiology has arisen from study of pathophysiology, and much of our knowledge of normal psychodynamics has arisen from study of psychopathology. By the same process, perhaps something can be learned of pleasure from studying perverse pleasure. Addiction is widely regarded as perverse pleasure. It is also an important clinical problem and, like most clinical problems which entail elements of perversity, addiction is generally rejected not only by the laity but also by many physicians. Published figures of the incidence of addiction may well be grossly erroneous, because addiction to some drugs is legally a crime, and, as with other crimes, only the unsuccessful are apprehended and included in statistical computations. Addiction to some agents is not widely recognized as true addiction and therefore is not entered into computations; yet such cases must be studied by anyone interested in addiction.

It is difficult to distinguish addiction from habituation or other misuse. The World Health Organization[33] has listed differential criteria as given in Table 1. Seevers[26] has recently published an excellent critique of the problem, showing that these criteria are not altogether adequate. Definition is difficult because the basic determinants of addiction are not yet fully understood. Moreover, the criteria listed are multidimensional, ranging from physiologic to sociologic effects of drugs. Opinion varies as to whether addiction is a psychologic or a pharmacologic phenomenon. Despite the difficulty of producing refined definitions, there is general agreement that some chemical substances of diverse forms are persistently used in such a way and to such an extent as to constitute "addiction." The elementary differences which distinguish addiction from other misuse are physical dependence and withdrawal symptoms. These crude statements will be the operational definition for addiction in the following discussion. Since all addiction consists of interactions between a chemical compound and the taker, one approach to a survey of addiction is to examine each of these interactions and to attempt to determine the common factors.

Like addiction itself, addicting agents are difficult to define. The tendency is strong to think only of opiates as addicting drugs; yet legally cocaine and marihuana are also included, even though neither of these causes tolerance, demands an increase in dosage, or produces withdrawal symptoms. Nevertheless, social consensus condemns these drugs, and since cocaine is a highly

TABLE 1. ADDICTION AND HABITUATION: DEFINITIONS
BY WORLD HEALTH ORGANIZATION

Addiction	Habituation
A state of periodic or chronic intoxication produced by repeated consumption of a drug (natural or synthetic)	A condition resulting from repeated consumption of a drug
Characteristics include: 1. Overpowering desire or need (compulsion) to continue taking the drug and to obtain it by any means 2. Tendency to increase dose 3. Psychic (psychologic) and general physical dependence on effect of drug	Characteristics include: 1. Desire (but not compulsion) to continue taking the drug for sense of well-being which it engenders 2. Little or no tendency to increase dose 3. Some degree of psychic dependence on effect of drug but absence of physical dependence and hence of abstinence syndrome
4. Detrimental effect on the individual and on society	4. Detrimental effects, if any, primarily on the individual

destructive agent, it is considered addicting. Other agents, however, which produce physiologic dependence are not legally considered addicting, e.g., ethyl alcohol and barbiturates and barbiturate-like drugs such as glutethimide, meprobamate, and chlordiazepoxide. Another host of agents is misused although not usually considered addicting; amphetamines, including methamphetamine and phenmetrazine, produce tolerance but not the major withdrawal syndrome. Bromides have fallen into perhaps undeserved disrepute because some people misuse them, and antipyretics are taken periodically in large doses by a great number of people. Recently, lysergic acid diethylamide has been reported to be misused.[4] The possible addictiveness of peyote, kavakava, and betel nut has been debated. Coffee and tobacco have been labeled addictive, and some people abuse food by excessive intake, to their own detriment if not that of society.

Ultimately, the definitions of what constitutes misuse and overuse are socially determined. Some people consider any use of certain agents as over-use, an attitude that is not always corroborated by objective criteria. Al-though the practice is widely disapproved, there is little evidence to show that chewing of coca leaf is directly harmful to Andean Indians. Probably the worst effect is that they spend a portion of their extremely limited in-come on coca instead of food. And although morphine addiction is depre-cated in this country, the retiring, inoffensive morphine addict is far less objectionable than the belligerent, abusive drunk at a "socially acceptable" cocktail party. The limits of use which society will accept vary greatly and not always rationally. The individual who transgresses these limits inevi-tably suffers some form and degree of social censure.

Historically, a vast range of agents has been ingested for actual or sup-posed pleasurable effect, ranging from glue-sniffing and ammonia cokes to atropine-containing plant products, to *Amanita muscaria* and other vari-ously poisonous mushrooms, to arsenic compounds (e.g., the "Count Drac-ula" habitués of Transylvania), to diethyl ether and nitrous oxide. Almost everything with any reasonably prompt action on the central nervous sys-tem has been tried, and only those which are plainly lethal have been completely eliminated.

All the well-known agents are used by large numbers of people. Hemp in various forms, tobacco, betel nut, and ethyl alcohol are steadily consumed by a sizable portion of the world population. Several points are worth not-ing here. First, most users of these agents do not flagrantly overuse them. Second, making an agent illegal does not hinder people from using it but usually lures new recruits or creates an illicit market aimed at expanding trade. The total failure of prohibition in this country is a striking example of this principle.

The diversity of agents ingested for pleasure is so great that for simplicity the rest of this discussion will be limited to the most commonly misused agents in this country: alcohol, barbiturates, and opiates. This selection loads the factorial odds, since all three are depressants, although qualita-tively somewhat different from each other in their depressant effects. Yet perhaps it is significant of our culture that if one discards such doubtful in-stances of addiction as coffee and tobacco, these three remaining agents, often used excessively, are all depressants. Moreover, all three produce the major withdrawal syndrome of delirium and seizures. Examination of phe-nomena of addiction to these agents therefore seems justified, since they can be considered addicting both pharmacologically and socially.

The first step in critical consideration of these three kinds of agents is the elimination of biased or untrustworthy assumptions based not on experi-mental observations but on prejudice. Attitudes toward addiction to opi-ates, alcohol, and barbiturates have varied widely. Some difference in the attitude toward barbiturates might be ascribed to their recent introduction, only 59 years ago. Alcohol and opium, on the other hand, have existed side by side throughout the known history of mankind. Cultural differences, nevertheless, have produced differences in attitudes toward the two.[22] Alcohol gained ascendency in the West, where aggressiveness was prized, and opium predominated in the East, where phlegmatism was cultivated. In our own time and country, opiate addiction retains an exotic quality, whereas alcohol in an acceptable range of dosage is an integral part of some of our social rituals from religious observances to the cocktail party.

There are other differences. For example, the possibility that alcoholism arises from some metabolic abnormality has been investigated widely. Mardones[19] has recently published a comprehensive review of such studies. Since many people drink alcohol without becoming obviously addicted, there must be something qualitatively different about those who are unable to do so, possibly a metabolic error which creates a craving for alcohol or which alcohol helps correct. In contrast, no one can take opium casually. Even the pet cat in the opium-smoking den becomes genuinely addicted merely by inhaling the smoky air. Pharmacologic dependence on opiates in all users is so great that no one has considered the possibility that predisposing biochemical factors may lead to addiction. Thus, social attitudes obviously influence scientists in the formulation of their scientific hypotheses.

Although withdrawal symptoms of delirium and seizures were reported as early as 1914, and in detail in 1934,[24] it remained for Isbell and coworkers[11-13] in 1950 to prove that barbiturates are addicting in every sense. Even now these drugs are by no means as closely regulated as opiates. In some sense they are less regulated than alcohol, the use of which is governed partly by heavy taxes. At 50 cents per capsule, the usual price on the illegal market, barbiturates give a more intense effect at less cost than alcohol.

A key question about alcohol, opiates, and barbiturates is whether they have some common characteristic which creates addiction. The belief that there is something about opiates, and particularly heroin, which, in itself, creates addiction is the basis of the Harrison Act and of attempts by the World Health Organization to suppress all use of heroin. The idea is that if a given drug is highly addicting—and some are in fact more addicting than others—and if that drug can be discarded medically, it should be discarded. Indeed, ketobemidone has been used only experimentally in this country for just that reason. But preferences are made by addicts only quantitatively, not qualitatively. In those uncommon instances in which supplies of heroin have been successfully interrupted, addicts have promptly shifted to other agents.

The assumption in repressive attempts is that a direct inverse relation exists between number of cases and force of repression (Fig. 1a). Experiences of the past 3 decades suggest that, in fact, no practicable amount of repression can eradicate a certain residual number of cases (Fig. 1b). This is not to say that opiates should be made freely available. The curves in Figure 1a and b allow for the fact that availability could influence a potentially large number of persons. The importance of availability is illustrated by the high incidence of addiction among physicians and other medical personnel (1 in 100 physicians, or about 10 times that in the total young population). On the other hand, it is illusory to suppose that current repressive efforts are effective in view of the conservative estimate that about 2 metric tons of heroin enter this country each year.

Addicts too have their preferences. Martin and Fraser[21] found that opiate addicts in double-blind experiments can distinguish heroin from morphine

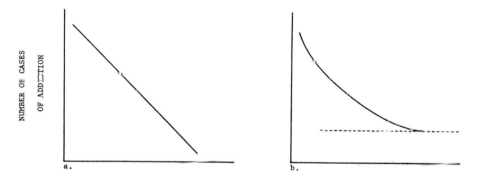

FORCE OF REPRESSION

FIG. 1. Possible effect of repressive measures on incidence of addiction.

and that they prefer heroin. The reason for this preference remains unclear. Despite this subtle difference, however, addicts can shift from agent to agent, and some indulge in what amounts to a bizarre polypharmacy.[4] This mobility explains the recent theory that all addiction is the same phenomenon and that the particular agent merely represents one variable. Even among the three classes of agents discussed here, the diversity of actions is so great as to eliminate the possibility of a special quality of the agent which engenders addiction, as distinguished from maintaining it.

Perhaps, however, there are common effects. The search for these is complicated by the necessity of distinguishing between acute and chronic effects. In consideration of etiology, it is the acute effect, the first experience, that is important.

In Table 2 are crudely summarized some of the more prominent effects of the three kinds of compounds, as compared with those of chlorpromazine, another kind of depressant. Only presence or absence of effects is recorded, so that the compounds appear to be more similar than they really are. Even so, the apparent similarity among them is also shared by the non-addictive chlorpromazine. These agents are all depressants, but the depression is always combined with stimulant and release mechanisms. The depression of opiates resembles that of chlorpromazine more than it does that of alcohol or barbiturates.

The local anesthesia produced by these agents is not clinically useful except in the case of semipermanent neural blocks produced by alcohol. But this, like respiratory depression and poikilothermia, is not a likely reason for addiction. Tolerance is a positive drawback to the addict; further-

TABLE 2. COMPARISON OF EFFECTS OF SOME ADDICTING
DRUGS AND OF CHLORPROMAZINE

Effect	Ethyl alcohol	Barbiturates	Opiates	Chlorpromazine
Central nervous system depression	+	+	+	+
Analgesia	+	?	+	+
Local anesthesia	?	?	+	+
Respiratory depression	[a]	+	+	0
Cardiovascular depression	[a]	+	[a]	+
Depression of sexual functions	+	+	+	+
Poikilothermia	+	+	+	+
Carbohydrate sparing	+	?	?	0
Tolerance	+	+	+	?

[a] Only follows other effects.

more, it is not an initial effect and therefore figures not in the etiology but only in the maintenance of addiction.

Effects on carbohydrate metabolism may possibly contribute to addiction. Ethanol is itself a food which yields 7.1 cal. per gram,[14] and it serves to spare carbohydrate and other metabolism. Barbiturates inhibit oxidative phosphorylation and through this mechanism may conceivably be slightly carbohydrate-sparing.[1] Effect on carbohydrate metabolism has been a point of debate about opiates. They initially cause hyperglycemia secondary to peripheral sympathetic discharge,[2, 17, 30] but as tolerance develops, this disappears. During withdrawal, hyperglycemia reappears. Opiates have so many actions that it is difficult to distinguish the important from the unimportant. But if hyperglycemia is the addict's desired effect, then a glass of orange juice would be much easier to take than more opiates.

Even if these three kinds of compounds could be shown to affect the same enzyme system, it does not necessarily follow that they work by the same mechanism. Wang and Bain[31] have shown that opiates act on the cytochromic system, but that morphine, methadone, and meperidine each act on a different subserving enzyme of the system. In addition, it is always dangerous to generalize about intact animals from in vitro experiments.

The analgesic effects of these compounds have been studied extensively. Ethyl alcohol and opiates can be clearly shown to have analgesic effects in experimental animals, whereas barbiturates can only potentiate this action of opiates and can, when given alone, produce amnesia for pain. All three classes of compounds modify greatly the emotional reaction to pain, as does chlorpromazine, which also potentiates this effect of opiates. Reactions to pain vary greatly from one person to another and so do the modifying effects of drugs, but the person himself is a much more important variable than the particular agent.

An important difference in addicting potential of these agents is in the threshold dosage for addiction. Plainly, many people can ingest significant amounts of ethanol or barbiturates more or less chronically without any evidence of addiction. Fraser[6] determined the average threshold dosage of barbiturates in healthy young men to be greater than 0.4 gm. per day for 42 days. Unfortunately, it is not clear from his report whether there might be individual variations in threshold dosage with respect to amount of daily dose and duration of administration, or whether addiction, as proved by withdrawal symptoms, is related to some total cumulative dose as well as a minimal daily amount. Furthermore, his subjects were former addicts, and his observations may not hold for other persons. A careful search of published reports discloses no such investigation with respect to opiates. The usual clinical doses of opiates are addicting if sustained, but careful study of minimal dose, rate, cumulative number of days, or cumulative dosage to produce addiction is lacking. Tolerance to opiates is acquired much sooner and lasts much longer than previously thought. A single large dose of morphine given to a rat has effects which can be measured at least 15 months later by suitably sensitive technics.[3] It is well known among addicts that even the 2-week "pleasure shooter" eventually gets hooked. And some maintain that once opiate-induced euphoria has been experienced, it is forever desired. This implies a lasting change, at least, in whatever memory is.

Once addiction has occurred, the ratio of maximal to minimal tolerance varies widely among the three kinds of agents. The most incorrigible alcoholic can manage no more than 3 to 4 times as much alcohol daily as a novice. Tolerance to barbiturates reaches the range of 10 to 50 times normal, whereas that to opiates reaches as high as 500 times normal.

It is part of clinical lore among anesthesiologists that cross tolerance exists between barbiturates and alcohol. An alternative possibility is that certain persons are resistant to alcohol and to barbiturates because they have an irritable, easily aroused nervous system. This concept is supported by the observation that thresholds for calming effects of alcohol and barbiturates are highly correlated in subjects nontolerant to either class of compound.[15] Goldstein and Warren[10] have also found that subjects who are resistant to disturbance of sleep by caffeine also tend to be resistant to induction of sleep by hexobarbital, so there may be significant differences in individual susceptibilities to centrally acting drugs. Cross tolerance between opiates and barbiturates or alcohol is not significant. Opiate addicts occasionally poison themselves by overestimating their tolerance when substituting barbiturates for opiates.

An alternative to the proposition that drugs possess some quality that engenders addiction is the possibility that the addict possesses a characteristic that makes him prone to addiction. Some have equated the etiology of addiction to one syndrome, such as "female troubles." Others related addiction to familial association with such a large number of common or vaguely defined disorders that no family is free from all of them. Marshall,[20] in 1878, advanced a fascinating hypothesis that the etiology of addiction lay in giving infants opiate-containing sleeping potions, such as Mrs. Winslow's Soothing Syrup, which produced a craving that lasted into adulthood. Stanley,[28] in 1915, was the first to implicate "the nervous strain of modern life."

In 1925 Kolb[16] proposed a much more sophisticated hypothesis: that addicts react to drugs differently from other people. Corollary to this, Rado[25] in 1933 advanced the thesis that the impulse to use a drug and not the toxic agent itself is the essential factor in addiction. He based his arguments on psychoanalytic case material rather than on uncritical or prejudicial concepts. We now know that many drugs can have widely varying effects in different individuals. Morphine is not always sedative; indeed man is the only species in which this is the usual effect. The subjective effect of morphine is commonly referred to as euphoria but, in fact, some persons become dysphoric from it. The property of barbiturates of cortical release, excitant rather than sedative, particularly in children and elderly people, is well known. And any cocktail party provides sufficient examples of the diversity of effects of alcohol.

Opiates also produce diverse effects,[18] the initial reaction sometimes being dysphoria. Chronic dosage, however, will change the initial reaction to euphoria about the third day,[17] probably because the beginnings of dependence are relieved, although these are difficult to evaluate, being subtle and subjective. In contrast, the empirically called "addiction-prone" person experiences intense pleasure from his first dose of opiate.

What are the possible explanations for this phenomenon? The popular explanation is that addicts are disreputable psychopathic characters who enjoy perverse pleasure. But alternative hypotheses based on differences in biologic constitution might be offered. To some persons the taste of phenyl-thiocarbamide is intensely bitter, but to others it is not, and this taste is genetically determined. Conceivably, similar genetic differences might exist in response to morphine. Differences in emotional make-up also merit examination, with observations and conclusions carefully censored of value judgments. Today, however, we reject any simple dichotomy of mental or emotional versus biologic, because it does not take into account complex subtle interactions among various bodily processes, some of which are subgrouped under "mind." Ideally, then, common actions among drugs and differences in reactions of people to them should be explored at all levels—molecular, cellular, organic, behavioral. Unfortunately, although a great deal is known of usual actions of the three kinds of drugs, almost nothing is known of pharmacologic determinants of individual differences in response.

A common effect of intoxication with many agents is the "great truth" phenomenon, a sense of some kind of magical realization of and communion with the infinite. This was eloquently described by Sir Humphry Davy after his first experience with nitrous oxide in 1799 and elaborately detailed by De Quincey[5] in the nineteenth century. These and other detailed descriptions strongly suggest some kind of emotional factor. Apparently the intensity of the experience varies greatly not only from one person to another but with time in the same person. The content of the fantasies under intoxication appears to be nonspecific. The ancient expression *in vino veritas* suggests that alcohol has no specific effect but merely brings truth to the surface. De Quincey said that a man whose talk is of oxen will have opium dreams of oxen.

There is, moreover, a sharp contrast between subjective and objective accounts of the effects of drugs. The inebriate at a party who considers himself the soul of wit and charm may appear sodden and boorish to others. Martin and Fraser[21] have catalogued in detail the contrast between addicts' descriptions of feeling relaxed and peaceful but energetic and their appearance of being somnolent, withdrawn, and irritably sullen. Indeed, some addicts seem to pursue their habit despite adverse pharmacologic effects. An experimental volunteer, after taking a dose of opiate and upon being asked "How do you feel?" may sit up, vomit in the wastebasket, smile blearily, and say, "I feel great, Doc. That's wonderful stuff." Such a person is apparently highly addiction-prone. But some persons cannot become addicts despite an earnest desire to do so because they cannot endure various pharmacologic effects or what they consider side effects. This was the case with one of Martin and Fraser's subjects, who asked to be released from studies involving experimental addiction to heroin because the experience was unbearably unpleasant.

In a consideration of the emotional origins of addiction, analgesia must be included. Any study of analgesia in human beings rapidly becomes complicated by emotional factors in the experimental subjects. By definition, analgesia means freedom from pain, but is freedom from pain equated with pleasure? Careful study of Freud's concept of the pleasure principle suggests an affirmative answer. Freud[7] described the pleasure principle as the guardian of the organism and the function of the pleasure principle as the striving for minimal tensions. By extrapolation, the ultimate goal of the pleasure principle would be death, which explains the concept of the death instinct. Physiologists tend to think of pain, not pleasure, as the guardian of the organism and offer in evidence the frequent damage to the rare person who appears to be without sense of pain. Freud[9] recognized that pain has "an inherently impelling quality in high degree," whereas pleasure does not. Moreover, the fact that pleasure is usually ephemeral would seem to invalidate the static view of pleasure as directly equal to a low tension state. An alternative and dynamic hypothesis would be that pleasure is an accompaniment, if not a result, of the process of tension release and reduction—in other words a first derivative function—and that its sequelae are satiation, fatigue, and exhaustion. Freud[8] alluded to this possibility briefly in *Beyond the Pleasure Principle* but never elaborated on it. Some people seem to gain pleasure by actively seeking strong excitation. But does the attraction reside in the preliminary great increase in tension or in the consequent correspondingly great reduction?

Some phenomena of addiction support the dynamic view. Euphoria due to alcohol occurs only while concentrations in blood and tissues are increasing. Euphoria disappears as these concentrations reach a maximum, whereupon it is superseded by depression and exhaustion. The intense euphoria experienced by heroin addicts occurs briefly after injection and is replaced by being "on the nod" as central nervous system concentrations reach a maximum. Orgastic tension release is then the intensely pleasurable part of the experience. Perhaps the addict gains his pleasure by greater than normal reduction in tension without suffering the increased tension of the excitement seeker. These considerations suggest that appropriately designed drug experiments could shed more light on the basic affective processes of pleasure. Possibly even the second derivative of tension state is important, i.e., the acceleration toward greater or less tension. In any case, the hypothesis of death instinct probably retains validity, whatever the differential aspects of tension levels may be, as attested by the front page of any newspaper.

Another consideration is that pleasure and pain are not unidimensional. Everyone in his fashion constantly endures frustrations and pains for ulterior pleasures. This is, of course, the basis of the reality principle. Addicts in their fashions do the same. Alcoholics endure wrenching nausea to down a drink. Opiate addicts endure the discomforts of intravenous injection to have a blast. In addiction, however, penalties become so great and pleasures so dubious that the question of masochistic satisfactions necessarily arises. The replacement of every other object attachment with drugs, amounting to an immolation, the self-mutilation of innumerable injections, of emaciation, of destroyed intellect and talents are all obviously closely parallel to self-destructive asceticism. Tabori[29] in 1933 was apparently first to refer to addiction as chronic suicide, an idea which was expanded greatly by Karl Menninger.[23]

One outstanding factor common to all forms of addiction is incorporation of some substance into the addict. Some complain that injection with a needle does not have the same symbolic significance as swallowing. However, in the inchoate world of oral fixation, route of entry is extremely indefinite, as are indeed the boundaries between self and other-than-self. Thus great oral need apparently combines with a rather broad range of pharmacologic effects in the etiology of addiction.

The effect of opiates in depressing sexual function may also be valued, albeit unconsciously, by addicts, since this may relieve them of tensions arising from profound sexual conflicts and inadequacies. As for alcohol, Shakespeare[27] described its effect thus:

> MACDUFF: What three things does Drinke especially provoke?
> PORTER: Marry, Sir, nose-painting, sleepe, and urine.
> Lecherie, Sir, it provokes, and unprovokes: it provokes the desire, but it takes away the performance. Therefore much drinke may be said to be an equivocator with Lecherie. . . .

The provoking of lechery is true only of smaller doses, since it results from the well-known release phenomenon of alcohol. As the dose is increased, the desire follows the performance into oblivion. The same holds true for barbiturates.

The conclusion emerges that the psychodynamics of addiction are, after all, the same, regardless of the particular agent. Careful psychodynamic studies, such as that of Wikler,[32] show also that drugs of themselves produce no significant alteration in the personality of the addict.

Certain secondary factors, however, help engender or maintain addiction. Although some which are commonly voiced, especially by addicts themselves, are specious, others have real validity. Among these are the reasons given for taking the first dose. For opiates, the most common reason offered is enticement by a "friend." Tabori[29] tried to distinguish between addicts who were intrinsically perverse and those who were seduced into addiction.

He correctly pointed out the sadism involved in deliberately introducing another to addiction. Adolescence is a naturally turbulent period, and the immature judgment and plasticity of adolescents enhance their vulnerability; the illicit trade takes profitable advantage of this, as shown by the steadily rising proportion of users who are teenagers. Correlated with this is the high incidence of crime and psychosis among adolescents. Suggestibility probably plays some role in the euphoria produced by the first dose. Moreover, probably only an individual with a particular make-up would try a first dose. Adequate internalization of widely expressed social rejection of addiction should serve a preventive function. A kind of maladjustment, making such internalization impossible, would explain the high correlation between addiction and psychopathy. Physician addicts frequently explain their first dose on the basis of excessive fatigue, an obvious rationalization. The factors which motivated them to become physicians and to become "overtired" and the underlying psychodynamic make-up are the real explanations.

Iatrogenic addiction to opiates is uncommon,[11] but iatrogenic addiction is a major factor with barbiturates. A sizable illegal market in barbiturates exists, ranging from the friendly corner druggist who does not demand a prescription to frank pushers. Social channels, of course, account entirely for addiction to alcohol.

Addiction is a communicable and social disease, acquired and maintained through others. Cultural differences in mores exist among countries and even within countries. In the United States, addicts, driven together by illegality and the necessity of maintaining contact with supplies of drug, have formed a pariah society, with a kind of hierarchal organization. "Mainliners" look down on "skinpoppers," and a "large habit" carries prestige. The clubhouse is the jail, where the uninitiated can join the brotherhood and learn the language and the criminal technics necessary to support the habit, or where the veteran can meet old friends and help inculcate addiction in the novice. Social pressures are not nearly as powerful on users of alcohol and baributrates as on opiate addicts, although there is some overlapping between barbiturates and opiates, and Skid Row is the well known terminus for alcoholics. Many "amateur" barbiturate addicts and alcoholics live outside these subcultures, however.

Finally, there is the relation between use of drugs and religion. Alcohol is used in religious rites throughout the Western world. Peyote is used in religious ceremonies in the American Southwest for the esthetic "great truth" experience it induces, and hemp has been used in Moslem countries for the same purpose. Christian Communion involves an incorporation, as does addiction. Addiction and religions have their own esoteric rituals and languages. It has been said that if religion is the opium of the people, opium is the religion of the addict. Some alcoholics substitute the quasi-religious society of Alcoholics Anonymous for their addiction.

SUMMARY

Substances which can cause dependence, if not actual addiction, are so heterogeneous in their effects as to defy cogent analysis for common pharmacologic factors. But many characteristics of addicts, both intrinsic and extrinsic, independent of any particular pharmacologic agent, serve to produce and maintain addiction. Moreover, rather clear-cut differences distinguish addicts from others. The basis of addiction, therefore, would seem to lie more in the addict than in his drug. This is not to say that there may not be measurable biochemical differences between addiction-prone persons and others to account for an abnormal response to pharmacologic agents. The range of action of drugs used by addicts is wide, and the variations among addicts are also great. The important matter is to discover the more uniform factors and hence the ones more likely to be causative. This emphasizes anew the gap between our knowledge of determinants of behavior at the molecular level and our knowledge at the social level; psychodynamics, our principal field of knowledge, is really an abstraction from the social interaction between patient and doctor.

The etiology of addiction is undoubtedly multifactorial, with drug and addict forming an alliance, and the symptom complex in the addict is undoubtedly overdetermined. On the basis of present evidence, it appears that pharmacy only provides a variety of agents, some of which are self-reinforcing, but that the addiction-prone person will always find some agent to fill his need.

REFERENCES

1. BAIN, J. A., and MAYER, S. E. Biochemical mechanisms of drug action. *Ann. Rev. Pharmacol. 2:*37, 1962.
2. CAMPOS, H. A. Role of central nervous system catecholamines in morphine hyperglycemia. *Fed. Proc. 19:*272, 1960.
3. COCHIN, J. and KORNETSKY, C. Factors influencing drug tolerance in the rat. *Fed. Proc. 20:*311, 1961.
4. COHEN, S., and DITMAN, K. S. Complications associated with lysergic acid diethylamide (LSD-25). *J.A.M.A. 181:*161, 1962.
5. DE QUINCEY, T. *Confessions of an English Opium-Eater.* London, Taylor and Hessey of Fleet Street, 1822.

6. FRASER, H. F. Minimum dose of barbiturates required to produce physical dependence. *Fed. Proc. 15*:423, 1956.
7. FREUD, S. "The Economic Problem in Masochism," in *Collected Papers*, Vol. 2. London, Hogarth Press and Institute of Psycho-analysis, 1950, pp. 255–268.
8. FREUD, S. *Beyond the Pleasure Principle*. London, Hogarth Press and Institute of Psycho-analysis, 1950.
9. FREUD, S. *The Ego and the Id*. London, Hogarth Press and Institute of Psycho-analysis, 1957.
10. GOLDSTEIN, A., and WARREN, R. Individual differences in sensitivity of people to the central effects of caffeine. *Fed. Proc. 20*:394, 1961.
11. ISBELL, H. Addiction to barbiturates and the barbiturate abstinence syndrome. *Ann. Int. Med. 33*:108, 1950.
12. ISBELL, H., ALSCHUL, S., KORNETSKY, C. H., EISENMAN, A. J., FLANARY, H. G., and FRASER, H. F. Chronic barbiturate intoxication: An experimental study. *Arch. Neurol. Psychiat. 64*:1, 1950.
13. ISBELL, H., and FRASER, H. F. Addiction to analgesics and barbiturates. *Pharmacol. Rev. 2*:355, 1950.
14. JACOBSEN, E. The metabolism of ethyl alcohol. *Pharmacol. Rev. 4*:107, 1952.
15. KAWI, A. A. The sedation threshold. *Arch. Neurol. Psychiat. 80*:232, 1958.
16. KOLB, L. Pleasure and deterioration from narcotic addiction. *J. Ment. Hyg. 9*:699, 1925.
17. KRUEGER, H., EDDY, N. B., and SUMWALT, M. The pharmacology of opium alkaloids, *Public Health Rep.*, Suppl. 165, Part 1, 1941; Part 2, 1943.
18. LASAGNA, L., VON FELSINGER, J. M., and BEECHER, H. K. Drug induced mood changes in man: 1. Observations on healthy subjects, chronically ill patients, and "post-addicts." *J.A.M.A. 157*:1006, 1955.
19. MARDONES, J. Experimentally induced changes in the free selection of ethanol. *Int. Rev. Neurobiol. 2*:42, 1960.
20. MARSHALL, O. The opium habit in Michigan. *Ann. Rep., State Board of Health, Michigan. 6*:61, 1878.
21. MARTIN, W. R., and FRASER, H. F. A comparative study of physiological and subjective effects of heroin and morphine administered intravenously in post addicts. *J. Pharmacol. Exp. Ther. 133*:388, 1961.
22. MAURER, D. W., and VOGEL, V. H. *Narcotics and Narcotic Addiction*. Springfield, Ill., Thomas, 1955.
23. MENNINGER, K. A. *Man Against Himself*. New York, Harcourt, 1938.
24. POHLISCH, K., and PANSE, F. *Schlafmittelmissbrauch*. Leipzig, Thieme, 1934.
25. RADO, S. The psychoanalysis of pharmacothymia (drug-addiction). *Psychoanal. Quart. 2*:1, 1933.
26. SEEVERS, M. H. Medical perspectives on habituation and addiction. *J.A.M.A. 181*:92, 1962.
27. SHAKESPEARE, W. "The Tragedie of Macbeth," Act II, Scene 3, in *Mr. William Shakespeare's Comedies, Histories, and Tragedies*. London, Jaggard & Blount, 1623.
28. STANLEY, L. L. Morphinism. *J. Amer. Inst. Crim. Law & Criminol. 6*:586, 1915–1916.

29. Tabori, J. Zur Kasuistik des induzierten Morphinismus. *Zbl. Psychother.* 6:88, 1933.
30. Vassalle, M. Studies on morphine hyperglycemia. *Fed. Proc. 19*:120, 1960.
31. Wang, R. I. H., and Bain, J. A. Analgesics and enzymes of the cytochrome chain. *J. Pharmacol. Exp. Ther. 108*:354, 1953.
32. Wikler, A. A psychodynamic study of a patient during experimental self-regulated re-addiction to morphine. *Psychiat. Quart. 26*:270, 1952.
33. Expert committee on addiction-producing drugs, seventh report. *WHO Techn. Rep. Ser. 116*:9, 1957.

FRED W. SCHUELER, PH.D.
Tulane University School of Medicine

Discussion

D R. STEIN, IN THE FIRST PAPER in this section, entitled Reciprocal Action
of Reward and Punishment Mechanisms, has presented data which
support a theory for reward and punishment of voluntary (operant)
behavior. In this theory, anticipation of reward or punishment directly
modifies operant behavior, the actual reward or punishment influencing
such behavior only by alteration of anticipation. The neuroanatomic
and physiologically active sites involved in the mechanism for anticipation,
conceived in Stein's work as Pavlovian, are said to be in the medial forebrain bundle region of the hypothalamus *for reward* and in the periventricular region of the diencephalon and midbrain *for punishment*. Data
and arguments are presented which support the concept that *reward* and
punishment mechanisms are operationally mutually antagonistic *and that
they "continually and jointly determine the net effect on operant behavior."*
(Italics mine.)

In the second paper in this section, Drug Dependence in the Monkey,
Drs. Deneau, Yanagita, and Seevers, in addition to reviewing other work
in this field, describe new experiments in which monkeys operate a mechanism for intravenous self-injection of a predetermined dose of a drug. The
mechanism is totally automatic insofar as refilling of the injection apparatus
and recording of the times of injection are concerned. The technic permits
testing in the animals of solutions of drugs as *dependence-producing* agents
or as substitutes for drugs known to produce dependence. It permits dupli-
cation of the human situation inasmuch as the monkey associates an operant
type of behavior (activation of the injection equipment) with its own
"desires," i.e., its state of anticipation. This represents a distinct advantage
over older procedures.

The third paper in this section, Addiction and the Pleasure Principle:
Pharmacodynamics versus Psychodynamics, by Dr. Murphree, is an excellent
smörgåsbord of the problems in this field. Its contribution to the symposium
constitutes a step-by-step presentation of the maze of definitions evolved
from pharmacologic problems, including matters of biochemical and nutri-

tional concern, problems of psychologic, social, and legalistic import, and matters of a general philosophic nature.

Dr. Murphree mentioned one of Martin and Fraser's subjects who requested that his experimental addiction be discontinued because it was intolerably unpleasant. Dr. Murphree's question of whether freedom from pain (analgesia) is equivalent to pleasure is relevant to the situation in Aldous Huxley's *Brave New World*, in which a whole society is oriented and conditioned by pharmacologic and psychologic methods to be happy! A small minority, the heroes, of course, find enforced happiness unpleasant. Whereas such instances of reverse connotation with respect to the pleasure-pain principle may be compatible with Dr. Stein's view of the reward and punishment mechanisms as *mutually inhibitory*, Stein's rather rigid concept may be only an excellent first approximation, in the present writer's opinion. Indeed, Dr. Murphree makes a suggestion from the standpoint of dynamics which may be relatable to Dr. Stein's concept in a useful way. Thus, Murphree, while reflecting on Freud's statement concerning pain as "an inherently impelling quality in high degree," which pleasure is not, proceeds to suggest that "an alternative and dynamic hypothesis would be that pleasure is an accompaniment, if not a result, of the process of tension release and reduction—in other words a first derivative function—and that its sequelae are satiation, fatigue, and exhaustion." Freud's undeveloped allusion to this possibility is mentioned by Dr. Murphree. If one attempts to read Dr. Murphree in the light of Dr. Stein's concept, then the state of the organism's anticipation which directly modifies operant behavior could be viewed as follows:

$$A = f[(R + P), t]$$

Anticipation (A) = function (f) of past rewards (R) plus past punishment (P) with respect to a given type of operant behavior with occurrence (O) at a given time (t) in the past.

Now with regard to anticipation (A) in a situation of the operant all-or-none type (e.g., monkey injects drug or does not inject drug), one may scale A as a graded function, where degree of A+ represents degree of anticipated reward or degree of A— represents degree of anticipated punishment, as in Figure 1.

This model represents a surface which gives the value of A as a function of the *two* variables, time (t) and reward plus punishment (R + P). The R + P is, according to Dr. Stein's mutually inhibitory hypothesis, an extension of the same axis. Whereas the anatomic loci of mechanisms which relate to reward (R) and punishment (P) are distinct, they are physiologically (functionally) summed by means of the mutually inhibitory principle of Dr. Stein. Time (t) is involved by physiologic and psychologic nulling out, repression, or other mechanisms, which may give a highly complex character to the surface representing A. Thus, at a given time (t_1) shortly after an occurrence (O_1) elicited by means of operant behavior, the value of A may be negative, and since punishment is anticipated, no further operant behavior (O), which is here all-or-none, takes place. At a later time (t_2), as a result of the complex character of the surface A, which depends on time, the value of A may become positive: Positive reward with reference to the operant act is anticipated, and the monkey again injects himself, i.e., O_2 occurs. The second time O occurs (i.e., O_2), the result is a new shift in the value of A, but not to the same place on the surface A, in general, as with O_1. This would be particularly true with an addicting drug, as I see it.

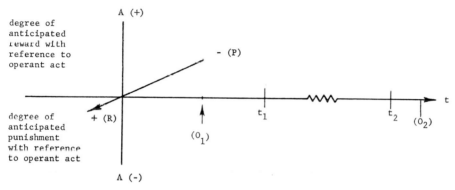

Fig. 1. Anticipation as a function of the variables reward and punishment and of the variable time.

Now, regarding the nature of pleasure within the present context, it does not appear to be identical with any of the variables A, R + P, or t. One might speculate that A+ is in itself a pleasure, but A+ might be associated with pain or anxiety. The state of pleasure or pain that accompanies an anticipated reward *may be* entirely independent at a particular time (t) of the pleasure of anticipation itself. Thus a state of anxiety or pain may accompany a sense of pleasurable anticipation of relief. The actual relation of over-all pleasure or pain or both at a given moment could be appreciated only by reference to the full surface characterizing A. Indeed, perhaps there is no such thing as over-all pleasure or pain at a given moment, i.e., they are not mutually exclusive. I have no proof, but I have the impression that reward (R) and punishment (P) are not necessarily mutually inhibitory, except with respect to certain areas of the surface A; that is, all of the variables, R, P, t, may be, in general, independent, but in certain special experimental designs (such as that of Dr. Stein), they may be mutually correlated either as sums, inverses, or in some more complex mathematical way.

What about Dr. Murphree's pleasure in a first derived function? In terms of the present variables, pleasure (P) may be related as the first derivative of A with respect to time (t):

$$P = F\left[\frac{dA}{dt}\right] = F\left[\frac{\partial A}{\partial t} + \frac{\partial A}{\partial (R + P)} \cdot \frac{d(R + P)}{dt}\right]$$
$$\text{where } A = f[(R + P), t]$$

If R and P are, in general, independent, then the expression for pleasure is considerably more complex. The main point to be made about pleasure is that after a given occurrence (O), the function (F) of the first derived function of A will be (according to Murphree) a relatively rapid monotonically decreasing function of t, which is asymptotic to zero. The final state, if pain and pleasure are considered mutually inhibitory, i.e., binary occurrences in the scheme, would lead to the sequelae of satiation, fatigue, and exhaustion. On the other hand, pleasure and pain may, in general, like plus (+) and minus (—) anticipation, be independent variables, in which case the scheme concerning pleasure and pain would be made still more complex. Fortunately, a night's sleep, another occurrence not embraced by the foregoing scheme of binary all-or-none relation to O, is also undoubtedly anticipated by mice and monkeys as well as by men, or these animals would never be able to survive our experiments. Unfortunately, such uncontrolled occurrences make it difficult to fit even the animals into our mathematical boxes. As should be already implicitly clear, attempts to elaborate mathematically analytic descriptions of such subjective responses as pleasure and pain without precise methods of measurement may provide a superficial aura of sophistication but actually only further obscure the subject.

To have served with the very scholarly contributors to this section has been a singular pleasure and honor. My comments are not intended as destructive criticism. First approximations are usually simpler than those evolved with time and, if cogently documented by experiment, lay a firm foundation for future work. The contributors to this symposium are to be congratulated on their outstanding presentations to this extremely difficult subject.

PART III

Physiologic Studies

E. GUERRERO-FIGUEROA, D.B.S.

R. GUERRERO-FIGUEROA, M.D.

ROBERT G. HEATH, M.D., D.M.SC.

Tulane University School of Medicine

Effects of Attention and Some Chemical Compounds upon Trigeminal Evoked Potential

Introduction

THE CLOSE, OFTEN EXTREMELY COMPLEX relation between pleasure and pain has long been recognized by philosophers and psychologists. Recently accumulated data demonstrate a close association between these feelings at the neurophysiologic level.[22, 23, 36, 37, 42]

Early clinical observations correlating activity of the central nervous system and pain were with epileptic subjects. The present report concerns the neurophysiologic basis for some types of pain perception. Studies of pain as an accompaniment of epileptic-like discharges from precise regions of the brain are presented, together with data derived from studying potentials evoked at various sites in the central nervous system by painful stimuli. Attention factors are known to be strong determinants in the subjective perception of pain. Data presented herein demonstrate the influence of attention factors, particularly those involving anticipation of pleasure, on physiologic responses to painful stimuli.

Early studies on human subjects first revealed a relation between activity of the central nervous system and intense feelings. Some crude correlations between sensory stimuli and activity of the nervous system were recognized clinically. In animal studies with use of newer technics and instrumentation, demonstration of paroxysmal or epileptic discharges has assisted in

Supported by funds provided by the Louisiana State Department of Hospitals and by Public Health Service Research Grant No. NB-04251-01, Institute of Neurological Diseases and Blindness.

establishing a relation between neural activity and emotional states. The animal experiments have also been of value in demonstrating the influence of sensory stimuli on activity of the nervous system.

Marshall Hall,[20] in 1833, divided epilepsy into centric and eccentric types. Centric seizures originated within the central nervous system, whereas eccentric seizures were induced by stimulation of the various nerves. Allen[2] reported cases in which seizures could be induced by loud noises; Cobb[7] postulated that photic driving is the precipitating factor of seizures; and Walter[47] demonstrated photic driving of larval wave and spike in some electroencephalographic records.

Gowers[15] and Jackson[31] reported that seizures could be provoked by sensory stimulation in patients with some types of epilepsy. This seizure has been called "reflex epilepsy" or evoked seizure. On the other hand, some types of epilepsy can be inhibited by sensory stimulation. Critchley[8] reported development of attacks in patients exposed to noise of a continuous or monotonous order. Adrian[1] noted that the operation of the brain seems to be related to particular fields of sensory information which vary from moment to moment with shifting attention. Electrically evoked potentials recorded from specific sensory pathways in the brain have been shown to be affected by functional states of the animal, such as alertness and distraction, or by the direction of attention.[19, 27, 28] Afferent impulses may be influenced by attention even at the first synaptic relay.[26] Fernandez-Guardiola and associates[13] demonstrated that stimulation of the reticular formation prevented development of convulsive activity in the cerebral cortex. Moruzzi and Magoun,[35] in 1949, with confirmation by Jasper and coworkers[32] in 1955, reported that "cortical recruiting" responses induced by stimulation of the specific nuclei of the thalamus are drastically reduced or abolished by reticular stimulation. This activating influence may block recruiting responses in all cortical areas, but sensory areas seem most affected.

In 1906, Dejerine and Roussy[9] correlated the thalamic syndrome with circumscribed lesions in parts of the ventral portion of the thalamus. The syndrome is associated with intractable pain and anesthesia in the involved region and additionally may be manifested by episodic laughing or crying. Coincident with the report from our laboratories[17] concerning the induction of petit mal seizures in kittens, we observed that introduction of crystalline aluminum oxide into the intralaminar thalamic nucleus induced an electroencephalographic pattern of 3-per-second spike and wave; the pattern was preceded by a short period of crying out.

In this report, experimental observations are presented which suggest an analogic model of the sensory aura that precedes the electroencephalographic pattern of 3-per-second spike and wave. This suggested model is interesting in two respects: (1) it permits study of the physiopathologic mechanism of focal epilepsy in relation to painful aura and (2) it provides an opportunity to study a possible association between some types of seizures and pain and the effects of acetylcholine (ACh) and gamma amino-butyric acid (GABA) on this phenomenon.

Human subjects with implanted semipermanent depth electrodes and under treatment for various neurologic disorders provided an excellent opportunity for extending studies to man. Preliminary data are presented which demonstrate the effects of sensory stimuli on cerebral activity in man.

METHODS

STUDIES IN ANIMALS

Experiments were performed on 15 kittens and 10 adult cats. By the technic of Becker and associates[4] and with the use of Nembutal as the anesthetic, electrodes were introduced into deep structures, including the intralaminar and ventroposteromedial nuclei of the thalamus, amygdala, hippocampus, spinal fifth sensory nucleus, and on the gyrus sigmoideus, gyrus coronalis, anterior gyrus ectosylvianus, posterior gyrus ectosylvianus, gyrus suprasylvianus, gyrus lateralis, posterior gyrus sylvianus, anterior gyrus sylvianus, medius gyrus ectosylvianus, and medius gyrus suprasylvianus.

Epileptogenic foci were induced by the technic of Guerrero-Figueroa and coworkers[18] with the introduction of aluminum oxide into the right intralaminar and ventroposteromedial nuclei of the thalamus. In addition, in some animals a single intracerebral cannula was implanted into the lateral ventricle or the thalamic nucleus by the technic of Heath and Founds.[21] ACh and GABA were administered through this cannula.

Evoked potentials were recorded in the spinal fifth sensory nucleus, ventroposteromedial nuclei of the thalamus, and sensory cortex by means of a cathode-ray oscilloscope or a Grass 8- or 16-channel electroencephalographic machine. Changes in recordings as a result of chemical stimulation were measured with one electrode placed on the active tissue and the other grounded.

A pair of insulated stainless steel wires, separated by 1.5 mm., was used for sensory stimulation of the tooth pulp. The ends were exposed for 0.5 mm. The stimulus consisted of rectangular pulses of 1 millisecond duration and the voltage threshold was determined for evoked responses. Clicks and flashes of light were also used to evoke potentials. Location of sites of electrodes and aluminum oxide was confirmed by histologic study. Two types of recording electrodes were used. A pair of small silver balls 4 to 6 mm. apart were fixed on the cortex. In deep structures bipolar stainless steel electrodes were most commonly used, with a separation of 0.4 to 0.8 mm. between two poles. The ends were exposed approximately 0.6 mm.

Animals were not used in the study until a minimum of 14 days had elapsed after implantation of electrodes and cannulae. Electrical recordings were made in freely moving cats during wakefulness. Some animals were given intravenous injections of sodium diphenylhydantoin and GABA.

STUDIES IN HUMAN SUBJECTS

This report includes data obtained from three patients in whom subcortical and cortical electrodes were implanted by the stereotaxic method. Studies began 3 months after electrode implantation. Subcortical electrodes were made of Teflon-insulated stainless steel wires (0.003 in. in diameter) with exposed contact areas approximately 2 mm. apart. Each exposed point, i.e., contact point, of the wire was approximately 0.3 mm. long. Silver ball electrodes were used for cortical recordings. Recordings were obtained from the following structures: optic tract, rostral end of the mesencephalic reticular formation (region of the tectobulbar tract), centromedian and paracentral nuclei of the thalamus, caudate nuclei, globus pallidus, amygdalae, hippocampi, putamen, hypothalamus, and acoustic and visual cortex. In all patients several leads were implanted into each of these structures.

Light flashes of 1 to 2 milliseconds' duration and of constant intensity were produced by a photic stimulator and were synchronized with audible clicks. Since the patient was seated in a mirror-lined enclosure, he could not avoid the light flashes. The click was delayed 10 to 20 milliseconds after the flash to allow for differences in times of excitation and transmission between the acoustic and visual areas. The sensory stimulation was given at intervals of 30 to 60 seconds. The recording was started after the patient was cooperative and completely relaxed. Grass S-4 stimulators and isolation units were used. Stimulation parameters were varied during the study, the duration of square (unidirectional) pulses ranging from 0.01 to 0.2 millisecond. Voltage thresholds were determined by the intensity required for this evoked response with suprathreshold values used during this experiment.

RESULTS

STUDIES IN ANIMALS

Injury in the pulp cavity is known to be followed by hyperemia and inflammation. Any type of stimulus applied to the tooth pulp, be it thermal, tactual, pressing, chemical, electrical, or noxious, is interpreted as pain.

Only painful sensations are manifested from the tooth pulp when the stimulus is sufficiently intense and confined within the pulp cavity. In dental exploratory work, repeated short impulses of electrical current have been noted to produce one sensation in a tooth with injured pulp and at the same time a separate sensation of pain in other teeth without pulp lesions. Pain in the tooth pulp can also be inhibited by the presentation of different, more significant stimuli, such as certain types of suggestion or other distracting stimuli which direct attention.

EVOKED POTENTIALS IN THE PRIMARY AFFERENT PATHWAYS FROM STIMULATION OF TOOTH PULP. Evoked potentials recorded in the fifth sensory nucleus (trigeminal nucleus) of some animals showed a biphasic or triphasic primary complex, consisting of an initial negative wave followed by a complex of three positive waves and, finally, by a negative wave. Latency and amplitude of responses were analyzed in all the animals. In each experiment the voltage threshold was determined for evoked response, but the voltage used was always supramaximal.

The effects of stimulation of the tooth on recordings in the trigeminal nucleus and visual, acoustic, and facial cortex are presented in Figure 1A. Very stable evoked responses were recorded in the trigeminal nucleus and the sensory cortex from the relaxed animal. Figure 1A also shows the effects of a combination of tooth and photic stimulation, which were characterized by a decrement of the amplitude of evoked responses recorded from the trigeminal nucleus. Evoked responses in the primary and secondary visual cortex are also shown; these responses have negative and positive waves.

EFFECTS OF INTRAVENTRICULAR ACH ON THE TRIGEMINAL NUCLEUS AND SENSORY CORTEX POTENTIALS. The effects of ACh introduced into the lateral ventricle are demonstrated in Figure 1B. These records from the fifth sensory nucleus, and sensory facial, visual, and acoustic cortex, demonstrate the potentials evoked by stimulation of the tooth pulp 5 minutes after injection of 0.5 μM of ACh into the lateral ventricle (Fig. 1B, left). The recording was characterized by progressive increments in amplitude of the evoked response beginning 1 minute after injection, reaching maximum 15 minutes later, and returning to base line 30 to 40 minutes after injection. The right side of Figure 1B also demonstrates the effect of light flashes combined with stimulation of the tooth pulp. There was generalized increment in amplitude of evoked responses on the sensory cortex. The novel stimulation (i.e., the photic stimulation) in animals treated with ACh did not inhibit the evoked potential recorded from the trigeminal nucleus.

EFFECTS OF INTRAVENTRICULAR GABA ON POTENTIALS EVOKED AT THE TRIGEMINAL NUCLEUS AND SENSORY CORTEX. The effects of 0.2 μM of GABA injected into the lateral ventricle are demonstrated in Figure 1C. Evoked potentials were recorded in the trigeminal nucleus 5 minutes after the

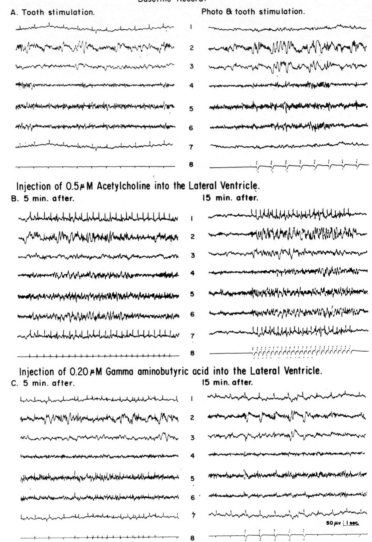

Baseline Record.

A. Tooth stimulation. Photo & tooth stimulation.

Injection of 0.5 μM Acetylcholine into the Lateral Ventricle.
B. 5 min. after. 15 min. after.

Injection of 0.20 μM Gamma aminobutyric acid into the Lateral Ventricle.
C. 5 min. after. 15 min. after.

50 μv ⌊ 1 sec

FIG. 1 *A*. Left column: Evoked response recorded from fifth sensory nucleus in response to stimulation of tooth. Right column: Decrement in amplitude of evoked response from fifth sensory nucleus when animal was under effects of simultaneous photic and tooth stimulation. *B*. Effect of injection of Ach into lateral ventricle upon evoked potentials with tooth stimulation recorded from fifth sensory nucleus, facial cortex, and visual cortex after 5 and 15 minutes, respectively. Left column: Increment in amplitude of evoked response from fifth sensory nucleus and facial cortex during tooth stimulation. Right column: When animal was under effects of Ach, addition of photic stimulation failed to produce change in evoked potential recorded from fifth sensory

intraventricular injection. No significant changes appeared in the evoked potentials, but the spontaneous cortical recording was characterized by desynchronized activity with low to moderate amplitude and fast mixed-frequency activity. When the photic stimulation and stimulation of the tooth were applied simultaneously, the potential evoked in the trigeminal nucleus showed an increment in the surface-positive phase of the response. The evoked response at the sensory cortex (visual and facial) was characterized by inhibition of the surface-negative and increment in the surface-positive phase.

EVOKED 3-PER-SECOND SPIKE AND WAVE COMPLEX BY STIMULATION OF TOOTH. Introduction of a small amount of solid alumina into the intralaminar and ventroposteromedial nuclei of the thalamus in kittens represents an extension of the report by Guerrero-Figueroa and associates[17] concerning induction of experimental petit mal. Spontaneous 3-per-second spike and wave complexes appeared in recordings from the site of the alumina and, after a short time, in the opposite thalamus and the mesen cephalic reticular formation. Shortly before the appearance of the electro encephalographic patterns of 3-per-second spike and wave complex, the animal uttered a cry. Figure 2A illustrates the paroxysmal bursts of spontaneous 3-per-second spike and wave discharges, and Figure 2B demonstrates the 3-per-second spike and wave complex provoked by stimulation in the left canine tooth. The evoked potential began in the right ventroposteromedial and intralaminar and centromedian nuclei of the thalamus. After brief, continued stimulation, the generalized 3-per-second spike and wave complex appeared in the opposite thalamus and over the cortex of both hemispheres. The experiment demonstrates that 3-per-second spike and wave discharges can be driven by stimulation of the tooth. Injection of $0.2 \mu M$ of ACh into the right thalamus also produced an increment of 3-per-second spike and wave complexes on the right side, which was reflected in recordings from the opposite side (Fig. 2C). Increment of this activity occurred without sensory stimulation or driving.

GABA, administered intravenously, significantly altered 3-per-second spike and wave activity in the kittens. Stimulation of the tooth in animals

---

nucleus. C. Left column: Effect of injection of GABA into lateral ventricle upon evoked responses from tooth stimulation recorded from fifth sensory nucleus and facial cortex. Right column: Effect of injection of GABA into lateral ventricle on evoked response recorded from fifth sensory nucleus, facial cortex, and visual cortex by tooth and photic stimulation. Responses of sensory cortex show decrement in surface-negative and increment in surface-positive phase of evoked potentials.

1. Trigeminal nucleus; 2. Prim. visual cortex; 3. Sec. visual cortex; 4. Acoustic cortical area; 5. Facial cortical area; 6. Facial cortical area; 7. Trigeminal nucleus; 8. Electrical and photo stimulation.

Baseline

A. 3-per-second spike and wave.

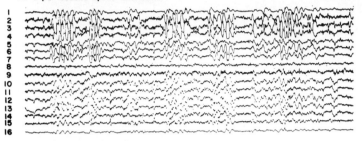

B. Tooth stimulation and 3-per-second.

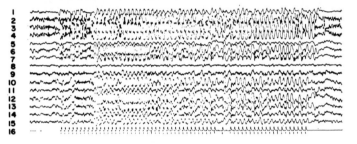

C. Injection of 0.2 µM Acetylcholine into the R. Thalamus 5 minutes after injection.

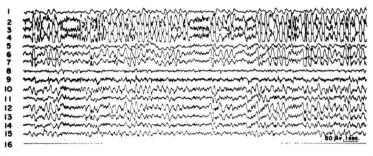

FIG. 2. *A*. Spontaneous pattern, consisting of 3-per-second spike and wave discharge in kittens with small amount of solid alumina introduced into intralaminar and ventro-posteromedial nuclei of thalamus. *B*. Three-per-second spike and wave complex precipitated by tooth stimulation. *C*. Effects of injection of Ach into right thalamus. Note increment of spontaneous 3-per-second spike and wave discharges.

1. R. Sigmoideus-R. Lateralis Gyrus; 2. R. C.M.N. Thal.-Indifferent; 3. R. V.M.N. Thal.-Indifferent; 4. R. V.P.M.N. Thal.-Indifferent; 5. R. Lateralis-R. Suprasylvianus Gyrus; 6. R. Sigmoideus-R. Coronalis Gyrus; 7. R. Coronalis-R. Sylvianus Gyrus; 8. R. Hippocampus-Amygdaloid Complex; 9. L. Hippocampus-Amygdaloid Complex; 10. L. C.M.N. Thal.-Indifferent; 11. L. V.M.N. Thal.-Indifferent; 12. L. V.P.M.N. Thal.-Indifferent; 13. L. Sigmoideus-Coronalis Gyrus; 14. L. Coronalis-Sylvianus Gyrus; 15. L. Lateralis-Suprasylvianus Gyrus; 16. L. Tooth Stimulation.

used in this study, as in those previously described, in which petit mal electrical patterns were created by the implantation of alumina into the intralaminar thalamic nucleus, also produced driving of the 3-per-second spike and wave complex. Again, the animals initially uttered cries (pain reaction, thalamic syndrome, Fig. 3*A*). Figure 3*B* and *C* shows the effects of intravenous injection of 30 mg. of GABA per kilogram of body weight in the animal. Three minutes after injection, the 3-per-second activity changed to low amplitude and fast activity (spindles) of low voltage, more apparent on the side opposite the alumina. Five minutes after GABA injection, stimulation of the tooth no longer evoked the 3-per-second spike and wave pattern. The spontaneous 3-per-second spike and wave complex also disappeared for a period of 50 minutes after the GABA injection. The electroencephalographic recording during the period that GABA was acting was characterized by desynchronized fast activity, and the animals' behavior was dominated by fear or rage with alertness. Effect of the addition of intravenous diphenylhydantoin sodium (Dilantin) (1 mg. per kilogram of body weight) to GABA (30 mg. per kilogram of body weight) is demonstrated in Figures 3*B* and *C* (right side). Ten hours after administration of this combination of drugs there was complete blocking of spontaneous and provoked 3-per-second spike and wave complex. The record was also characterized by fast activity of low amplitude and spindling, more predominant in the side opposite the alumina lesion. Recordings from the hippocampus and amygdaloid complex on the alumina side, however, showed a remarkably lasting effect from the GABA and Dilantin. For 2 to 3 days there were no spontaneous discharges and, additionally, the 3-per-second spike and wave complex could not be evoked with stimulation of the tooth.

Figure 4 demonstrates the effects of intraventricular ACh in recordings of the brain of adult animals in which small amounts of alumina had been implanted into the posterior hypothalamus. Figure 4*A* is a base line recording in an animal so prepared during stimulation to the posterior hypothalamus through bipolar electrodes at 10-second intervals. Recordings were obtained from the following structures: anterior hypothalamus, mesencephalic reticular substance, hippocampus, amygdala, and septal region. Effects of intraventricular injection of ACh are illustrated in Figure 4*B*. The alumina-epileptic focus was highly activated, as demonstrated by the electroencephalographic epileptiform discharges. These epileptiform discharges were also demonstrable in some deep structures which have synaptic connection with the posterior hypothalamus. Effects of intravenous injection of 30 mg. per kilogram of body weight of GABA in an animal under the maximal effect of ACh are demonstrated in Figure 4*C*. Epileptiform discharges were blocked and electrical activity approached the base line (characterized by fast activity of low voltage). The slow and high-amplitude

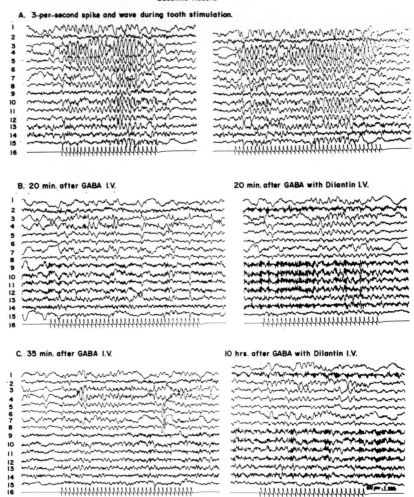

Baseline Record

A. 3-per-second spike and wave during tooth stimulation.

B. 20 min. after GABA I.V.   20 min. after GABA with Dilantin I.V.

C. 35 min. after GABA I.V.   10 hrs. after GABA with Dilantin I.V.

FIG. 3. A. Three-per-second spike and wave discharges provoked by tooth stimulation in kitten with alumina previously implanted into intralaminar and ventroposteromedial nuclei of thalamus. *B, C.* Left column: Effects of intravenous injection of GABA characterized by inhibition of 3-per-second spike and wave and absence of evoked discharges during tooth stimulation. Right column: Effects of adding diphenylhydantoin sodium to GABA, administered intravenously. Note blockade of spontaneous discharges and reflex effect provoked by tooth stimulation. Record shows desynchronization of pattern and potentiation of effect of GABA by diphenylhydantoin sodium.

1. R. Coronalis-R. Sigmoideus; 2. R. Hippocampus.-R. Amygdaloid; 3. R. C.M.N. Thal.-Indifferent; 4. R. V.M.N. Thal.-Indifferent; 5. R. V.P.M.N. Thal.-Indifferent; 6. R. Lateralis-R. Suprasylvianus Gyrus; 7. R. Coronalis-R. Sylvianus Gyrus; 8. R. Sigmoideus-R. Lateralis Gyrus; 9. L. Hippocampus-L. Amygdaloid; 10. L. C.M.N. Thal.-Indifferent; 11. L. Coronalis-L. Sigmodeus; 12. L. C.M.N. Thal.-Indifferent; 13. L. V.P.M.N. Thal.-Indifferent; 14. L. Coronalis-L. Sylvianus Gyrus; 15. L. Lateralis-L. Suprasylvianus Gyrus; 16. L. Tooth Stimulation.

waves activated by ACh were blocked by GABA after a period of 5 minutes, and throughout the period that GABA was effective the electroencephalographic patterns were characterized by fast activity of low voltage. The

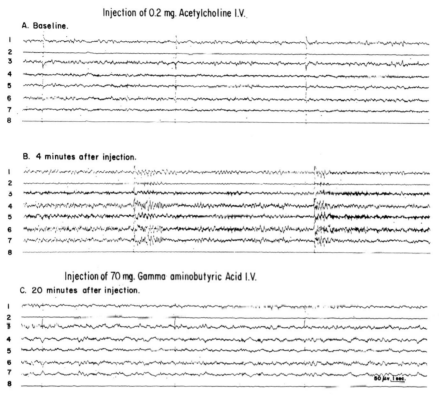

FIG. 4 *A, B*. Effect of intraventricular injection of Ach in animal with epileptogenic focus in posterior hypothalamus. Tracing is characterized by activation of electroencaphalographic epileptiform discharges and increment in amplitude of evoked responses. *C*. Effect of intravenous injection of GABA, characterized by blocking of epileptiform discharges and return to base line.

1. Ant. Hypothalamus; 2. Subst. Reticularis Mesencephalica; 3. L. Hippocampus; 4. L. Amygdala; 5. R. Hippocampus-Septum; 6. R. Hippocampus; 7. R. Amygdala; 8. Post. Hypo. Elect. Stimulation.

evoked response also returned to base line while the animal was under the influence of GABA.

EFFECTS OF ATTENTION ON THE 3-PER-SECOND SPIKE AND WAVE COMPLEX AND EVOKED RESPONSES FROM THE FIFTH SENSORY NUCLEUS AND SENSORY (FACIAL) CORTEX. While focusing attention on a rat, the cats consistently showed extreme reduction in amplitude of evoked potentials recorded from the sen-

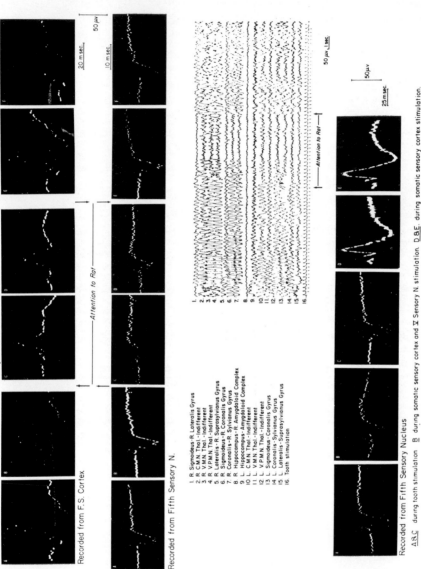

Before —— During —— After

20 m.sec.

50 μv

10 m.sec.

Recorded from F.S. Cortex.

Attention to Rat

Recorded from Fifth Sensory N.

1. R Sigmoideus - R Lateralis Gyrus
2. R C.M.N. Thal. - Indifferent
3. R V.M.N. Thal. - Indifferent
4. R V.P.M.N. Thal. - Indifferent
5. R Lateralis - R Suprasylvianus Gyrus
6. R Sigmoideus - R Coronalis Gyrus
7. R Coronalis - R Sylvianus Gyrus
8. R Hippocampus - R Amygdaloid Complex
9. L. Hippocampus - Amygdaloid Complex
10. L. C.M.N. Thal. - Indifferent
11. L V.M.N. Thal. - Indifferent
12. L V.P.M.N. Thal. - Indifferent
13. L Sigmoideus - Coronalis Gyrus
14. L Coronalis - Sylvianus Gyrus
15. L Lateralis - Suprasylvianus Gyrus
16. Tooth stimulation

◄—— Attention to Rat ——►

50 μv

25 m.sec.

50μv

Recorded from Fifth Sensory Nucleus

A,B,C during tooth stimulation   B during somatic sensory cortex and Ⅴ Sensory N. stimulation.   D & E during somatic sensory cortex stimulation.

Fig. 5. Correlation between 3-per-second spike and wave discharges and evoked responses from fifth sensory nucleus and sensory (facial) cortex when animal focused attention on a rat. Top tracings show diminution in amplitude of evoked potentials obtained from fifth sensory nucleus and sensory (facial) cortex. Middle tracings show blocking in epileptiform discharges while animal focused attention on rat. Bottom records show decrement in amplitude of evoked response recorded from fifth sensory nucleus under effect of electrical stimula-tion of sensory (facial) cortex.

sory (facial) cortex and the fifth sensory nucleus and notable change in 3-per-second spike and wave complex response to driving by stimulation of the tooth (Fig. 5). The electrical activity of the cat while it watched the rat was characterized by low amplitude and fast frequency.

Stimulation of the sensory (facial) cortex consistently evoked a response from the fifth sensory nucleus (Fig. 5). When stimulation of the sensory (facial) cortex and tooth pulp were applied simultaneously, the recording from the fifth sensory nucleus contained a decided reduction in amplitude of potentials evoked by stimulation of the tooth pulp. Stimulation of the tooth pulp affected principally the later components of the evoked response.

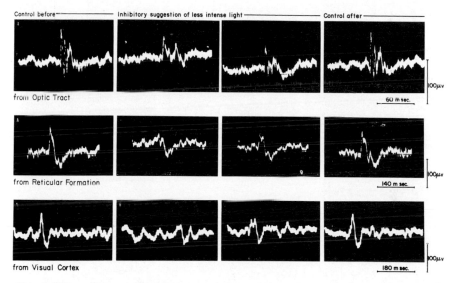

FIG. 6. Effect of repeated inhibitory verbal suggestion upon evoked potentials recorded from optic tract, mesencephalic reticular formation, and visual cortex. Patient was told that intensity of next two flashes of light would be diminished. Note diminution of amplitude of response evoked by such negative suggestion.

STUDIES IN HUMAN SUBJECTS

EFFECTS OF SUGGESTION. Our preliminary studies in human subjects with semipermanent electrodes in a variety of subcortical and cortical structures showed some correlation with the reports of Jouvet and Courjohn[33] and of Hernández-Péon and Donoso.[26] These investigators have reported the effect of selective visual attention and intrusion of distracting stimuli (various sensory stimuli and suggestion) on recordings obtained from the scalp and over the visual cortex in man. The data presented here result from record-ing evoked potentials from the optic tract, reticular formation (tectobulbar tract), and visual sensory cortex during stimulation by light flash in a patient. Changes in recordings occurred with altered attention (e.g., with suggestion and during changing motivation) and with electrical stimulation of the mesencephalic reticular formation.

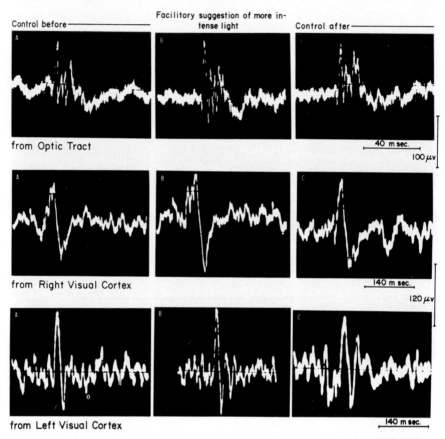

FIG. 7. Effect of repeated facilitory verbal suggestion upon evoked potentials recorded from optic tract and visual cortex. Patient was told that intensity of next flash would be greater. Note increment of amplitude of potential evoked by such positive suggestion.

The evoked potentials decreased in amplitude during repeated verbal suggestion that light intensity would be lessened in the next two flashes and increased in amplitude with verbal suggestion that the next flash would be of greater intensity (Fig. 7). Parameters of photic stimulation were actually maintained constant during the course of the experiment. Each evoked response correlated with the patient's subjective report: that the intensity was less (Fig. 6) and that it was greater (Fig. 7). Increment and diminution in amplitude of evoked potentials were demonstrated in recordings from the optic tract, from the mesencephalic reticular formation, and from the occipital cortex. Stimulation to the mesencephalic reticular formation by single pulses or by different frequencies inhibited the evoked potentials recorded from the visual pathways in response to photic flashes (Fig. 8).

DISCUSSION

From these studies of evoked potentials from the fifth sensory nucleus, perception of pain consequent to stimulation of the tooth pulp appears to

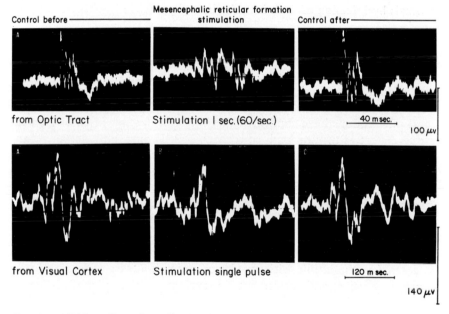

FIG. 8. Inhibiting effect of amplitude of evoked responses during stimulation of mesencephalic reticular formation recorded from optic tract and visual cortex in man in response to photic stimulation.

be inhibited by new and significant stimuli (i.e., the effect of flashes of light on visual attention). Results corroborate the observations of Hernández-Péon and colleagues[25] that a stimulus can elicit changes in activity of the lowest synapses of sensory pathways, provided the stimulus is significant and related meaningfully to the past experience of the animal. Richter and Crossland[40] have pointed out that the total ACh content of the brain depends on the physiologic state of the animal. It seems to vary inversely with the activity of the animal, increasing during sleep and decreasing in emotional states or after electrical stimulations. In the Tulane laboratory we have noted that injections of ACh into the lateral ventricle of normal cats induced the electroencephalographic pattern of sleep. Feldberg and Sherwood[12] observed catatonia in cats after intraventricular injections of ACh, physostigmine, and diisopropyl fluorophosphate. Our data indicate that intraventricular injection of ACh induced an increment of amplitude of the evoked potentials recorded from the trigeminal sensory nucleus and from the sensory cortex in addition to the electroencephalographic pattern of spindle bursts and slow waves. These observations may suggest activation or lowering of threshold of the cholinergic neurons in subcortical structures which are close to the ventricle. The data also suggest that novel stimulation in animals by injection of ACh into the lateral ventricle is without effect on the potentials evoked with pain, demonstrating that ACh can be involved in the mechanism for inhibition of attention.

A number of studies attest to the role of GABA in activity of the central nervous system. Awapara and associates,[3] Roberts and Frankel,[41] and Udenfriend[46] identified GABA in brain. Elliott and Florey[10] isolated factor I from the mammalian brain and identified one of the factors as GABA. Several publications have confirmed the inhibitory action of GABA on the nervous system. Purpura and coworkers,[38, 39] Iwama and Jasper,[30] and Elliott and Jasper[11] have demonstrated that GABA causes an immediate reversible depression in the surface-negative component of the evoked potential in the somatosensory cortex and also changes the recruiting response from surface-negative to surface-positive.

Our results and the data of others demonstrate the following electroencephalographic changes in the cat during wakefulness when GABA is administered: (1) desynchronized low to moderate amplitude and fast or mixed activity compatible with an alerted animal, (2) extreme diminution in surface-negative and increment in surface-positive phase of evoked potentials from the sensory cortex, and (3) increased surface-positive phase of the evoked potential from the fifth sensory nucleus. We postulate, on the basis of existing data, that GABA may increase alertness by inhibiting the nonspecific thalamic reticular system which is implicated in the regulation of sensitive changes in levels of attention, consciousness, and sleep.

Topical application of GABA on the cerebral cortex has been interpreted by Jasper and associates[32] as a selective blockade of excitatory synapses. Tower[43] reported that patients with various types of seizures experienced significant improvement and, in one instance, complete control of seizures. Our data suggest that GABA exerts inhibitory effects upon focal epilepsy by inhibiting the mechanism for certain types of seizural discharge. With the thalamic type or sensorial epilepsy, the effects are more pronounced, characterized by blockage in slow, abnormal, 3-per-second activity, which it seems reasonable to consider as dependent on the non-specific thalamic system. A possible relation between GABA and the mode of activity of sodium diphenylhydantoin in the relief of neuralgic pain can be postulated.

We have observed that GABA can inhibit perception of pain. Sodium diphenylhydantoin was introduced by Bergouignan[5] for treating pain of trigeminal neuralgia because this condition was often accompanied by epileptiform discharges in the fifth sensory nucleus. Iannone and associates[29] and Morrell and coworkers[34] reported that diphenylhydantoin has an in-hibitory effect on peripheral nerve conduction. According to Fromm and Landgren,[14] diphenylhydantoin has an inhibiting effect on synaptic trans-mission, which is probably more significant than its effect on excitability of peripheral nerve conduction. Our experiments corroborate the strong action of diphenylhydantoin on the synaptic level and suggest that it may poten-tiate the effects of GABA.

We have demonstrated in several animals that an epileptiform focus in the intralaminar and ventroposteromedial nuclei of the thalamus can in-duce a generalized pattern of 3-per-second spike and wave discharges. This recording pattern can be activated and driven by stimulation of the tooth pulp. The spontaneous appearance of the 3-per-second spike and wave pat-tern was often preceded by a short cry, which may represent a symptom related to the thalamic syndrome of Dejerine-Roussy or central pain. The data suggest a relation between this electroencephalographic pattern and pain. Some of the experimental animals seemed to experience a painful aura activated by sensory stimuli and of the type seen in some epileptics.

The relation of ACh to the brain's electrical activity has been investi-gated. Ward and Jenkner[48] studied monkeys with electrolytic lesions in the reticular formation and observed the appearance of a static tremor in the animals, which become hypersensitive to ACh. Tower[43] noted that the epileptogenic cortex appeared to be characterized biochemically by impair-ment of ACh-binding, metabolic loss of glutamic acid, and failure to main-tain concentration of potassium in the tissues. This, he reasoned, caused a greater tendency to depolarization with firing of the neurons. Guerrero-Figueroa and coworkers,[19] in 1961, described a disturbance of ACh in cer-tain types of epilepsy which was modified by administration of hydro-chlorate of quinacrine. Brenner and Merritt[6] postulated that a disturbance in ACh metabolism might be etiologically important in certain varieties of epilepsy. Wolfe and Elliott[50] concluded that convulsive activity appears to be associated with accelerated liberation of free ACh and its consequent destruction, so that ACh content momentarily declines and the fall stimu-lates rapid resynthesis. Tower and Elliott[44, 45] demonstrated that focal epileptogenic tissue produced free ACh at about the same rate as normal human tissue, but its content of bound ACh failed to increase during incubation. Our data demonstrate the capacity of some sensory stimuli to initiate and drive trains of 3-per-second spike and wave discharges in animals with a chronic thalamic epileptogenic focus. This observation suggests that sensory stimuli may initiate the appearance of 3-per-second spike and wave activity by stimulating the liberation of free ACh.

Our data concerning the effect of suggestion on evoked potentials in human subjects demonstrate a physiologic correlation for the frequently reported psychologic effects of suggestion. Although the light stimulus remained constant, the evoked potential in both the mesencephalic reticular formation and the primary sensory pathway increased in amplitude with the suggestion of a more intense light and diminished in amplitude with the suggestion of a dimmer light. Different patients in our series responded in varying degrees to this type of suggestion, as would be expected. The specific neural mechanism involved in this process is under investigation. A similar neural mechanism was probably basic to the clinical observations of Wolfe and Goodell,[49] who demonstrated that pain thresholds could be raised by suggestion. In animal studies, Hernández-Péon and Donoso[26] also observed that the magnitude of evoked potentials could be varied according to degree of attention to the stimulus and suggested that the transmission of light stimuli was modified at the retina by centrifugal influences.

By direct stimulation to the mesencephalic reticular formation at frequencies from 50 to 100 cps, we were able to produce significant inhibition in amplitude of the potential evoked by photic stimulation. Similar results were reported in cats by Granit[16] and by Hernández-Péon and associates,[27] who further demonstrated that this tegmental stimulation reduced photically induced activity of the ganglion cells of the retina. In our human studies, stimulation of the mesencephalic reticular system was followed by an activated electroencephalographic recording, i.e., one characterized by fast, desynchronized, low-voltage activity. The patients were alerted and exhibited intense degrees of emergency emotion (i.e., fear and rage) with stimulation at frequencies ranging between 6 and 100 cps. During this highly emotional alerted state, the patients were unable to pay attention to the sensory stimulus, and this probably accounts for the diminution in amplitude of the evoked response to the light flash.

SUMMARY

Studies in cats and human subjects are presented which demonstrate certain neural mechanisms for perception of pain and pleasure, the effects of attention on perception, and the manner in which certain chemical compounds, principally GABA and ACh, affect the neural mechanism for sensory perception. Stimulation of the reticular activating system was followed by (1) inhibition of evoked potentials in sensory pathways, which was observed from the first synaptic relay; (2) inhibition of the mechanism in recruiting responses recorded from sensory cortex; and (3) inhibition of the mechanism in patients with focal sensory epilepsy. This stimulation was characterized by electroencephalographic patterns of low to moderate amplitude voltage and fast to mixed frequency activity (desynchronized). The patterns can be compatible with alerting with selective attention, certain types of suggestion, and certain emotional states.

Intravenous injection of GABA into the lateral ventricle was followed by (1) inhibition of the surface-negative component in the evoked sensory cortex responses and increment in the surface-positive component, (2) inhibition of the spontaneous 3-per-second spike and wave discharges consequent to an epileptogenic focus induced with introduction of alumina into the intralaminar thalamic nucleus, (3) inhibition of the recruiting responses elicited by stimulation of the midline thalamic nuclei, and (4) inhibition of a painful aura which may be related to the thalamic syndrome of Dejerine-Roussy or central pain. The electroencephalographic recording of the GABA effect was characterized by low to moderate amplitude and fast or mixed activity (desynchronized), followed by excited emotion suggesting fear, rage, or anxiety.

REFERENCES

1. ADRIAN, E. D. "The Physiological Basis of Perception," in *Brain Mechanisms and Consciousness*. Springfield, Ill., Thomas, 1954, pp. 237-248.
2. ALLEN, I. M. Observation on cases of reflex epilepsy. *New Zeal. Med. J. 44*:135, 1945.
3. AWAPARA, J., LANDUA, A. J., FUERST, R., and SEALE, B. Free gamma aminobutyric acid in brain. *J. Biol. Chem. 187*:35, 1950.
4. BECKER, H. C., FOUNDS, W. L., PEACOCK, S. M., HEATH, R. G., and LLEWELLYN, R. C. "Improvements in the Technique for Implanting Subcortical Electrodes by a Stereotaxic Method," in Heath, R. G., and the Department of Psychiatry and Neurology, Tulane University. *Studies in Schizophrenia*. Cambridge, Mass., Harvard, 1954, pp. 565-570.
5. BERGOUIGNAN, M. Cures heureuses faciales essentielles par le diphenylhydantoinate de sonde. *Rev. Laryng. (Bordeaux) 63*:34, 1942.
6. BRENNER, C., and MERRITT, H. H. Effect of choline derivatives on electrical activity of cortex. *Arch. Neurol. Psychiat. 48*:382, 1942.
7. COBB, S. Photic driving as a cause of clinical seizures in epileptic patients. *Arch. Neurol. Psychiat. 58*:70, 1947.

8. CRITCHLEY, M. Musicogenic epilepsy. *Brain 60*:13, 1937.
9. DEJERINE, J., and ROUSSY, G. Le syndrome thalamique. *Rev. Neurol. 14*:521, 1906.
10. ELLIOTT, K. A. C., and FLOREY, E. Assay and properties of an inhibitory factor from the brain. Presented at the Twentieth International Physiologic Congress, Brussels, 1956.
11. ELLIOTT, K. A. C., and JASPER, H. Gamma aminobutyric acid. *Physiol. Rev. 39*:383, 1959.
12. FELDBERG, W., and SHERWOOD, S. Behavior of cats after intraventricular injections of eserine and DFP. *Brit. J. Pharmacol. 125*:488, 1954.
13. FERNANDEZ-GUARDIOLA, M., ALCARAZ, V., and GUZMAN, F. C. Inhibition of convulsive activity by the reticular formation. *Acta Neurol. Lat. Amer. 7*:30, 1961.
14. FROMM, G. H., and LANDGREN, S. Effect of diphenylhydantoin on single cells in the spinal trigeminal nucleus. Presented at the Annual Meeting of the American Academy of Neurology, New York City, 1962.
15. GOWERS, W. Epilepsy and other chronic convulsive diseases. *London J. 24*:108, 1901.
16. GRANIT, R. Centrifugal and antidromic effects on ganglion cells of retina. *J. Neurophysiol. 18*:388, 1955.
17. GUERRERO-FIGUEROA, R., BARROS, A., DEBALBIAN VERSTER, F., and HEATH, R. G. Experimental "petit mal" in kittens. *Arch. Neurol. 9*:297, 1963.
18. GUERRERO-FIGUEROA, R., DEBALBIAN VERSTER, F., and HEATH, R. G. Mirror focus in specific subcortical nuclei: Its production and its modification through chemical agents in cats. *Trans. Amer. Neurol. Ass. 87*:207, 1962.
19. GUERRERO-FIGUEROA, R., GONZALEZ, G., BARROS, A., and LAVERDE, R. Effects of 7-methoxy-3 cloro-9-(1 methyl-4-diethylamino) butylaminoacridine hydrochloride on the myoneural plate, the superior cervical sympathetic ganglion, cortical areas, and subcortical nuclei. *Rev. Fac. Med. (Bogota) 29*:59, 1961.
20. HALL, M. On the reflex function of the medulla oblongata and medulla spinales. *Philos. Trans.*, pp. 635–665, 1833.
21. HEATH, R. G., and FOUNDS, W. L. A perfusion cannula for intracerebral microinjections. *Electroenceph. Clin. Neurophysiol. 12*:930, 1960.
22. HEATH, R. G., and MICKLE, W. A. "Evaluation of Seven Years' Experience with Depth Electrode Studies in Human Patients," in *Electrical Studies on the Unanesthetized Brain*, ed. by Ramey, E. R., and O'Doherty, D. S. New York, Hoeber-Harper, 1960, pp. 214–247.
23. HEATH, R. G., and the Department of Psychiatry and Neurology, Tulane University. *Studies in Schizophrenia*. Cambridge, Mass., Harvard, 1954.
24. HERNÁNDEZ-PÉON, R. Centrifugal control of sensory inflow to the brain and sensory perception. *Acta Neurol. Lat. Amer. 5*:279, 1959.
25. HERNÁNDEZ-PÉON, R., BRUST-CARMONA, H., PENALOZA-ROJAS, J., and BACY-Y-RITA, G. The efferent control of afferent signals entering the central nervous system. *Ann. N.Y. Acad. Sci. 89*:866, 1961.
26. HERNÁNDEZ-PÉON, R., and DONOSO, M. "Influence of Attention and Suggestion upon Subcortical Evoked Electric Activity in the Human Brain," in *First Inter-*

national Congress of Neurological Sciences, Vol. 3. Ed. by van Bogaert, L., and Radermecker, J. New York, Pergamon Press, 1959, pp. 385–396.

27. HERNÁNDEZ-PÉON, R., SCHERRER, H., and JOUVET, M. Modification of electrical activity in the cochlear nucleus during attention in unanesthetized cats. *Science 123*:331, 1956.

28. HERNÁNDEZ-PÉON, R., SCHERRER, H., and VELASCO, M. Central influences on afferent conduction in the somatic and visual pathways. *Acta Neurol. Lat. Amer. 2*:8, 1956.

29. IANNONE, A., BAKER, A. B., and MORRELL, F. Dilantin in the treatment of trigeminal neuralgia. *Neurology 8*:126, 1958.

30. IWAMA, K., and JASPER, H. The action of gamma-aminobutyric acid upon cortical electrical activity in the cat. *J. Physiol. 138*:365, 1957.

31. JACKSON, J. H. "Neurological Fragments," in *Selected Writings of John Hughlings Jackson,* ed. by Taylor, J. London, Hodder & Stoughton, 1931, pp. 362–365.

32. JASPER, H., NAQUET, R., and KING, E. E. Thalamocortical recruiting responses in sensory receiving areas in the cat. *Electroenceph. Clin. Neurophysiol. 7*:99, 1955.

33. JOUVET, M., and COURJOHN, J. Variations des responses visuelles souscorticales au cours de l'attention chez l'homme. *Rev. Neurol. 99*:177, 1958.

34. MORRELL, F., BRADLEY, W., PTASHNE, M. Effect of diphenylhydantoin on peripheral nerve. *Neurology 8*:140, 1958.

35. MORUZZI, G., and MAGOUN, H. W. Brain stem reticular formation and activation of the electroencephalogram. *Electroenceph. Clin. Neurophysiol. 1*:455, 1949.

36. OLDS, J. Approach-avoidance dissociation in rat brain. *Amer. J. Physiol. 199*:965, 1960.

37. OLDS, J., and MILNER, P. Positive reinforcement produced by electrical stimulation of septal area and other regions of rat brain. *J. Comp. Physiol. Psychol. 47*:419, 1954.

38. PURPURA, D. P., GIRADO, M., and GRUNDFEST, H. Selective blockade of excitatory synapses in the cat brain by gamma-aminobutyric acid. *Science 125*:1200, 1957.

39. PURPURA, D. P., and GRUNDFEST, H. Nature of dendritic potentials and synaptic mechanisms in cerebral cortex of cat. *J. Neurophysiol. 19*:573, 1956.

40. RICHTER, D., and CROSSLAND, J. Variation in acetylcholine content of brain with physiological state. *Amer. J. Physiol. 159*:247, 1949.

41. ROBERTS, E., and FRANKEL, S. Gamma-aminobutyric acid in brain: Its formation from glutamic acid. *J. Biol. Chem. 187*:55, 1950.

42. ROBERTS, W. W. Both rewarding and punishing effects from stimulation of posterior hypothalamus of cat with same electrode at same intensity. *J. Comp. Physiol. Psychol. 51*:400, 1958.

43. TOWER, D. "The Administration of Gamma-Aminobutyric Acid to Man: Systemic Effects and Anticonvulsant Action," in *Inhibition in the Nervous System and Gamma-Aminobutyric Acid,* ed. by Roberts, E. New York, Pergamon Press, 1960, pp. 562–577.

44. Tower, D., and Elliott, K. A. C. Activity of acetylcholine system in human epileptogenic focus. *J. Appl. Physiol. 4*:669, 1952.
45. Tower, D., and Elliott, K. A. C. Activity of acetylcholine system in cerebral cortex of various unanesthetized mammals. *Amer. J. Physiol. 168*:747, 1952.
46. Udenfriend, S. Identification of gamma-aminobutyric acid in brain by the isotope derivative method. *J. Biol. Chem. 187*:65, 1950.
47. Walter, W. G. Analysis of the electrical response of the human cortex to photic stimulation. *Nature (London) 18*:540, 1946.
48. Ward, A. A., and Jenkner, F. L. The bulbar reticular formation and tremor. *Trans. Amer. Neurol. Ass. 78*:36, 1953.
49. Wolfe, H. G., and Goodell, H. The relation of attitude and suggestion to the perception of and reaction to pain. *Res. Publ. Ass. Res. Nerv. Ment. Dis. 23*:434, 1943.
50. Wolfe, L. S., and Elliott, K. A. C. "Chemical Studies in Relation to Convulsive Conditions," in *Neurochemistry,* ed. by Elliott, K. A. C., Page, I. H., and Quastel, J. H. Springfield, Ill., Thomas, 1962, pp. 694–727.

RAUL HERNÁNDEZ-PÉON, M.D.
Unidad de Investigaciones Cerebrales

Attention, Sleep, Motivation, and Behavior

B EHAVIOR MAY BE NEUROPHYSIOLOGICALLY DEFINED as the response of the
entire organism to a stimulus or stimulatory constellation, according to
past experience and present motivations. Therefore, a complete understanding of behavior requires basic knowledge about the processes involved in
sensory perception, including learning and memory, as well as those concerned with motivation.

In most of my own work I have been concerned with the first group of
neurophysiologic events, in an attempt to understand how sensory experiences arise and how they are stored. On the other hand, the rapid developments recently achieved in the psychophysiology of motivation are leading
scientists to the desired and inevitable *rapprochement* in studies concerned
with the executive integrating mechanisms of behavior. In this paper, I
shall present a synthesis of some observations made with various collaborators and a discussion of the basic alternating patterns of cerebral activity
during wakefulness and sleep.

SENSORY TRANSMISSION IN SPECIFIC
AND POLISENSORY SYSTEMS

Contrary to traditional views, it is now established that neural impulses
arising from sensory receptors not only are transmitted along the classic
afferent pathways or Pavlovian analyzers but also propagate to a considerable number of anatomic structures within the central nervous system from
the spinal cord up to the cortex. Because each of these sensory neurons undoubtedly belongs to specific functional systems in spite of receiving impulses of two or more sensory modalities, I have proposed the term
"polisensory system"[8] to replace the ambiguity expressed by "nonspecific

Supported in part by the United States Air Force under Grant No. AF-AFOSR-62-364
monitored by the Air Office of Scientific Research, Office of Aerospace Research.

system." Although sensory transmission in the polisensory system, because of its convergence and polisynaptic architecture, is more labile than in the specific systems, transmission along the paucisynaptic pathways of the specific systems is not rigid and fixed, as was thought for many years. Physiologic evidence accumulated during the past 8 years has established that afferent transmission can be modified at each specific sensory synapse from the lowest central level up to the cortex, and even at the receptor itself. A great deal of evidence substantiates the idea that the central core of the brain stem plays an important role in the aforementioned sensory regulation.[9] More work is necessary to elucidate the functional significance of the laterally located paraspecific descending pathways described by anatomists long ago.

RETICULOFUGAL TONIC INHIBITION ON FIRST SENSORY SOMATIC SYNAPSE

The observation that electrical stimulation of the mesencephalic reticular formation blocked the postsynaptic potentials at the spinal cord[5] and at the spinal fifth sensory nucleus[23] evoked by stimulating the first-order sensory neurons suggested the existence of a reticulofugal inhibitory mechanism acting upon the first sensory synapse. More convincing evidence about the physiologic nature of the postulated descending sensory inhibition was provided by experiments with lesions. An extensive lesion of the midbrain tegmentum[6, 25] resulted in enhancement of the bulbar trigeminal potentials elicited by stimulating the infraorbital nerve. Although this experiment demonstrated a tonic inhibitory influence during wakefulness, the source of such an influence was by no means determined. Subsequent studies by Hernández-Péon and Brust-Carmona[13, 14] have shown that the tonic descending influence arises in the hindbrain and does not require supramesencephalic structures. In decerebrate preparations, tactile potentials recorded from the lateral column of the spinal cord were immediately and remarkably enhanced after high transection of the spinal cord.

LIMITATION OF SPAN OF ATTENTION AND GATING OF SENSORY SIGNALS AT FIRST SENSORY SYNAPSE

The limitation of our span of perception even during maximal voluntary effort was one of the earliest psychologic discoveries. It implies that only a limited amount of sensory information can reach the level of consciousness at any given moment.

The limitation of the span of perception is associated with a corresponding limitation of the span of attention. Furthermore, not all the items within the field of attention are equally perceived. Only objects located in the focus of attention leave a well-defined conscious experience; objects located in the fringe of attention receive less recognition.

During study of the reticulofugal inhibitory influences which block transmission at the first sensory synapse, I considered it logical that such a

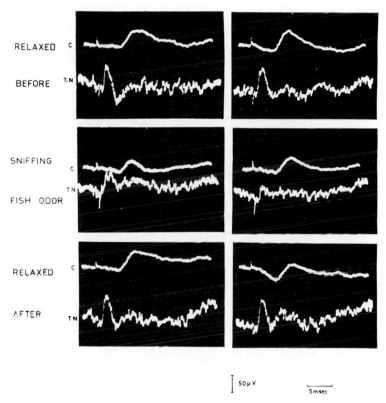

FIG. 1. Tactile potentials evoked by single shocks applied to skin of cat's face. Simultaneous recordings from facial area of somatic sensory cortex (C) and from spinal fifth sensory nucleus (T.N.). This figure shows reduction of cortical and bulbar evoked potentials when cat was sniffing fish odor.

mechanism would reasonably explain our intrinsic limitation of sensory perception. Therefore, reticulofugal inhibition should be associated with shiftings of attention for excluding at a particular moment those sensory channels which otherwise would be activated by irrelevant signals.

With the collaboration first of Scherrer[25] and later of Jouvet,[26] I tested this hypothesis by recording auditory evoked potentials from the dorsal cochlear nucleus with electrodes permanently implanted in cats during wakefulness. The auditory evoked potentials had a stable magnitude as long as the cat was in a state of relaxed wakefulness. Then he was presented a couple of mice inside a closed beaker, and when he was attentively looking at the mice, the auditory evoked potentials were considerably reduced. When the mice were removed and the cat became relaxed again, the poten-

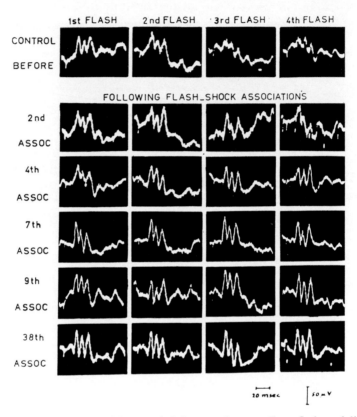

FIG. 2. Photic evoked potentials recorded from optic tract. Four flashes of light were presented at a rate of 1 per second. Following a control series, a painful electric shock was applied to a leg of the cat during fourth flash. Potentials evoked by third and fourth flashes of each series increased after a few associations.

tials recovered their initial magnitude. A similar phenomenon was observed when the cat's attention was attracted by a significant olfactory stimulus, such as fish odor introduced into the cage through a tube.

In an effort to determine whether the afferent blockade at the first sensory synapse during distraction is a general mechanism occurring in all sensory pathways, I have recorded, with various collaborators, photic retinal potentials from the optic tract,[22, 39] tactile potentials from the lateral column of the spinal cord,[14] and tactile and nociceptive evoked potentials from the spinal fifth sensory nucleus.[8, 9] In all the pathways tested, the evoked potentials representing volleys from second-order sensory neurons were significantly reduced when the animal was distracted by a stimulus more significant than the test stimulus (Fig. 1).

If distraction from a stimulus is accompanied by sensory inhibition, attention to a given stimulus should be accompanied by a selective sensory facili-

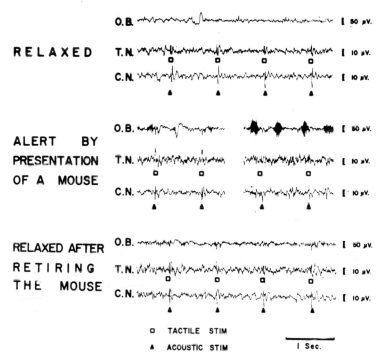

FIG. 3. Simultaneous recordings from olfactory bulb (O.B.), spinal fifth sensory nucleus (T.N.), and cochlear nucleus (C.N.). Single shocks applied to skin of face and clicks were simultaneously presented. Changes during alertness are described in text.

tation. This hypothesis was tested experimentally with use of the Pavlovian conditioning technic. Indeed, after associating the test conditional indifferent stimulus (clicks or flashes of light) with a nociceptive stimulus (a painful electric shock to a leg of the animal), the magnitude of the auditory evoked potentials from the dorsal cochlear nucleus[24] and of the photic evoked potentials from the optic tract[39] increased significantly (Fig. 2). Therefore, it appears that transmission of afferent impulses evoked by a stimulus occupying the focus of attention is facilitated at the level of the first sensory synapse.

The oscillating nature of attention and of the accompanying centrifugal influences which filter the sensory inflow to the brain can be demonstrated by recording simultaneously both the background and the evoked activity at the first synapse of several sensory pathways. Hernández-Péon and associates[15] have observed in the cat that an alerting stimulus produced at first activation of the olfactory bulb, enhancement of tactile evoked potentials at the spinal trigeminal nucleus, and reduction of the auditory evoked poten-

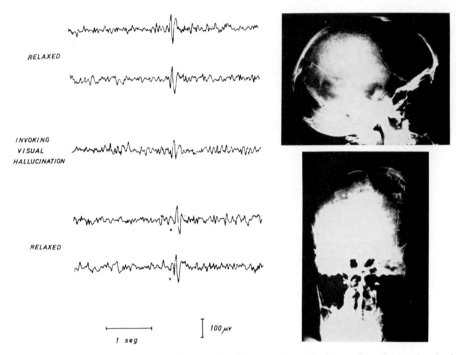

RELAXED

INVOKING
VISUAL
HALLUCINATION

RELAXED

1 seg   100 μν

FIG. 4. Photic evoked potentials recorded from optic radiations of patient who had previously presented visual hallucinations. When he was asked to recall the hallucinations, photic evoked potentials were remarkably decreased.

tials at the dorsal cochlear nucleus. These changes were followed a few seconds later by further activation of the olfactory bulb, decrease of the trigeminal potentials, and further diminution of the auditory potentials (Fig. 3). Besides sensory inhibition in several afferent pathways, an alerting stimulus may simultaneously produce release of inhibition of sensory transmission in previously habituated pathways.

As to the source of the aforementioned centrifugal influences, the available experimental evidence indicates an important participation of the brain-stem arousal system. Both alertness and sensory inhibition at the first sensory synapse can be elicited by direct electrical stimulation of the mesencephalic reticular formation.[9] However, the massive and indiscriminate effects produced by the electrical stimulus can never be compared to the selective neuronal activation occurring in physiologic situations.

VARIETIES OF ATTENTION.   In addition to being able to focus his attention upon the external environment or upon any part of his own body, man has the capacity for memories and ideas. Thinking is nothing more than the process of forming ideas, and it becomes creative when, by association of ideas, new and valuable concepts arise. Therefore, according to the object focused upon, attention is either sensorial or ideational. On the other hand, the process of attention can be triggered directly by a sensory stimulus (so-called nonvoluntary or reflex attention), or it can be focused at will (so-called voluntary attention). Since even the so-called voluntary behavior is

TABLE 1. VARIETIES OF ATTENTION

Origin	Development	Object
Nonvoluntary (passive, reflex) exo-evoked	Immediate (direct)	Sensorial
Voluntary (active) auto-evoked	Derived (indirect)	Intellectual

triggered by sensory stimuli as a function of past experiences and present motivations, I have proposed the terms "exo-evoked attention" and "auto-evoked attention" for the aforementioned types (Table 1). Sensorial exo-evoked attention can be studied in animals as previously described. However, auto-evoked ideational attention can be studied only in human subjects.

ELECTROPHYSIOLOGIC RECORDINGS IN NORMAL HUMAN
SUBJECTS DURING RELAXED WAKEFULNESS AND DURING
VOLUNTARY ATTENTION

Hernández-Péon and Donoso[20, 21] first studied changes of sensory transmission during attention focused upon mental processes in subjects with electrodes implanted in the optic radiations. The potentials evoked by flashes of light were considerably reduced when the subject was engaged in conversation, when he was solving an arithmetical problem, or when he was asked to remember a particular past experience (Fig. 4). Thus subcortical sensory inhibition appears to be a general phenomenon accompanying all varieties of attention.

These studies also indicated that repeated verbal instructions of the experimenter, suggesting variations of intensity of the light stimuli, led to corresponding modifications of the magnitude of the evoked potentials. For instance, announcement of extremely bright flashes of light elicited enhancement of the photic evoked potentials in two highly suggestible subjects. Correspondingly, previous suggestions of less intense light led to diminished photic evoked potentials (Fig. 5).

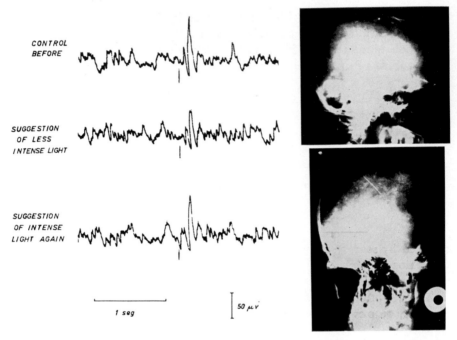

CONTROL
BEFORE

SUGGESTION
OF LESS
INTENSE LIGHT

SUGGESTION
OF INTENSE
LIGHT AGAIN

1 seg

50 μ v

FIG. 5. Effects of suggestion upon photic evoked potentials recorded from optic radiations. Potentials decreased when subject was warned that light would be less intense.

Since the method of recording sensory evoked potentials proved adequate for studying attention in both animals and human subjects, more extensive application to human psychology and psychiatry was obtained by recording the evoked potentials from the scalp without penetrating the brain. The small size of the evoked signals makes them undetectable from the random background activity with the conventional electroencephalographic technic. However, a photoelectronic method described by Kozchesnikov[29] permits the averaging of a given number of evoked responses and thus brings out the specific response from the random background activity. Using this method, Hernández-Péon and Aguilar-Figueroa[11, 12] have recorded somatic evoked potentials through the scalp of a group of normal and abnormal subjects. The stimuli, consisting of single rectangular pulses, were applied

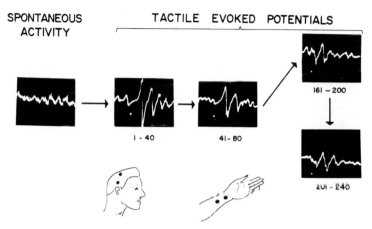

SPONTANEOUS
ACTIVITY

TACTILE   EVOKED   POTENTIALS

161 - 200

1 - 40   41- 80

201 - 240

FIG. 6. Averaged potentials evoked by single shocks of tactile intensity applied to skin of forearm. Recording electrodes were placed on scalp of contralateral side. As stimuli were regularly repeated (at a rate of 1 per second), potentials diminished (habituation).

to the skin of the forearm, and the recording electrodes were placed on the contralateral side of the head in the region overlying the perirolandic area. In normal subjects the somatic evoked potentials were considerably reduced or abolished during conversation or during solution of an arithmetical problem as compared with those during relaxed wakefulness. If the tactile

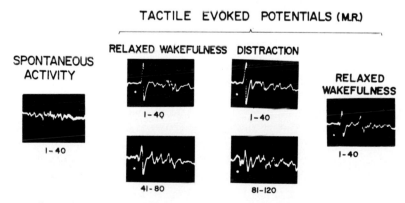

TACTILE   EVOKED   POTENTIALS (M.R.)

SPONTANEOUS
ACTIVITY

RELAXED WAKEFULNESS   DISTRACTION

RELAXED
WAKEFULNESS

1-40   1-40   1-40

1- 40   41- 80   81-120

FIG. 7. Effects of distraction upon averaged tactile evoked potentials in a mentally retarded subject (15 years old). Reduction produced by conversation appeared after first 40 seconds of onset of the distracting stimuli.

stimuli were repeated monotonously, the size of the evoked potentials progressively diminished (habituation) (Fig. 6). This phenomenon is similar to that observed in the cat.[8]

ELECTROPHYSIOLOGIC RECORDINGS IN MENTALLY RETARDED SUBJECTS

Hernández-Péon and Aguilar-Figueroa[11, 12] used the photoelectronic method for studying the deficiencies of attention in mentally retarded subjects. The following experiments provided evidence that such persons have slow and unstable mechanisms of attention. During the recording of somatic

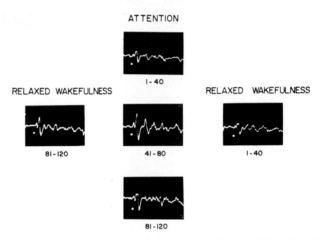

FIG. 8. Averaged tactile evoked potentials in a mentally retarded subject (16 years old). Potentials increased after first 40 seconds of instruction to focus attention upon tactile stimulus.

evoked potentials, extremely simple instructions were given for directing their attention away from or toward the test stimulus. In each case, the maximal reduction (Fig. 7) or enhancement (Fig. 8) of the evoked potentials occurred with a latency of about 40 seconds. The potentials evoked by tactile stimuli of low intensity were exceedingly small at first, progressively increasing in magnitude as the stimuli were repeated (Fig. 9). This phenomenon contrasts with the observation in normal subjects in whom the first potentials were initially large, decreasing subsequently as the stimuli were monotonously repeated. Thus, mentally retarded subjects seem to have unimpaired subcortical inhibitory and facilitory mechanisms for sensory filtering but deficient corticoreticular mechanisms involved in triggering and maintenance of attention.

CONTROLLING MECHANISMS OF ATTENTION IN FOREBRAIN

Although the vigilance system located in the rostral brain stem is undoubtedly indispensable for wakefulness, control and maintenance of attention require higher forebrain structures. Descending corticofugal projections

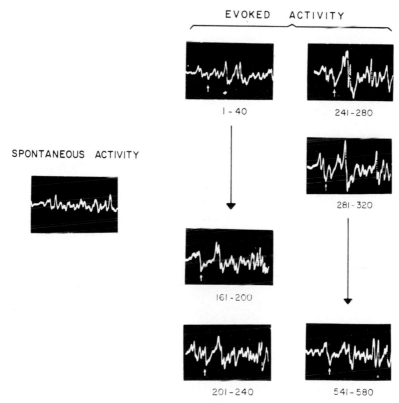

FIG. 9. Averaged tactile evoked potentials recorded in a mentally retarded subject (14 years old). Maximal size was attained after 280 successive tactile stimuli applied at a rate of 1 per second.

extending from localized cortical areas into the reticular or vigilance system of the brain stem have been traced anatomically and neurophysiologically.[4] Furthermore, the existence of arousing components in these projections has been demonstrated by cortical electrical stimulation.[44] Of all the corticofugal projections, those arising in the frontal lobes appear to be importantly related to maintenance of attention, since ablations of the frontal cortex in monkeys[28, 40] and frontal lobotomies in human subjects interfere with the performance of tasks that require sustained attention. If this interpretation is correct, adequate activation of those corticoreticular projections should induce a state of sustained attention upon objects otherwise incapable of attracting attention for prolonged periods.

In experiments designed to study the behavioral and electrographic effects of localized chemical stimulation of the brain with minute crystals of substances introduced through cannulae permanently implanted, Chavez-Ibarra and I[16] have found that application of carbachol in the inferior lateral supracommissural septum produced in the cat a state of specific alertness which may be followed by or associated with rage. In this state, the cat's gaze was focused upon and followed any nonsignificant object (such as

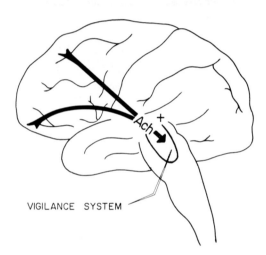

VIGILANCE SYSTEM

Fig. 10. Diagram illustrating proposed corticoreticular projections involved in maintenance of attention of septal cholinergic synapses.

a pencil or a finger of the experimenter) moving within its visual field just as iron filings are attracted by a moving magnet. I should like to propose the descriptive term "magnetic attention" for this peculiar behavioral response. Cholinergic magnetic attention probably results from depolarization of postsynaptic membranes of septal neurons included within a multisynaptic pathway descending from the cortex to the brain-stem reticular formation (Fig. 10).

The discovery that attention can be sustained for unusually long periods by localized chemical subcortical stimulation in animals with a poorly developed cortical mantle may foster fruitful research in human beings. Such research may eventually provide improvement of the ill-defined and unattractive world of mentally retarded subjects by furnishing a method to achieve better control of their attention.

SOMATIC THALAMOCORTICAL TRANSMISSION DURING SLEEP

Until recently, little attention has been devoted by neurophysiologists to the pattern of cerebral activity during complete sleep. Much to the surprise of the neurophysiologists who considered wakefulness and sleep as invariably associated with desynchronized and synchronized electroencephalographic tracings, it has been found that when the cat passes from light to deep sleep, the high-voltage slow waves of the electroencephalograph are replaced

LIGHT   SLEEP

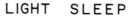

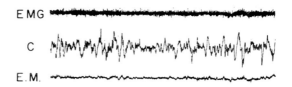

DEEP   SLEEP

FIG. 11. Electrical activity of cortex (C), of cervical muscles (EMG), and movements of eye (E.M.) in a cat during light and deep stages of sleep.

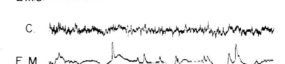

2 sec.

by a low-voltage fast activity similar to that recorded during wakefulness. Furthermore, during the deep stage of sleep, fast ocular movements appear as well as observable jerks of the animal's body, and the electromyographic activity of the cervical muscles practically disappears (Fig. 11).

The two phases of sleep which can now be electrographically defined probably result from a progressive degree of inhibition within the brainstem arousal system proceeding from a hypnogenic circuit to be described hereinafter. Unpublished studies by Dr. Allison in my laboratories on somatic thalamocortical transmission during the two phases of sleep have shown that the primary cortical response evoked by a single shock applied to the ventral posterolateral thalamic nucleus or to the medial lemniscus increases during light sleep and is further enhanced during deep sleep. Contrariwise, the secondary response to a lemniscal stimulus is reduced during the deep stage of sleep (Fig. 12). Since the secondary response results from sensory transmission within polisensory structures which form part of the brain-stem arousal system, these results support the view that the rostral

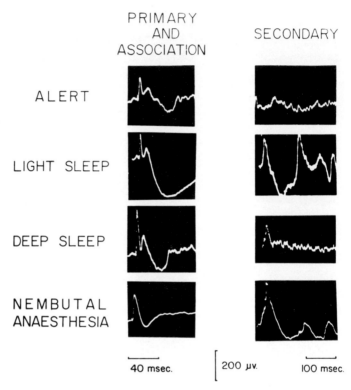

FIG. 12. Cortical potentials evoked by single shocks applied to ventral posterolateral thalamic nucleus. Primary spike was maximally enhanced during deep sleep. Secondary wave was smaller during deep than during light sleep.

brain stem may be maximally inhibited during deep sleep. As a consequence, the reticulofugal sensory inhibition is released, and the specific afferent pathways are opened.

ANATOMIC SUBSTRATE AND FUNCTIONAL ORGANIZATION
OF SLEEP SYSTEM

The existence of hypnogenic central structures has been suggested by experiments dealing with electrical stimulation as well as with procedures involving lesions. However, because the anatomic hypnogenic areas pointed out by different investigators were apparently unrelated, these workers were reluctant to admit the existence of a localized sleep system in contradistinction to the widely accepted localized arousal or vigilance system.[30] Hess[27] demonstrated that sleep is induced by electrical stimulation of a thalamic area in the vicinity of the massa intermedia. More recently, sleep has also been elicited by electrical stimulation of a number of regions including limbic structures[2, 3, 10, 16, 43] and all of the reticular systems in the brain stem.[41, 42] Evidence obtained from experiments with lesions indicates that the preoptic region[33] and the most caudal part of the brain stem behind the midpons[1]

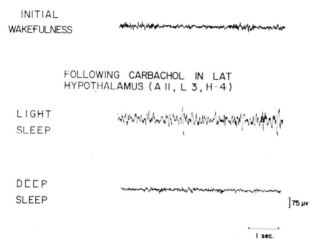

FIG. 13. Behavioral and electrocortical manifestations of light and deep sleep induced by application of carbachol in medial forebrain bundle at lateral hypothalamus.

have a tonic hypnogenic influence. This puzzle has been solved by a systematic investigation to be described.

In experiments of electrical stimulation of subcortical structures,[43] the activation of the medial forebrain bundle at the preoptic region proved most effective in producing sleep. Furthermore, in experiments designed to test the nature of possible chemical synaptic transmitters within the neuronal pathway subserving sleep, atropine, parenterally administered at a dose of 1.5 mg. per kilogram, prevented sleep otherwise induced by electrical stimulation of the preoptic region.[16] These results encouraged me to map out the anatomic substrate of the hypnogenic system by localized chemical stimulation of the brain with minute crystals of cholinergic substances applied through cannulae permanently implanted in the brain of cats. In brief, Hernández-Péon and associates[17-19] noted that local application of acetylcholine (alone or with eserine) or carbachol elicited sleep only from an extremely circumscribed pathway extending from the medial upper preoptic region into the medial pontine tegmentum along the medial forebrain bundle, the interpeduncular nucleus, and Bechterew's and Gudden's nuclei. This hypnogenic pathway corresponds to anatomic connections described by Nauta[34] within the limbic system–midbrain circuit.[35] From 20 seconds to 2 minutes after a few crystals of the previously mentioned cholinergic substances were tamped into the cannula, the cat fell asleep, often reaching the deep stage with the characteristic manifestations of the electrical activity of the cortex (Fig. 13) and olfactory bulb, disappearance of electromyographic activity of the cervical muscles, and rapid ocular movements.

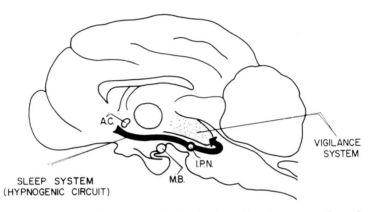

Fig. 14. Diagram illustrating hypnogenic circuit descending from preoptic region below anterior commissure into medial pontomesencephalic tegmentum. Caudal end of this descending pathway would inhibit directly vigilance system in brain stem.

The hypnogenic impulses along this circuit are conducted caudally, since a lesion in the medial forebrain bundle behind a hypnogenic site previously tested prevented sleep otherwise elicited by cholinergic stimulation of that site. Further evidence supporting the view of cholinergic synaptic transmission within this recently disclosed hypnogenic circuit has been provided by experiments designed to test the effects of eserine and atropine locally applied along this circuit. Indeed, eserine elicited light sleep when applied in the hypnogenic upper medial preoptic area, and atropine prevented sleep otherwise induced by cholinergic stimulation of the same site or of a distant site of the hypnogenic circuit rostral to the atropinized locus.[45] This new evidence indicates that the sleeplessness obtained by Nauta[33] and by Moruzzi's[31] group resulted from interruption of the rostral and caudal ends, respectively, of the descending hypnogenic circuit.

Since the caudal end of the hypnogenic circuit lies behind the vigilance system, the terminal hypnogenic segment must follow a curved trajectory, along which the descending hypnogenic impulses turn back in a rostral direction to reach the vigilance system (Fig. 14). The final inhibitory link between the hypnogenic and vigilance systems may be subserved at least partially by the diffuse fiber system known as Weisschedel's[46] radiatio grisea tegmenti, which extends from the region of the central gray substance to the entire cross section of the midbrain tegmentum. As a lesion in the rostral part of the hypnogenic circuit would be compensated by activity in the remaining part of the system, more complete and long-lasting effects would

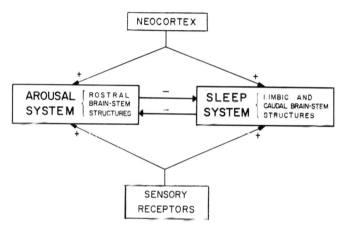

FIG. 15. Hypothetical organization of vigilance and sleep systems in reciprocal antagonism. Dynamic equilibrium can be unbalanced by impulses coming from sensory receptors or from neocortex.

be expected if the caudal end of the circuit were interrupted as it occurs in the midpontine preparation.[1]

RECIPROCAL ANTAGONISM AND COMMON SOURCES OF ACTIVATION FOR VIGILANCE AND SLEEP SYSTEMS

It is likely that the vigilance and the sleep systems are reciprocally connected in dynamic equilibrium, as depicted in Figure 15. This sleep system appears to inhibit the vigilance system and vice versa. The level of activity within each system is probably determined by intrinsic rhythms. The level also can be affected by impulses coming from sensory receptors and from the cortex. The reticular arousing system in the brain stem can be activated either by multiple modalities of sensory stimulation or by corticifugal impulses. On the other hand, sleep is often induced by certain monotonous sensory stimuli. It remains to be demonstrated whether the corticifugal projections to the brain-stem reticular formation carry hypnogenic components along with those concerned with arousal.

SIMILARITIES BETWEEN THE SLEEP-VIGILANCE SYSTEMS AND THE POSITIVE-NEGATIVE MOTIVATIONAL SYSTEMS

When the anatomic and functional organizations of the neuronal systems subserving sleep and wakefulness are compared with those concerned with basic motivations, several similarities become apparent. As far as the ana-

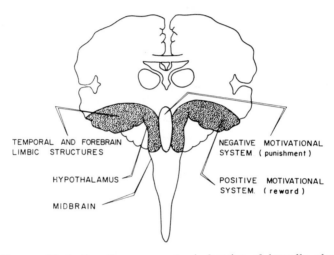

FIG. 16. Diagram illustrating the gross anatomic location of laterally placed positive motivational system and more medially placed negative motivational system.

tomic localization of those systems is concerned, there is certain overlapping of the sleep pathway and that yielding positive reinforcement.[37] The medial forebrain bundle appears to contain elements of both systems. It remains to be determined whether the interpeduncular nucleus and the medial pontomesencephalic tegmentum behind it also produce positive reinforcement. On the other hand, there is a partial overlapping of the mesodiencephalic regions from which arousal and negative reinforcement can be elicited (Fig. 16).

The brilliant investigation on self-stimulation of the brain carried out by Olds[37] suggested reciprocal connections between the positive and negative motivational systems. Although in recent experiments of Olds and Olds,[38] constant stimulation of a positive reinforcing point in the lateral hypothalamus facilitated negatively reinforced behavior from a tegmental point, other data[36] suggest mutual antagonism between those subcortical systems, as illustrated in Figure 17. Since both pleasant and unpleasant sensations can be elicited directly by sensory stimuli of various modalities, or indirectly through associated memories, the subcortical motivational systems must be activated selectively by sensory and corticifugal inflows.

In summary, the basic wakefulness-sleep and motivational functions appear to be subserved by two mutually antagonistic and balanced subcortical systems, the activity of which can be directly or indirectly modified by impulses arising from sensory receptors or from the cerebral cortex. The reasonable suggestion made by Murray[32] to consider sleep as one of the basic motivations falls in line with this idea.

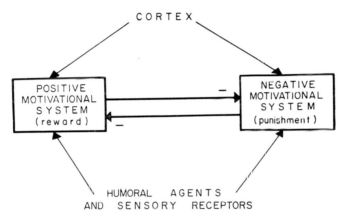

FIG. 17. Organization of subcortical positive and negative motivational systems in reciprocal antagonism. Activity in each system is modified by humoral agents or by impulses arising in sensory receptors and neocortex.

SUMMARY

The organization of inhibitory systems operating during wakefulness and sleep is described. Reticulofugal descending inhibitory influences act tonically during wakefulness at second-order afferent neurons to prevent excessive sensory bombardment of the brain. During attention, reticulofugal inhibition selectively excludes sensory channels otherwise activated by irrelevant signals. As a consequence of inhibition at the entrance gates of the brain, the span of attention and of perception is limited. Simultaneously with the extensive sensory inhibition accompanying distraction, centrifugal facilitation occurs in the sensory pathway activated by the stimulus on which attention is focused. Sensory inhibition has been demonstrated during all varieties of attention, including the so-called voluntary attention to memories or ideas.

In mentally retarded subjects, the subcortical inhibitory and facilitory mechanisms for sensory filtering appear to be unimpaired, whereas the corticoreticular mechanisms necessary for triggering and maintenance of attention are deficient.

A state of prolonged attention (magnetic attention) to otherwise unattractive objects (a pencil, for example) has been obtained in animals with a poorly developed cortex, such as the cat, by localized cholinergic stimulations of the septal region. It is suggested that there might be cholinergic septal synapses in the corticoreticular pathways involved in the maintenance of attention.

A subcortical cholinergic hypnogenic circuit has also been mapped out by the method of localized chemical stimulation of the brain. This circuit extends from the medial preoptic region into the medial midbrain and pontine tegmentum involving the medial forebrain bundle, the interpeduncular nucleus, and Bechterew's and Gudden's nuclei. The hypnogenic impulses are conducted caudally within this circuit, since electrolytic lesions or atropine blockade of different sites of the pathway prevent sleep otherwise induced by cholinergic stimulation of rostral hypnogenic areas.

It is proposed that the wakefulness-sleep systems and the positive-negative motivational systems subserved by common anatomic subcortical limbic-midbrain structures are reciprocally connected in dynamic equilibrium and that the level of activity in each system is modified by impulses coming from sensory receptors or from the neocortex.

REFERENCES

1. BATINI, C., MORUZZI, G., PALESTINI, M., ROSSI, G. F., and ZANCHETTI, A. Persistent patterns of wakefulness in the pretrigeminal midpontine preparation. *Science 128*:30, 1958.

2. CLEMENTE, C. D., and STERMAN, M. B. Cortical recruitment and sleep patterns in acute restrained and chronic behaving cats. *Electroenceph. Clin. Neurophysiol. 14*:420, 1962.

3. CLEMENTE, C. D., and STERMAN, M. B. "Cortical Synchronization and Sleep Patterns in Acute Restrained and Chronic Behaving Cats Induced by Basal Forebrain Stimulation," in *The Physiological Basis of Mental Activity*, ed. by Hernández-Péon, R. *Electroenceph. Clin. Neurophysiol.*, *Suppl. 24*. In press.

4. FRENCH, J. D., HERNÁNDEZ-PÉON, R., and LIVINGSTON, R. G. Projections from cortex to cephalic brain stem (reticular formation) in monkey. *J. Neurophysiol. 18*:74, 1955.

5. HAGBARTH, K.-E., and KERR, D. I. B. Central influences on spinal afferent conduction. *J. Neurophysiol. 17*:295, 1954.

6. HERNÁNDEZ-PÉON, R. Central mechanisms controlling conduction along central sensory pathways. *Acta Neurol. Lat. Amer.* *1*:256, 1955.

7. HERNÁNDEZ-PÉON, R. The centrifugal control of afferent inflow to the brain and sensory perception. *Acta Neurol. Lat. Amer.* *5*:279, 1959.

8. HERNÁNDEZ-PÉON, R. Neurophysiological correlates of habituation and other manifestations of plastic inhibition (internal inhibition). Moscow Colloquium on Electroencephalography of Higher Nervous Activity. *Electroenceph. Clin. Neurophysiol. Suppl. 13*:101, 1960.

9. HERNÁNDEZ-PÉON, R. "Reticular Mechanisms of Sensory Control," in *Sensory Communication,* ed. by Rosenblith, W. A. Cambridge, Mass., Massachusetts Institute of Technology, 1961, pp. 497–520.

10. HERNÁNDEZ-PÉON, R. Sleep induced by localized electrical or chemical stimulation of the forebrain. *Electroenceph. Clin. Neurophysiol. 14*:423, 1962.

11. HERNÁNDEZ-PÉON, R., and AGUILAR-FIGUEROA, E. Effects of distraction and habituation upon somatic evoked potentials recorded with an averaging technique in normal human subjects. To be published.

12. HERNÁNDEZ-PÉON, R., and AGUILAR-FIGUEROA, E. Disturbances of attention in mentally retarded subject revealed by averaged evoked potentials. To be published.

13. HERNÁNDEZ-PÉON, R., and BRUST-CARMONA, H. "Functional Role of Subcortical Structures in Habituation and Conditioning," in *Brain Mechanisms and Learning.* Oxford, Blackwell, 1961, pp. 393–408.

14. HERNÁNDEZ-PÉON, R., and BRUST-CARMONA, H. Inhibition of tactile and nociceptive spinal evoked potentials in the cat during distraction. *Acta Neurol. Lat. Amer. 7*:289, 1961.

15. HERNÁNDEZ-PÉON, R., BRUST-CARMONA, H., PEÑALOZA-ROJAS, J., and BACH-Y-RITA, G. The efferent control of afferent signals entering the central nervous system. *Ann. N. Y. Acad. Sci. 89*:866, 1961.

16. HERNÁNDEZ-PÉON, R., and CHAVEZ-IBARRA, G. "Sleep Induced by Electrical or Chemical Stimulation of the Forebrain," in *The Physiological Basis of Mental Activity,* ed. by Hernández-Péon, R. *Electroenceph. Clin. Neurophysiol. Suppl. 24.* In press.

17. HERNÁNDEZ-PÉON, R., CHAVEZ-IBARRA, G., MORGANE, J. P., and TIMO-IARIA, C. Cholinergic pathways for sleep, alertness and rage in the limbic midbrain circuit. *Nature (London).* In press.

18. HERNÁNDEZ-PÉON, R., CHAVEZ-IBARRA, G., MORGANE, J. P., and TIMO-IARIA, C. Induction of sleep by direct cholinergic stimulation of the brain. *Clin. Res.* In press.

19. HERNÁNDEZ-PÉON, R., CHAVEZ-IBARRA, G., MORGANE, J. P., and TIMO-IARIA, C. Limbic cholinergic pathways involved in sleep and emotional behavior. *Exp. Neurol.* In press.

20. HERNÁNDEZ-PÉON, R., and DONOSO, M. Subcortical photically evoked activity in the human waking brain. Fourth International Congress of Electroencephalography and Clinical Neurophysiology. *Excerpta Med.,* International Congress Series 11, p. 155, 1957. (Abst.)

21. HERNÁNDEZ-PÉON, R., and DONOSO, M. "Influence of Attention and Suggestion

upon Subcortical Evoked Electric Activity in the Human Brain," in *First International Congress of Neurological Science,* Vol. 3, ed. by van Bogaert, L., and Radermecker, J. New York, Pergamon Press, 1959, pp. 385–396.

22. HERNÁNDEZ-PÉON, R., GUZMAN-FLORES, C., ALGARA, M., and FERNANDEZ-GUARDIOLA, A. Sensory transmission in visual pathway during "attention" in unanesthetized cats. *Acta Neurol. Lat. Amer. 3*:1, 1957.

23. HERNÁNDEZ-PÉON, R., and HAGBARTH, K.-E. Interaction between afferent and cortically induced reticular responses. *J. Neurophysiol. 18*:44, 1955.

24. HERNÁNDEZ-PÉON, R., JOUVET, M., and SCHERRER, H. Auditory potentials at cochlear nucleus during acoustic habituation. *Acta Neurol. Lat. Amer. 3*:144, 1957.

25. HERNÁNDEZ-PÉON, R., and SCHERRER, H. "Habituation" to acoustic stimuli in cochlear nucleus. *Fed. Proc. 14*:71, 1955.

26. HERNÁNDEZ-PÉON, R., SCHERRER, H., and JOUVET, M. Modification of electric activity in cochlear nucleus during "attention" in unanesthetized cats. *Science 123*:331, 1956.

27. HESS, W. R. *Das Zwischenhirn: Syndrome, Lokalisationen, Funktionen.* Basel, Schwabe, 1949.

28. JACOBSEN, C. F. Functions of the frontal association areas in primates. *Arch. Neurol. Psychiat. 33*:558, 1935.

29. KOZCHESNIKOV, V. A. Photo-electric method of selecting weak electrical responses of the brain. *J. Physiol. (U.S.S.R.). 44*:801, 1959.

30. MAGOUN, H. W. *The Waking Brain.* Springfield, Ill., Thomas, 1958.

31. MORUZZI, G. Synchronizing influences of the brain stem and the inhibitory mechanisms underlying the production of sleep by sensory stimulation. *Electroenceph. Clin. Neurophysiol. Suppl. 13*:231, 1960.

32. MURRAY, E. J. *Sleep and Motivation.* New York, Appleton. In press.

33. NAUTA, W. J. H. Hypothalamic regulation of sleep in rats: An experimental study. *J. Neurophysiol. 9*:285, 1946.

34. NAUTA, W. J. H. Hippocampal projections and related neural pathways to the midbrain in the cat. *Brain 81*:319, 1958.

35. NAUTA, W. J. H. "Some Neural Pathways Related to the Limbic System," in *Electrical Studies on the Unanesthetized Brain,* ed. by Ramey, E. R., and O'Doherty, D. S. New York, Hoeber-Harper, 1960, pp. 1–16.

36. OLDS, J. "Studies of Neuropharmacologicals by Electrical and Chemical Manipulation of the Brain in Animals with Chronically Implanted Electrodes," in *International Congress of Neuro-psychopharmacology, Proceedings,* ed. by Bradley, P. B. Amsterdam, Elsevier, 1958, pp. 20–32.

37. OLDS, J. Hypothalamic substrates of reward. *Physiol. Rev. 42*:554, 1962.

38. OLDS, M. E., and OLDS, J. Approach-escape interactions in rat brain. *Amer. J. Physiol. 203*:803, 1962.

39. PALESTINI, M., DAVIDOVICH, A., and HERNÁNDEZ-PÉON, R. Functional significance of centrifugal influences upon the retina. *Acta Neurol. Lat. Amer. 5*:113, 1959.

40. PRIBRAM, K. H., MISHKIN, M., ROSVOLD, H. E., and KAPLAN, S. J. Effect on

delayed-response performance of lesions of dorsolateral and ventromedial frontal cortex of baboons. *J. Comp. Physiol. Psychol. 45*:565, 1952.

41. ROSSI, G. F. Sleep-inducing mechanisms in the brain stem. *Electroenceph. Clin. Neurophysiol. 14*:428, 1962.

42. ROSSI, G. F. "Sleep Inducing Mechanisms in the Brain Stem," in *The Physiological Basis of Mental Activity*, ed. by Hernández-Péon, R. *Electroenceph. Clin. Neurophysiol. Suppl. 24*. In press.

43. RUSSEK, M., and HERNÁNDEZ-PÉON, R. Olfactory bulb activity during sleep induced by stimulation of limbic structures. *Acta Neurol. Lat. Amer.* 7:299, 1961.

44. SEGUNDO, J. P., ARANA, R., and FRENCH, J. D. Behavioral arousal by stimulation of the brain in the monkey. *J. Neurosurg. 12*:601, 1955.

45. VELLUTI, R., and HERNÁNDEZ-PÉON, R. Atropine blockade within a cholinergic hypnogenic circuit. *Exp. Neurol.* In press.

46. WEISSCHEDEL, E. Die zentrale Haubenbahn und ihre Bedeutung für das extrapyramidal-motorische System. *Arch. Psychiat. Nervenkr. 107*:443, 1937.

ROBERT G. HEATH, M.D., D.M.SC.*

Tulane University School of Medicine

Pleasure Response of Human Subjects to Direct Stimulation of the Brain: Physiologic and Psychodynamic Considerations

S TUDIES CONDUCTED AT TULANE UNIVERSITY over the past 12 years have yielded a quantity of data concerning pleasurable, as well as uncomfortable, feelings experienced by fully conscious human subjects in association with direct stimulation of the brain.[6-8, 12] The procedures permitted both electrical and chemical stimulations to specific, predetermined cerebral regions. The chemical stimulation procedure,[9, 10] introduced in January 1960, was applied to the last 10 of the total 54 patients studied with electrical stimulation.

The most consistent and striking alterations with stimulation, as determined by psychiatric technics, were observed in affect and levels of consciousness. Changes in verbal reports or content of speech were consistent with changes in underlying affect, and as one would expect, the content reflected the past experiences of the patients in the context of the affect created. Other behavioral indicators, such as facial expression and other motor movements, similarly reflected the altered affect and level of consciousness. Only in a few instances were primary motor areas stimulated. Therapy was the fundamental goal in these studies, and the induced alterations in affect generally proved beneficial. The studies in man reported herein were based on extensive animal experimentation which always preceded the clinical investigations.

Supported by funds provided by the Louisiana State Department of Hospitals and by grants-in-aid from The Commonwealth Fund.

* With the technical assistance of Charles J. Fontana, electroencephalographic technologist.

MATERIAL AND METHODS

Fifty-four patients have been studied since 1950, and 3 of these are still under investigation. Of the 51 subjects for whom studies have terminated, 37 were undeniably schizophrenic by all accepted clinical criteria. Of 6 epileptic patients, 2 were afflicted with seizures only and the other 4 displayed serious behavioral symptoms, with episodes of psychosis in addition to seizures. Eight of the 51 patients had nonpsychiatric diseases, including Park-

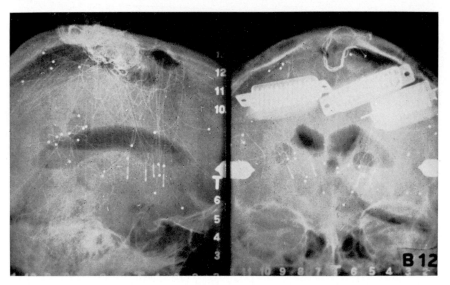

Fig. 1. Roentgenogram of Patient No. B-12 taken at conclusion of operative procedure, with residual air in ventricular system. Silver ball electrodes and cannulae are visible. Stainless steel electrodes cannot be seen.

insonism, carcinoma with intractable pain, severe advanced rheumatoid arthritis, and narcolepsy.

Grass electroencephalographs were used for all recordings. A single 8-channel machine was used early in the study for recordings from patients prepared with a few electrodes. More recently, as many as four electroencephalographs (two 16-channel and two 8-channel machines) have been used simultaneously to allow synchronized recordings from deep and cortical sites, together with conventional 8-channel scalp recordings. Recordings from the four machines were synchronized with a multi-electroencephalographic synchronizing apparatus.

During the first year of the Tulane depth electrode studies in man, technics permitted electrodes to remain in position for only a few days to a few weeks. Procedures were developed to hold the electrodes in place for longer periods, and since 1952 they have remained in patients for 1 to 3 years. The intracerebral cannula[10] used in the last 10 patients in the series also has been demonstrated to remain in accurate position for periods up to 3 years. Methods for implanting and maintaining electrodes and cannulae by the stereotaxic technic have undergone continuing modification.[1, 2, 11]

TABLE 1. ELECTRODE PLACEMENTS IN SCHIZOPHRENIC
PATIENT NO. B-12[a]

Site	Electrodes
L. temporal cortex	8 regular
R. temporal cortex	8 regular
L. occipital cortex	5 regular
R. occipital cortex	5 regular
L. frontal cortex	2 regular + 1 stainless steel[b]
R. frontal cortex	3 regular
L. parietal cortex	2 regular
R. parietal cortex	2 regular
L. centromedian	1 stainless steel
R. centromedian	1 stainless steel
L. caudate	1 regular + 1 stainless steel
L. ventricle	1 regular
R. ventricle	1 regular
L. hippocampus	1 stainless steel
R. hippocampus	1 stainless steel
L. hypothalamus	1 stainless steel
R. hypothalamus	2 stainless steel
L. septal	1 stainless steel
R. septal	1 regular + 1 stainless steel
R. amygdala	1 stainless steel

[a] White man, aged 35 years.
[b] Each stainless steel electrode has six contact points 2 mm. apart.

We currently implant two types of electrodes: a No. 316 stainless steel wire (0.003 in. in diameter) with quad Teflon-coated leads with six contact points 2 mm. apart, and a silver ball electrode with a silver ball 0.05 in. in diameter welded to No. 34-gauge vinyl chloride acetate insulated wire (Fig. 1 and Table 1).

In the 51 patients prepared with silver ball electrodes only, recordings were obtained from over the pia of the cingulate gyrus and other cortical areas (frontal, parietal, temporal, and occipital) and from the following deep structures: septal region, caudate nucleus, hippocampus, amygdala, thalamus, globus pallidus, hypothalamus, mesencephalic tegmentum, and cingulate gyrus. Since the stainless steel electrodes were introduced in combination with the silver ball electrodes, a larger number of leads have been implanted into all of these sites and additionally into the medial geniculate, lateral geniculate, and more extensively through the thalamus into specific nuclei, including the intralaminar group and the posterior ventral lateral thalamus. In most patients studied, scalp recordings were obtained synchronously with the deep recordings.

ELECTRICAL STIMULATION TECHNICS

Parameters of electrical stimulation were varied in initial studies, but since 1951 a 1-millisecond pulse with a frequency of 100 per second, and with alternating polarity of one pulse up and the next one down, has been most extensively used. The effects of altering frequency, pulse duration, and intensity were, however, explored during the search for reward and aversive sites in each patient studied. Intensity of stimulation varied minimally from subject to subject and from one cerebral region to another, ranging generally from 1 to 5 ma.

INTRACRANIAL SELF-STIMULATION TECHNICS. Recently a self-stimulating transistorized apparatus[8] was built to deliver similar parameters of stimulation to selected cerebral regions. The train duration of the self-stimulating device is 0.5 second with each push of the button. Stimuli delivered through the specially constructed transistorized, self-contained unit, which is worn on the subject's belt, are monopolar; the indifferent pole is a plate strapped to the subject's leg. Different purposes have established the designs for intracranial self-stimulation (ICSS) studies, one of which is reported by Bishop and associates in this monograph.

ICSS studies were conducted in two subjects. Patient No. B-7, aged 28 years, with a diagnosis of narcolepsy and cataplexy, had failed to respond to conventional treatment. Electrodes were then implanted into 14 predetermined cerebral regions, including the right anterior and posterior septal region, left anterior and posterior septal region, right anterior hypothalamus, midline mesencephalic tegmentum, left anterior and posterior hippocampus, left anterior and posterior caudate nucleus, and over the right frontal cortex, right and left midtemporal cortex, and left anterior temporal cortex. The three buttons of the self-stimulation unit were attached to electrodes in the septal region, hippocampus, and mesencephalic tegmentum, and the patient was free to stimulate any of these three sites as he chose. He wore the unit for 17 weeks. Our primary interest in this patient was to determine the cerebral region in which electrical stimulation was most effective in abolishing the pathologic sleep pattern.

The second subject, Patient No. B-10, aged 25 years, was a psychomotor epileptic with brief episodes of impulsive behavior uncontrolled by the usual treatments. He had 51 leads implanted into 17 sites of the brain: left and right centromedian, left caudate nucleus, right ventricle, left and right hippocampus, midline mesencephalic tegmentum, left and right septal region, left amygdaloid nucleus, left para-olfactory area, and over the left and right temporal cortex, left and right occipital cortex, and left and right frontal cortex.

A number of different experimental designs were used to investigate the effects of ICSS. In the first part of the study, 17 different cerebral regions, selected at random, were stimulated, the unit permitting three sites to be connected at any one time. Various combinations of three cerebral sites were arranged, and the patient was allowed to stimulate each electrode for a minimal period of 2 hours. The design for this study was based on well-documented animal data which indicate that rate of stimulation to a given cerebral site will vary, depending on the region stimulated beforehand. Data were recorded with the three automatic counters of the transistorized unit. Additionally, the same site of the brain was attached to different buttons to determine whether the subject would relate a response to a given button.

In the second part of the study, the three electrodes in the cerebral sites which the subject had stimulated most frequently during the first phase of the study (centromedian thalamus, septal region, and mesencephalic tegmentum) were attached to the three buttons of the transistorized unit. The patient was permitted to stimulate himself at random for a 6-hour period to enable the investigators to evaluate the objective data of number of button presses to a given region with the patient's subjective explanations for preferring one stimulus over another.

CHEMICAL STIMULATION

To date we have implanted cannulae into specific cerebral regions of 10 patients: 3 patients had three cannulae each and 7 patients had four cannulae each. Sites of implantation were left and right septal region, left and right hippocampus, left and right hypothalamus, left and right caudate nucleus, left and right ventral lateral thalamus, left and right globus pallidus, and left ventricle. Compounds administered through the intracerebral cannula were acetylcholine, atropine, levarterenol bitartrate, epinephrine, phenobarbital, phenobarbital combined with levarterenol bitartrate, histamine, serotonin, substance P, d-amphetamine sulfate, physostigmine, gamma aminobutyric acid, dopa, dopamine, and morphine.

RESULTS

Some data obtained by members of the Tulane group working with the special patient population are presented in Paper 4 in this monograph. In the present report some of the behavioral changes experienced by the subjects, as determined by psychiatric technics of interview and observation, will be described. In the absence of efficient methods for reducing data collected through these studies, observations have been recorded in anecdotal material and the objective medium of sound movie films. Extensive data have been obtained, but this presentation will be limited to studies in which pleasurable responses were induced.

In all stimulation studies, electrical and chemical, the schizophrenic patients were less responsive than the nonschizophrenic population.

ELECTRICAL STIMULATION

GENERAL.   Studies in our laboratories suggest that the distribution of cerebral sites which human subjects prefer to have stimulated is similar to that mapped for animals. These reward sites are grouped through the septal region and its principal outflow pathway, the medial forebrain bundle, into the interpeduncular nuclei of the mesencephalic tegmentum. Aversive sites are close to the reward sites and similarly scattered through deep cerebral regions, principally the midline diencephalon and mesencephalon.

PASSIVE ELECTRICAL STIMULATION.   With parameters ranging from 1 to 5 ma., a pleasurable response, as described by patients capable of reporting their feelings, was consistently induced with stimuli applied to the septal region. Electrical stimuli were applied to this region in all 54 patients in the series. Six severely deteriorated schizophrenic subjects did not describe a pleasurable feeling, although they showed objective changes suggestive of a rewarding experience. With septal stimulation the patients brightened, looked more alert, and seemed to be more attentive to their environment during, and for at least a few minutes after, the period of stimulation. With this basic affective change, most subjects spoke more rapidly, and content was more productive; changes in content of thought were often striking, the most dramatic shifts occurring when prestimulation associations were pervaded with depressive affect. Expressions of anguish, self-condemnation, and despair changed precipitously to expressions of optimism and elaborations of pleasant experiences, past and anticipated. Patients sometimes appeared better oriented; they could calculate more rapidly and, generally, more accurately than before stimulation. Memory and recall were enhanced or unchanged. Psychomotor activity accelerated during stimulation, as indicated by tests developed by King.[14] (These tests were not administered with all stimulation procedures.)

Subjects were not informed when stimuli were applied. When questioned concerning changes in mental content, they were generally at a loss to ex-plain them. For example, one patient on the verge of tears described his father's near-fatal illness and condemned himself as somehow responsible, but when the septal region was stimulated, he immediately terminated this conversation and within 15 seconds exhibited a broad grin as he discussed plans to date and seduce a girl friend. When asked why he had changed the conversation so abruptly, he replied that the plans concerning the girl sud-denly came to him. This phenomenon was repeated several times in the patient: Stimulation was administered to the septal region when he was describing a depressive state, and almost instantly he became gay. Another severely agitated and depressed subject whose verbalizations expressed self-condemnation and hopelessness (a condition that had prevailed for over 2 years) smiled broadly and related a sexual experience of his youth within 1 minute after onset of septal stimulation.

Only rarely was there objective evidence of sexual arousal. Three male patients, all nonschizophrenic, experienced penile erection during septal stimulation. The most striking sexual response occurred in a female epi-leptic patient with administraton of acetylcholine to the septal region (see "Chemical Stimulation"). A sexual motive state of varying degree consist-ently developed in association with the pleasure response resulting from stimulation to the septal region, whereas a specific kind of behavior was not evident in association with the pleasure response resulting from stimulation to other areas of the brain.

Striking and immediate relief from intractable physical pain was consist-ently obtained with stimulation to the septal region of three patients with advanced carcinoma, two with mestastases from primary breast carcinoma to bone and one with carcinoma of the cervix and extensive local proliferation. The patients were stimulated at intervals ranging from twice a day to once every 3 days over periods of 3 weeks to 8 months. Stimulation to the septal region immediately relieved the intense physical pain and anguish, and the patients relaxed in comfort and pleasure.

Stimulation in the vicinity of the centromedian nucleus in one patient, a psychomotor epileptic, induced a pleasurable response, but only at a fast frequency (60 to 100 cps). The other two patients, both schizophrenics, re-ported neither pleasure nor extreme discomfort with stimulation to the centromedian nucleus.

Behavioral responses with stimulation at 100 cps to other cerebral regions have previously been reported.[13] Affect was not significantly altered with stimulation to the corpus striatum (caudate nucleus, the putamen, or globus pallidus). Drowsiness or sleep, however, without affective changes, was frequently noted with stimulation to the caudate nucleus. Introduction of the 1-millisecond pulse at an intensity of 1 to 5 ma. to other deep structures induced feelings ranging from mild discomfort to extreme pain. Stimulation of the deep midline or periventricular structures extending from the rostral hypothalamus to the tegmentum of the mesencephalon induced pain. When the rostral hypothalamus was stimulated, patients complained of discomfort of the type usually associated with intense autonomic nervous system imbalance, i.e., abdominal discomfort, feelings of warmth, fullness in the head, and pounding heart. Application of stimuli to the midline tegmental region produced intense rage or fear or both, with impairment of ability to calculate and perform motor tests. Stimuli to more lateral sites in the hypothalamus and mesencephalic tegmentum, in contrast, yielded more positive responses; patients volunteered, "This is a good feeling," and sometimes asked that the stimulus be repeated. No characteristic sexual motive state was reported by the patient, however, as it was with septal stimulation. Extremely uncomfortable emotional reactions were induced with stimulation at these parameters to the amygdaloid nucleus. Stimuli to the hippocampus were accompanied by pronounced anxiety, and one patient described a *déjà vu* phenomenon.

With other parameters of stimulation designed to provide a more focal activation (i.e., of much less intensity and shorter train duration), as reported by Bishop and associates earlier in this monograph,[4] numerous apparent reward areas have been detected in the posterior hypothalamus and mesencephalic tegmentum, regions where only adverse responses were obtained in our early studies. The intensity of stimulations with earlier parameters probably resulted in spread of the stimulus to activate adverse areas, a possibility suggested some time ago by Stein.[17]

The character of recordings from those electrodes through which stimuli were introduced frequently changed and persisted for varying periods of a few minutes up to 1 hour or, on one occasion, for a day after prolonged stimulation. Recording patterns after stimulation varied somewhat. Common effects were the appearance of a slow-wave pattern, or a rapid-spindling pattern, or, occasionally, sharp waves and spikes which lasted only a few minutes. Prolonged after-discharges of high-amplitude spindling appeared occasionally and inconsistently after stimulation to deep olfactory structures, the septal region and hippocampus, but never after stimulation to diencephalic, mesencephalic, or striatal structures.[13]

SELF-STIMULATION. Data presented herein suggest an explanation for the motivation for ICSS and include further information concerning the nature of the subjective responses. After randomly exploring the effects of stimulation with presses of each of the three buttons of the transistorized unit,

Patient No. B-7 pressed the septal button almost exclusively (Fig. 2). He complained of intense discomfort, looked fearful, and requested that the stimulus to the mesencephalic tegmentum not be repeated, although it induced alerting. To make certain that the region was not stimulated again, he ingeniously modified a hairpin to fit under the button which directed a pulse train to the mesencephalic tegmentum so it could not be depressed. The patient found stimulation to the hippocampus to be mildly aversive, whereas stimulation to the septal region was most rewarding and caused alerting. By virtue of his ability to control severe symptoms of narcolepsy with the stimulator, he was employed part-time, while wearing the unit, as an entertainer in a night club. Fellow patients and friends, recognizing that button-pressing promptly awakened him, occasionally pushed the button

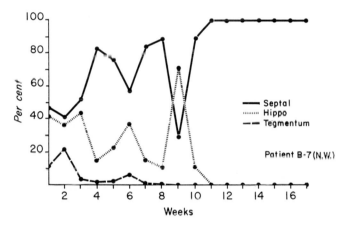

FIG. 2. Comparative sites of intracranial self-stimulation. Frequency of stimulation to various intracranial sites in patient with narcolepsy and cataplexy.

for him if he fell asleep too rapidly to stimulate himself. When asked why he pressed the septal button with such frequency, the patient said the feeling was "good" and made him feel as if he were building up to a sexual orgasm. He was unable to achieve the orgastic end point, however, and explained that his frequent, sometimes frantic, pushing of the septal button was an attempt to reach a "climax," although at times this was frustrating and produced a "nervous feeling."

ICSS studies with the psychomotor epileptic patient, No. B-10, were more varied and provided more information concerning subjective responses. The average number of button presses per hour and the principal subjective responses to stimulation of various regions of the brain are summarized in Tables 2 and 3. The patient reported a consistent response to stimulation of a given electrode regardless of the button to which it was attached.

The patient elected to push most frequently the button which provided a stimulus to the centromedian thalamus, although this stimulus did not elicit the most pleasurable response but rather induced irritability. During this stimulation the subject was almost able to recall a memory but could not quite grasp it and repeatedly depressed the button in an effort to bring the elusive memory into focus. Pleasurable feelings resulted from stimulation to two electrodes in the septal region and one in the mesencephalic

TABLE 2. ICSS IN PATIENT NO. B-10: REWARD SITES

Average No. button presses/hour	Cerebral region	Subjective response
488.8	Left centromedian thalamus	Partial recall of a memory; anger and frustration
394.9	Right posterior septal region	"Feel wonderful"; sexual thoughts; elimination of "bad" thoughts
373.0	Left caudate nucleus	"Cool" taste; "feel OK"; pleasant feeling
280.0	Mesencephalic tegmentum	"Drunk feeling"; "happy button"; elimination of "bad" thoughts
257.9	Anterior amygdaloid nucleus	Somewhat pleasant feeling, but not intense
224.0	Posterior amygdaloid nucleus	Moderately rewarding; increase of current requested

TABLE 3. ICSS IN PATIENT NO. B-10: AVERSIVE SITES

Average No. button presses/hour	Cerebral region	Subjective response
1.77	Right hippocampus	Intensely aversive; "feel sick all over"
0.36	Left para-olfactory	Moderately aversive; general discomfort
0.50	Right parietal cortex	
0.00	Right frontal cortex	No significant response
0.00	Right occipital cortex	
0.00	Right temporal cortex	

tegmentum. The patient's response to septal stimuli frequently had sexual association. Regardless of his base-line recording or the topic under discussion, the patient would introduce a sexual subject, usually accompanied by a broad grin, upon receiving septal stimulation. When asked about his response, he said, "I don't know why that came to mind—I just happened to think of it." The pleasurable feelings from mesencephalic stimulation were not associated with sexual thoughts. The patient also liked the response he obtained with stimuli to the amygdaloid nucleus and the caudate nucleus, and he stimulated other septal electrodes and one other electrode in the amygdaloid nucleus a considerable number of times, but his reports concerning these stimulations did not suggest as intense a pleasure as described previously.

A "sick feeling," the most aversive response observed in this patient, occurred with stimulation to one hippocampal electrode and one lead in the para-olfactory area. He complained of light flashes, probably due to spread to the optic nerve, and general discomfort with stimulation to the para-olfactory area.

Stimulation to the 12 cortical leads dispersed widely over the cortical surface, including the frontal, temporal, occipital, and parietal lobes, produced no consistent changes, either aversive or rewarding.

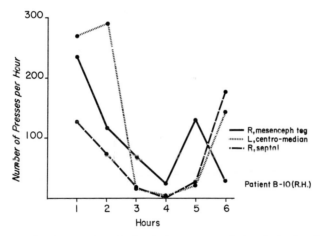

Fig. 3. Comparative frequencies of stimulation to reward sites in brain of patient with psychomotor epilepsy.

Data in the second phase of the study indicated that the combination of sites available (centromedian thalamus, the septal region, and the mesencephalic tegmentum) influenced the number of times a given region of the brain was stimulated (Fig. 3). When coupled with subjective reports, the data also suggested that the general state of the subject at a given moment was a determinant for selection of the region to be stimulated. The centromedian thalamus, for example, was stimulated up to 1,100 times per hour when relatively inactive sites were being stimulated and only 290 times per hour when two other highly rewarding areas, the septal region and the mesencephalic tegmentum, were being stimulated. The patient discovered that the frustration and anger resulting from stimulation of the centromedian thalamus were relieved by stimulation of the septal region and of

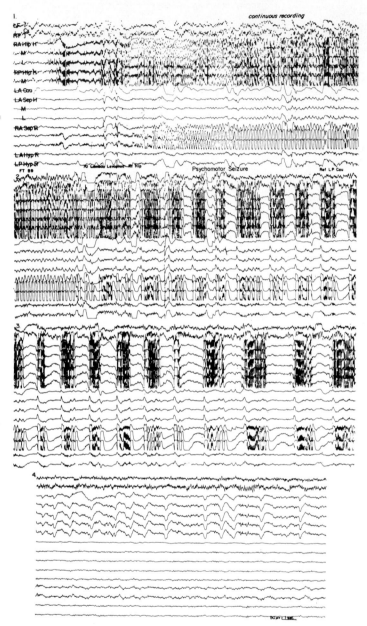

FIG. 4. Electroencephalogram of Patient No. B-9, showing response to 140 μg. of levarterenol bitartrate in 70 λ injected through intracerebral cannulae into both hippocampi. A focal seizural discharge was induced. LF, left frontal; RF, right frontal; Cx, cortex; RA, right anterior; Hip, hippocampus; H, M, L, highest, middle, and lowest, respectively, of the three leads of the triple electrode; Sep, septal, Hyp, hypothalamus; LP, left posterior.

the mesencephalic tegmentum. As indicated in Figure 3, the patient stimulated the centromedian thalamus most frequently during the first 2 hours, despite the discomfort induced when he attempted to recapture a fleeting memory. Stimulation to the other sites relieved the discomfort. The patient was largely inactive during the next 2 hours. Stimulation to septal and tegmental leads increased during the fifth and sixth hours of the study. The mesencephalic tegmentum was stimulated most frequently during the fifth hour and the septal lead most frequently during the sixth hour. To minimize the feeling of frustration, the subject evolved a pattern coupling the stimulus to the centromedian thalamus (which stirred his cusiosity concerning the memory) with stimuli to the more pleasurable sites.

CHEMICAL STIMULATION

In 1960 the Tulane investigators presented data on chemical stimulation of the brain derived from studies in animals and in a few human subjects.[9] General results of our experience with chemical stimulation can be summarized as follows:

1. A compound which produced either a recording or recognizable behavioral response, or both, when introduced into a specific cerebral region in one patient rarely produced the same response, and sometimes produced no response, in other patients when introduced into the same cerebral region (Figs. 4 and 5).

2. Exact repetition of a treatment in a patient, i.e., introduction of the chemical into the same cerebral site, did not consistently result in the same change in behavior and electrical recordings. The effects with some chemicals were more consistent than with others: Acetylcholine (ACh) and atropine were most consistent, and epinephrine was least consistent.

3. When a chemical was active, behavioral or electroencephalographic responses, or both, varied, depending on which loci within the brain were used. For example, activation of the septal region with a given chemical might induce one type of behavior, whereas activation of the hippocampus by the same chemical might be associated with a different type of behavior.

4. A compound that was active at one cerebral site was usually not active at another cerebral site. This suggests the possibility of specific receptor sites in certain anatomic regions, although with variations in sensitivity between patients and within the same patient. For example, several chemicals produced recording and behavioral changes when introduced into the septal region but failed to produce a physiologic or behavioral change when introduced into the corpus striatum cr hypothalamus.

5. The most meaningful correlation was between behavior and electroencephalographic recordings. A frequent recording change when the septal

region was chemically stimulated was the appearance of fast spindle-like activity of 12- to 16-per-second frequency with or without slow-wave activity. This was associated with feelings of pleasure, usually sexual. In

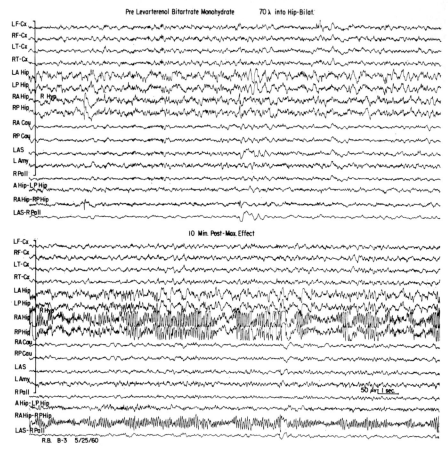

FIG. 5. Electroencephalogram of Patient No. B-3, showing response to 140 μg. of levarterenol bitartrate injected through intracerebral cannulae into both hippocampi. Note focal high-amplitude spindle. LT, left temporal; RT, right temporal; LA, left anterior; Cau, caudate; RP, right posterior; S, septal region; Amy, amygdaloid nucleus; Pall, globus pallidum. (For interpretation of other labeling, see legend for Figure 4). Figures 4 and 5 demonstrate the widely different electroencephalographic effects obtained with introduction of a compound into a cerebral site.

schizophrenic patients, chemical stimulation to the septal region occasionally resulted in *increased* spiking similar to the type we have consistently recorded from this region in psychotic patients, and in nonschizophrenic patients stimulation with some compounds *induced* spiking (Figs. 6 and 7).

This change was accompanied by intensification of psychotic behavior in the schizophrenic subjects. The appearance of spike and slow-wave activity in the hippocampus was associated with agitation and painful emotions of fear and rage. These correlations of behavior and electrical activity were consistent, although the response to a given compound from one patient to the next was unpredictable.

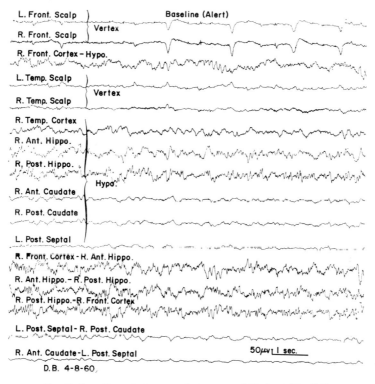

FIG. 6. Base-line electroencephalogram of Patient No. B-2.

In keeping with the theme of this symposium, I shall focus on the pleasure response with chemical stimulation. The two compounds most consistent in inducing pleasurable responses were ACh in a dose of 200 to 450 μg., and levarterenol bitartrate in a dosage of 150 to 500 μg. (All subjects were average-sized adults.) The pleasurable responses were obtained only with injection into the septal region. On occasion, however, ACh and levarterenol bitartrate failed to induce behavioral or electroencephalographic changes when introduced into the septal region. Injection of the two compounds into the hippocampus generally resulted in no changes, although infrequently the hippocampal injection induced electroencephalographic changes associated with unpleasant feelings of anxiety or anger. ACh and levarterenol bitartrate were also introduced into the caudate nucleus, hypothalamus, globus pallidus, and the ventricle with no changes resulting.

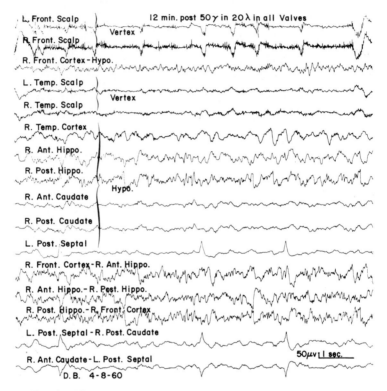

Fig. 7. Electroencephalogram demonstrating effects of 50 μg. of atropine in 20 λ introduced into septal region of Patient No. B-2. Note sharp wave or slow spike in all leads from left posterior septal region. With recording change, patient became overtly psychotic, with depersonalization and agitation evidenced by appearance of muscular activity in scalp recordings.

Of the compounds administered, atropine, in a dose of 25 to 100 μg., was most consistent in inducing undesirable behavioral changes when it was introduced into the septal region and hippocampus. Typical patterns were increased psychotic symptoms, agitation, and irritability, which were associated with appearance or increase of spiking in the septal region. Atropine introduced into the caudate nucleus, ventricle, globus pallidus, and hypothalamus induced no change. Other compounds (see "Material and

Methods") produced inconsistent behavioral and electroencephalographic responses; when changes occurred, effects were not as great.

Pleasure responses to ACh and levarterenol bitartrate were obtained only in nonschizophrenic patients. ACh was administered to four schizophrenic patients without behavioral or significant electroencephalographic changes. The effects of atropine appeared in both schizophrenic and nonschizophrenic groups.

The most consistent response to intracerebral stimulation occurred after introduction of ACh into the septal region of female epileptic patient, No. B-5: Her response was pleasurable and activated septal recordings (seven out of seven times). This patient also experienced pleasurable feelings with

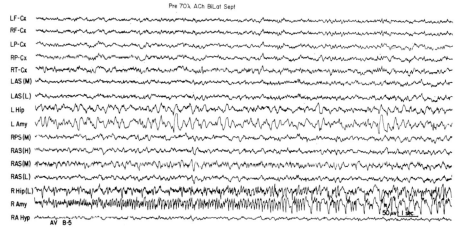

FIG. 8. Electroencephalogram from Patient No. B-5 before injection of ACh. The spindling and spiking in amygdaloid nucleus and hippocampus were associated with feelings of despair. (See legend for Figs. 4 and 5 for interpretation of labeling.)

other compounds. Levarterenol bitartrate activated the septal recordings and induced pleasurable feelings two out of eight times. In one of four times, the combination of levarterenol bitartrate and phenobarbital produced a pleasurable response accompanied by spindling in septal recordings.

On three occasions, ACh was introduced first through the cannula to activate the hippocampi and then into the septal region of Patient No. B-5. The rage-fear, and sometimes depression, associated with the hippocampal activation was replaced within minutes by intense pleasure as the recordings from the septal region were activated. On other occasions the chemical stimulus was applied to the septal region during periods of spontaneous depression (Fig. 8), and again anguish and despair were supplanted within minutes by pleasurable feelings as the electrical recordings changed (Fig.

9). Consistently, strong pleasure was associated with sexual feelings, and in most instances the patient experienced spontaneous orgasm with the recording change. This patient, now married to her third husband, had never experienced orgasm before she received chemical stimulation to the brain, but since then has consistently achieved climax during sexual relations.

The behavioral and electroencephalographic responses of Patient No. B-10 to chemical stimulation of the septal region with ACh were similar to those of Patient No. B-5.* The behavioral pattern characterized by intense

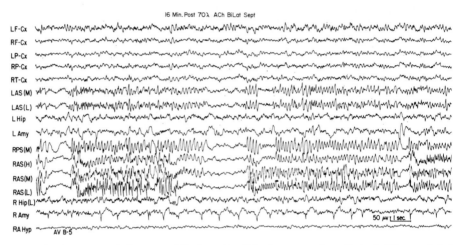

16 Min. Post 70λ ACh BiLat Sept

LF-Cx
RF-Cx
LP-Cx
RP-Cx
RT-Cx
LAS (M)
LAS (L)
L Hip
L Amy
RPS(M)
RAS(H)
RAS(M)
RAS(L)
R Hip(L)
R Amy
RA Hyp
AV B-5
50 μv⎿1 sec.⎾

Fig. 9. Electroencephalogram of Patient No. B-5, demonstrating effect of 400 μg. of Ach in 70 λ injected bilaterally into septal region. Fast spindling at onset was followed by slower, high-amplitude activity appearing in paroxysms. These changes were associated with feelings of intense pleasure and strong sexual arousal.

---

* At the time of the symposium, a 16-mm. sound film was shown to demonstrate effects of electrical stimulation (including ICSS) and chemical stimulation to specific cerebral regions of human subjects. The film is on file in the Department of Psychiatry and Neurology, Tulane University School of Medicine, and is available for review. A brief description follows.

1. Electrical stimulation to the hippocampus of Patient No. B-10, a psychomotor epileptic, induces spikes into the septal region. With the spiking, the patient displays an altered contact with reality and a painful emotional reaction. The film frame is split: The left half shows the interview of the patient and the right half a 16-channel recording of his brain waves.

2. Two patients, No. B-7 and No. B-10, stimulate their own brains by depressing a button on a transistorized self-stimulation box, which is worn attached to the belt. The subjects describe the feelings they experience with electrical stimulation to precise regions of the brain.

3. Demonstration of the pain-pleasure phenomenon. Part 1: The intractable pain of Patient No. A-9, who is suffering from carcinoma of the cervix, is relieved immediately by electrical stimulation to the septal region. Part 2: Injection of ACh into the septal region

rage or fear, or both, often associated with depersonalization and sometimes with overt delusional and hallucinatory experiences, was repeatedly
induced with electrical stimulation to the hippocampus at a slow frequency

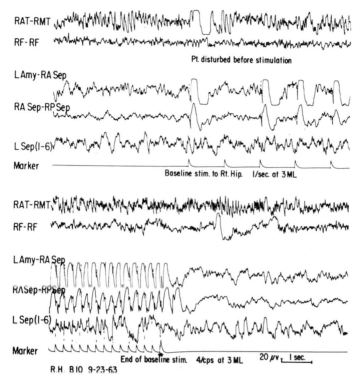

FIG. 10. Electroencephalogram of Patient No. B-10, showing effect of 1-per-second
and 4-per-second stimuli to hippocampus. Spike and slow-wave activity appeared in septal
leads, and patient displayed pronounced behavioral changes. The significant recording
and behavioral changes outlasted stimulation.

(3 to 6 cps). With the behavioral change, a spike and slow-wave pattern
appeared in the recording from the septal region (Fig. 10). At the peak
of this behavioral response, we introduced, on two occasions, 500 μg. of
ACh into the septal region. Within 1 minute the spike and slow-wave

and hippocampus bilaterally of epileptic Patient No. B-5 induces spindling in the septal
region. As the spindling begins, the patient's mood changes from depression to euphoria.
Split film frame shows interview of patient on one side and electroencephalographic recordings on the other. Part 3: Sequence shows psychomotor epileptic Patient No. B-10 having
an attack characterized by rage and poor contact with reality. With stimulation to the
septal region, the mood changes immediately from intense rage to a feeling of pleasure
and happiness.

activity in the septal region was replaced by a fast, high-amplitude, 16- to
18-cps spindle similar to that displayed by Patient No. B-5 (Fig. 11). With
the recording change, the patient's affect changed dramatically: He smiled,
became euphoric, and switched his conversation to topics with sexual
content.

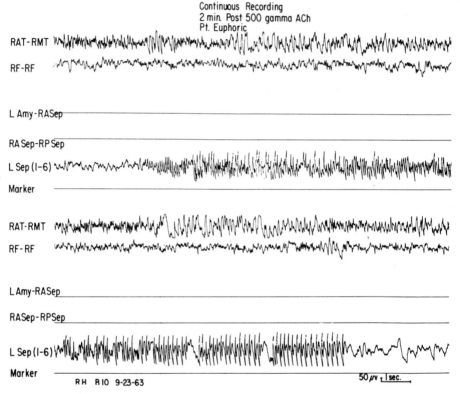

FIG. 11. Electroencephalogram of Patient No. B-10, showing effects of 500 μg. of Ach
introduced into septal region. Some channels of recording were discontinued because
of artifacts. Patient experienced intense feelings of pleasure and sexual arousal.

DISCUSSION

Electroencephalographic patterns and behavioral responses to electrical
stimulation were consistent, whereas these responses to a given chemical
varied considerably from one patient to the next and from time to time in
the same patient. With chemical stimulation, however, a consistent relation
was observable between recording and behavioral changes. A pleasurable

response was associated with focal activation of the septal region, as evidenced by a fast, high-amplitude spindle in the recording. Painful affects of rage and fear accompanied activation of a spike and slow-wave pattern from the hippocampus and amygdala. Psychotic behavior accompanied activation of spiking in the septal region. These observations are consistent with electroencephalographic changes in the olfactory brain during spontaneous behavioral fluctuations. The complementary nature of the two observations suggests that physiologic activity in the septal region is basic to the pleasure response. Psychotic schizophrenics, who characteristically lack ability to experience pleasure, have a spike and slow-wave recording from the septal region which suggests impaired cerebral function, whereas activation of the septal region by chemical or electrical stimulation, as evidenced by a fast high-amplitude recording from the septal region, enhances feelings of pleasure. The observation that nonschizophrenic patients experience more intense pleasurable reactions to stimulation of the brain than schizophrenic patients also seems noteworthy, in view of the history of anhedonia in the schizophrenic patients. The schizophrenic process may somehow raise the threshold for responsivity of those cells or pathways involved in the pleasurable response.

The observation that a recording change (whether activation, as suggested by spindling, or impairment in function, as suggested by spike and slow-wave activity) is focal by our technics does not mean that the particular site from which it is recorded is a center for a particular function—in this instance, pleasure. The septal region, for example, is richly interconnected with many parts of the brain. Its main efferent pathway is the median forebrain bundle to the interpeduncular nuclei of the mesencephalic tegmentum, and most reports concerning the apparent induction of pleasure in animals by self-stimulation, together with the few studies in human subjects, implicate this system.

Studies in human subjects, which have permitted collection of subjective reports simultaneously with objective data, fill gaps in the animal data and somewhat reduce speculations concerning the self-stimulation phenomenon studied extensively in animals. Patients' explanations for button-pressing indicate that ICSS is not solely for pleasure. In Patient No. B-7, the highest rate of button-pressing occurred when he was somewhat frustrated in his attempt to achieve an orgasm. In Patient No. B-10, the highest rate of button-pressing occurred with frustration in his attempt to recall a vague memory that ICSS had evoked. In this instance, the subject became extremely angry. He pressed the button which stimulated the region within the centromedian thalamus less frequently, however, when buttons providing more pleasurable septal and tegmental stimulation were also available. According to the subject's report, the pleasurable feelings resulting from pushing the septal button alleviated the painful emergency state and thereby provided him comfort to pursue his quest for the fleeing memory in a more leisurely fashion. We have induced sexual arousal in other patients with stimulation to the septal region but not during stimulation to other regions. Maclean[15] has described a relation between sexual feelings and stimulation to the septal region in monkeys. These observations partially answer questions raised by Galambos[5] regarding ICSS: "What motivates these animals to do such unheard-of-things? Is it some exquisite pleasure they receive, as several students of the problem staunchly contend, or the feeling of utter and complete well-being as others claim?"

Olds[16] has indicated the difficulty in appraising the influence of cerebral stimuli on learning in animals. Stimulation to areas considered to be rewarding seemingly produces greater impairment in the learning score than does stimulation to areas which yield negative reinforcement. Olds offers several possible explanations, one of which is that a positive emotional background may produce partial reinforcement of the wrong response, which may be disorganizing to the associative mechanism. Stein, earlier in this monograph, has suggested that access to subjective reports of the pleasurable sphere of behavior activated with cerebral stimulation may contribute to an understanding of this complex problem. For example, induction of a sexually pleasurable state seriously impairs interest in food. Induction of this pleasurable state by a cerebral stimulus would reinforce behavioral patterns associated with sexual arousal and would thereby interfere with patterns of response contingent upon food reward. Thus the motivational state of the human subject or animal must be known for appraisal of a behavioral act.

Psychodynamic theory should suggest applications of this therapeutic modality to correction of clinical disorders. In experiments in animals and human subjects, electrical and chemical stimulation which instantly induced pleasure obliterated feelings of pain, both physical and emotional. The possibility of relieving such pain is important not only from a therapeutic but also from a pathogenic standpoint. Moreover, this observation has further significance in relating activity of the brain and perception, since administration of analgesics or of euphoria-inducing drugs alters recordings through these olfactory structures (Heath and Gallant, this symposium). The physiologic-behavioral relation is evident in correlation of electroencephalographic and stimulation data with the behavioral characteristic of pleasure deficiency in the schizophrenic. The abnormal recordings from the septal region of the schizophrenic, the site from which pleasure can be induced by stimulation, suggest a defective mechanism. Electrically induced pleasure in such patients temporarily modifies both primary and secondary symptoms of the disease.

The pleasure ingredient may have even greater significance for persons with intact brains than for schizophrenics who suffer impairment of cerebral function from some yet unidentified product of abnormal metabolism. According to our theory, behavioral patterns are established on the basis of reward (pleasure) and punishment (pain). The self-operating behavioral mechanism of adults is established in early years as a result of relations with other people, usually parents or parental surrogates, who provided reward or punishment. Adaptive or normal behavior results when the person learns, through these early relations, to avoid realistic danger (pain) in the interest of self and society and to approach benefits (pleasure) in the same interests. The neurotic or maladapted person, in contrast, acquires faulty learning habits through his early interpersonal relations, so that painful emergency emotions develop with situations that should be pleasurable or neutral. This is the nucleus of maladaptive or neurotic behavior. The descriptive symptoms listed in textbooks represent attempts to neutralize the inappropriate emotional responses.

If this dynamic formulation of normal and neurotic behavior is correct, then elimination of unwarranted, inappropriate fear or rage in the neurotic person through introduction of pleasure with stimuli to the brain should be therapeutic. Theoretically, the neurotic person's inappropriate fear of a nonhazardous situation would be replaced instantly with a pleasurable feeling, and the reparative patterns which represent the neurotic maneuvers would disappear. Our current therapeutic approach to the neuroses involves manipulation of interpersonal relations, through which we attempt to expose the inappropriate or neurotic pattern—to show the illogical basis for the inappropriate fears and to dispense love (reward) to alter the behavioral pattern. Results in altering long-established behavioral patterns with psychotherapy have been disappointing.

Although most of our patients have enjoyed septal stimulation and many have asked to have the procedure repeated, none have exhibited reactions to it which are comparable to those manifested by addicts to pain-killing, euphoria-inducing drugs. Published reports[4] indicate that some drugs which kill pain and induce euphoria initiate electrical activity in the same regions of the brain that we have activated by pleasure-inducing stimuli.

The methods we have used to induce the pleasure response, i.e., electrical stimulation through implanted electrodes or chemical stimulation through implanted cannulae, are obviously impractical, and their use is justified only in a limited number of severely ill patients. The observation that pleasure can be induced by a direct approach to the brain, however, may accelerate the search for a chemotherapeutic agent which will induce the desirable pleasurable effect with heightened level of awareness but without complicating addiction and reduction in level of psychologic awareness.

Manipulation of the basic regulators of behavior, pain and pleasure, alters the core of behavior. Enhancement of pleasure and consequent reduction of rage-fear may facilitate psychotherapeutic correction of faulty learning involved in the neurotic process. Moreover, a compound with this effect might conceivably aid in correcting the deficiency that is basic to schizophrenia.

SUMMARY

Our experiences in eliciting pleasure responses from human subjects prepared with electrodes and cannulae implanted into precise cerebral regions for long-term study have been reviewed. Responses were induced by (1) electrical stimulation administered to the patient by a physician, (2) electrical self-stimulation by the patient, and (3) chemical stimulation administered by a physician. Information gathered through the studies complements extensive animal data on ICSS. Conceivably, knowledge obtained from these experiments can be applied practically to the correction of psychiatric disorders.

REFERENCES

1. BECKER, H. C., FOUNDS, W. L., PEACOCK, S. M., HEATH, R. G., and LLEWELLYN, R. C. "Improvements in the Technique for Implanting Subcortical Electrodes in Man by a Stereotaxic Method," in *Studies in Schizophrenia*, by Heath, R. G., and the Department of Psychiatry and Neurology, Tulane University. Cambridge, Mass., Harvard, 1954, pp. 565–570.
2. BECKER, H. C., FOUNDS, W. L., PEACOCK, S. M., HEATH, R. G., LLEWELLYN, R. C., and MICKLE, W. A. A roentgenographic stereotaxic technique for implanting and maintaining electrodes in the brain of man. *Electroenceph. Clin. Neurophysiol. 9*:533, 1957.
3. BISHOP, M. P., ELDER, S. T., and HEATH, R. G. Intracranial self-stimulation in man. *Science 140*:394, 1963.
4. EIDELBERG, E., LESSE, H., and GAULT, F. P. "An Experimental Model of Temporal-Lobe Epilepsy: Studies of the Convulsant Properties of Cocaine," in *EEG & Behavior*, ed. by Glaser, G. H. New York, Basic Books, 1963, pp. 272–283.
5. GALAMBOS, R. Neurophysiological studies on learning and motivation. *Fed. Proc. 20*:604, 1961.
6. HEATH, R. G., and the Department of Psychiatry and Neurology, Tulane University. *Studies in Schizophrenia*. Cambridge, Mass., Harvard, 1954.
7. HEATH, R. G. Physiological and biochemical studies in schizophrenia with particular emphasis on mind-brain relationships. *Int. Rev. Neurobiol. 1*:299, 1959.

8. HEATH, R. G. Electrical self-stimulation of the brain in man. *Amer. J. Psychiat.* *120*:571, 1963.

9. HEATH, R. G., and DEBALBIAN VERSTER, F. Effects of chemical stimulation to discrete brain areas. *Amer. J. Psychiat.* *117*:980, 1961.

10. HEATH, R. G., and FOUNDS, W. L. A perfusion cannula for intracerebral microinjections. *Electroenceph. Clin. Neurophysiol.* *12*:930, 1960.

11. HEATH, R. G., JOHN, S., and Foss, O. Stereotaxic biopsy. *Arch. Neurol.* *4*:291, 1961.

12. HEATH, R. G., and MICKLE, W. A. "Evaluation of Seven Years' Experience with Depth Electrode Studies in Human Patients," in *Electrical Studies on the Unanesthetized Brain,* ed. by Ramey, E. R., and O'Doherty, D. S. New York, Hoeber-Harper, 1960, pp. 214–237.

13. HEATH, R. G., PEACOCK, S. M., MONROE, R. R., and MILLER, W. H. "Electroencephalograms and Subcorticograms Recorded Since the June 1952 Meetings," in *Studies in Schizophrenia,* by Heath, R. G., and the Department of Psychiatry and Neurology, Tulane University. Cambridge, Mass., Harvard, 1954, pp. 573–608.

14. KING, H. E. *Psychomotor Aspects of Mental Disease: An Experimental Study.* Cambridge, Mass., Harvard, 1954.

15. MACLEAN, P. D., ROBINSON, B. W., and PLOOG, D. W. Experiments on localization of genital function in the brain. *Trans. Amer. Neurol. Ass.* *84*:105, 1959.

16. OLDS, M. E., and OLDS, J. Emotional and associative mechanisms in rat brain. *J. Comp. Physiol. Psychol.* *54*:120, 1961.

17. STEIN, L. Verbal communication.

L. M. N. BACH, PH.D.

Tulane University School of Medicine

Discussion

THE THREE PAPERS, by Dr. Guerrero-Figueroa and associates, Dr. Hernández-Péon, and Dr. Heath, represent an important and intriguing examination into certain basic processes relevant to the production of pleasure and pain in animal and human subjects. The first two papers deal with the relation of the reticular arousal system to the expression of emotion and have in common a consideration of the influence of acetylcholine (ACh). Dr. Guerrero-Figueroa and coworkers have demonstrated that intraventricular administration of ACh will enhance the evoked potential response to pain at several levels of the neuraxis and will impede any interruption due to a simultaneous novel stimulus. Dr. Hernández-Péon has shown that septal application of ACh induces a hypnotic attraction to an indifferent stimulus. Allowing for different sites of action due to varying methods of administration of ACh, one may consider that ACh-sensitive elements in the septal region enhance attentiveness to the point of hypnotic induction of sleep, whereas the demanding nature of pain is enhanced by ACh to the point of blockage of attention to any less crucial, albeit novel, stimulus. Yet Dr. Heath's presentation reveals that ACh stimulation of septal elements in human subjects yields overwhelming attention to pleasure in the sexual sphere, despite preceding states of depression. Pleasure and pain each appears to be prepotent as a source of attention, an experience common to all of us but here demonstrated in terms of anatomic structures and putative neurohumoral transmission. The paradox of hypnosis, which can focus attention upon insignificant stimuli to a degree sufficient to induce sleep, clearly suggests the fragile distinction between attention and sleep and consequently recalls the difficulty in distinguishing that point (anatomic, conscious, experimental, or whatever) which separates pain from pleasure. Thus, one is reminded of experiments by Miller, in which cats, self-stimulating in a fashion definable as pleasurable, nevertheless exhibited a profound rage response with each self-stimulation.

The patients discussed in Dr. Heath's paper demonstrate the important relation between facial expressions of pain and pleasure (midbrain versus septal stimulation) and verbalized sensations, both current and remembered. In studies with animals, we are inevitably faced with the assumption that the animals' reactions to pain or pleasure indicate the nature of the sensation which they experience. Witnessing the conjunction of reaction and communicable sensation permits us to appreciate Sherrington's remark in response to Penfield's description of the effects of stimulation of the temporal lobe in conscious human patients: "It must be great fun to put a question to 'the preparation' and have it answer!"

Each speaker has discussed, to some degree, possible anatomic connections between the septal areas and the brain-stem reticular arousal system. Dr. Hernández-Péon perhaps has discussed such connections most specifically, and whereas those pathways are the most obvious candidates anatomically, the integrity of each of these bundles and commissures should be proved essential for the effects variously of pleasure manifestation, reciprocal inhibition of arousal systems in the midbrain regions, and the proposed functional relation or identities of the sleep-wake and pain-pleasure systems.

It is tempting and natural to think of two opposing systems, reciprocally inhibitory, and compromising a pleasure-sleep-cholinergic complex against a pain-wakefulness-adrenergic complex. The data of Dr. Guerrero-Figueroa and associates, difficult to interpret because of the uncertain site of action of ventricularly administered drugs, would not be consistent with such a simple scheme because they report that pain-evoked responses are amplified throughout the recording sites by ACh. In contrast, both Dr. Heath's and Dr. Hernández-Péon's experimental observations suggest a cholinergic-pleasure-hypnapagogic system involving the septal regions. The studies with GABA by Dr. Guerrero-Figueroa and associates and with adrenergic and other compounds by Dr. Heath are not as easily interpreted, but the midbrain evocation of pain in human subjects and the relation of arousal or voluntary attention to facilitation of selected sensory channels of input through reticulofugal paths contribute to the notion.

Two other points deserve comment. The discussion by Dr. Hernández-Péon of apparent failure of cortical triggering of reticulofugal systems essential to attention in mentally retarded subjects and the indifferent selection by a relatively oligoneocortical subject, such as the cat, of objects worthy of attention emphasize the necessity of reverting always to inclusion of the cerebral cortex in any systems which regulate pain, pleasure, sleep, or wakefulness, despite our obvious eagerness to describe presumably more obscure subcortical relations. We do not know as much about the cerebral cortex as we may suggest by our casual disregard of its involvement in these discussions.

The rather dramatic demonstration by Dr. Heath, in which responses of patients are filmed simultaneously with the electrical events recorded from several cortical and subcortical sites, re-emphasizes the necessity for inclusion of the most important and least regarded element of any biologic investigation—*time*. By providing a continual display of the temporal sequence of behavioral and electrical changes together—unique enough in itself—we should all be effectively impressed with the revelations, too easily dismissed or ignored in experimental designs, available when we include time as a parameter of our observations.

PART IV

Psychodynamic Studies

JAMES K. FEIBLEMAN
Tulane University

A Philosophic Analysis of Pleasure

E VER SINCE SOCRATES'S EXPLANATION[7] that pleasure is generated from the restoration of harmony by "the passage and return of all things to their nature," philosophers have been trying to understand pleasure. The highest kind of pleasure, Socrates asserted, was the pleasure of hope or expectation. There was speculation on this topic even before Socrates, however; Empedocles, for instance, thought pleasure could be explained by the attraction of like for like.[4]

In their analysis of pleasure, the ancients were chiefly concerned with which pleasures were moral and which immoral, and why. Plato was no exception; he suspected it of being "the greatest incitement of evil" and, as such, "fearful and avoidable."[9] Unfortunately, the topic has remained chiefly in the hands of moralists ever since. There is little doubt that pleasure has its moral aspect, that according to the way in which we handle pleasure we are influenced toward good or evil. But this is a problem for the morality of pleasure, not an analysis which will tell us what pleasure is, for moralists are not concerned with the nature of pleasure so much as they are with its effects. But its effects upon morality are accidental to it and not necessary, since everyone admits that it can sometimes have such effects and sometimes not. What is involved in such a connection is moral approval or disapproval, not the analysis of pleasure. And so we shall have to look elsewhere for what we want.

Am I mistaken in supposing that no attempts were made to understand the nature of pleasure apart from its moral aspects until contemporary experiments in neurophysiology brought it before the attention of serious investigators? Undoubtedly much knowledge has been lost to the world, but we can judge only from what remains. In any case, the studies of the neurophysiologists in producing self-stimulation through the technic of permanently implanted electrodes is intriguing and suggestive. The best interpretation seems to indicate that the stimulated animals are experiencing pleasure.

There is no such thing in the world as a useless truth. Few scientific developments offer as much hope of important disclosures as recent neurophysiologic investigations. These investigations, however, must be supplemented, for they tell us what *produces* pleasure, not what it *is*. They tell us that the experience of pleasure is in some way connected with the brain, so that there seems good reason to suspect that pleasure can be initiated at either end of the nervous system, at the center as well as from the peripheral end organs. Yet this is no explanation of pleasure—only of one set of circumstances which serves to bring it about. Like morality, such considerations are, strictly speaking, extraneous. They bring us no nearer an understanding of the nature of pleasure in itself. Neurophysiologically, the work is of immense significance; psychologically, we are no closer to an answer.

There are inherent difficulties in the way of a psychologic explanation. Pleasure is generally recognized as a quality, and qualities are impossible to describe; they are intelligible only to those who have experienced them. All that we can hope to achieve, then, is to tag the quality and describe the nature of its associations.

The hypothesis advanced here is that pleasure is the quality of consistency in a living system. By "consistency" is meant the compatibility of parts, the absence of conflict. And by "quality" is meant that property which is contained in a feeling. For logical purposes (and since our definition of pleasure is a logical definition), let us agree to accept the definition of a quality as that which is ultimately simple.[2] Qualities as such are incapable of further analysis. The analytic elements of that mechanism which has produced the quality are logical and have their own qualities. But such elements are always one analytic level below that of the quality itself. Consistency for purely logical purposes is that property of a system which indicates that it is a system but which cannot be demonstrated within the system. In a living system, then, pleasure is the system-feeling, the feeling within the organism that it *is* a system, the feeling of integrality, of perfection of organization.

"Pleasure is the result of a growing systematization; pain is the result of a decreasing systematization," wrote Paulhan.[6] Pleasure spreads from specific zones to the whole somatic organism, and so all such feelings are body-wide.

One characteristic of pleasure is that it is always the same. As a disturbance which spreads throughout the whole organism, it does not change in feeling, varying only in intensity, never in pervasiveness. There are, of course, relative degrees of intensity of the feeling of pleasure, reaching, say, from the sharpness of an orgasm to the vagueness of the reception of good news. Pleasure is always all-pervasive. However, the cause of it or the occasion for it may differ; i.e., the environing events which trigger it may be various. A man may experience pleasure at the sound of music or in the act of eating candy; one form of pleasure may persist longer, the other seem more intense; but pleasure is pleasure in every instance.

We shall have to describe the analytic levels now in order to show the functioning of pleasure in living systems. The human organism as a whole constitutes an entity at an integrative level containing many sublevels: physical, chemical, biologic, psychologic, and even cultural. Justification for recognizing the divisions between the integrative levels, as we do, is found in the organizational breaks and the qualitative emergents. The organism's interactions with its immediate environment occur in terms of these same levels, which exist also, of course, in the environment, for the world external to the organism is one containing physical objects, chemical elements, biologic organisms, other minds, and collections of artifacts. Interactions are originally instituted by events in the external world and trigger interchanges which result in effects both on the organism and on segments of its environment.

Each of the aforementioned sublevels can also be subdivided. Thus, at the higher level at which such phenomena as feelings exist, there also exist sublevels. Herbert Spencer[8] spoke of "presentative feelings," that is to say, of "mental states in which, instead of regarding a corporeal impression as of this or that kind, or as located here or there, we contemplate it in itself as pleasure or pain: as when inhaling a perfume." Here is that second level of feeling in which there is an awareness of feeling—the *feeling* that there is a feeling.

Feelings, however integral, may be intensified by compounding. The complexity can be measured by the number of levels involved. We take pleasure at the physical level in the mere absence of pain, as when a sprained ankle stops hurting; at the biologic level in the reduction of organic needs, as when food reaches the stomach; at the psychologic level in the pride of achievement, as when something we have made is highly valued; and at the cultural level in a shared experience, as when there is genuine social communication.

Such complexity conceals the fact that pleasure, or pain, is always present in some degree in the organism. Every span of consciousness has the quality of either pleasure or pain. Mere awareness, as in daydreaming, is perhaps the lowest grade of pleasure, that grade which contains the least degree of intensity. But it is still pleasure. Although pleasurable experience is always basically the same, a certain amount of novelty is necessary to produce it. "All consciousness," as Mill[5] said, "is of difference." Consciousness, it has been shown by experiment, would not be possible without differences in the objective field of consciousness.[6] Trains of nerve impulses, initiated at the peripheral end organs, are all alike,[7] and we should never be able to account for the differences in patterns between them without reference to stimuli in the external world. We owe to Walter[10] and others the knowledge that consciousness breaks down with monotony of input. Thus pleasure, upon some degree of which consciousness depends, itself depends in turn upon novelty among the stimuli.

But this very necessity has a tremendous significance. Because the human organism is a living system, it is appropriate to consider in this connection the properties of systems. If I understand mathematics to be "all deductive systems" and logic to be "the theory of systems," then the study of systems falls within the province of the logician and mathematician, who have in fact so understood it. And they have considered systems to possess, in the main, two properties. Systems must be consistent, and they must be complete. Let us say a few words about these, one at a time.

Systems must be, above all, consistent. A system is said to be consistent if it contains no contradictions. The consistency of a system can never be demonstrated within the system; nevertheless, it is there as the one essential ingredient.

But there is another property recognized by logicians and mathematicians, and this is the property of completeness. A system is said to be complete if for every element, A, which lies within its domain of relevance, either A or non-A is included.

Now let us turn back in order to apply these ideas to our earlier discussion of the organism's need for novelty. Evidently, for living as for non-living systems, consistency, however important, is not enough. The novel experience gives pleasure but also introduces additional elements into the living system, for clearly what is novel must be something that was not there before. Hence, novelty means that more must be included within the organism and so constitutes a call for completeness. Paulhan[6] called attention to the fact that, as with "all affective phenomena and indeed all conscious events," both pleasure and pain imply that "the systematization is imperfect."

Thus far I have contended that pleasure is the quality of consistency, that it is a characteristic of living systems, that it is body-wide, that it is always the same, that it involves self-consciousness, that consciousness itself depends upon its presence in some measure, and that it, in turn, depends upon the presence of novelty in the immediate environment. It remains to show how it functions in the organism—what, in other words, the mechanism is by which it is produced.

The activity of the animal is the result of the operation of its needs. These are felt as hungers of some sort, and hungers are varieties of pains, ranging in intensity from mild discomfort to intense ache. Activity begins with an orienting response when a material object in the environment holds out to the animal the promise of need reduction, so that the need is transformed into a drive and the animal moves tropistically toward the object. After such a preparatory response, there is a consummative response by means of which the need is satisfied and the drive reduced. The pain subsides, and this in itself is pleasurable. Pleasure, in other words, is the qualitative concomitant of drive reduction. But this has its positive side: It is not merely negative, for all feelings qua feelings are positive; they have a content. Pleasure is, in other words, the feeling of attainment that accompanies a completion.

But pleasure is not confined to consummation, even though there it is at its zenith. Pleasure exists also in the drive itself, in the effort at need reduction. The activity itself is capable of furnishing the drive reduction for a need other than the need specific to its aim. There exists a need to do, a need just to be active, to move and exert the muscles, which like other organs have their own requirements. But the drive reduction of one need is often a by-product of the activity intended to satisfy another. For instance, when a lion stalks, kills, and then eats a deer, not only is the lion's hunger reduced but also his generic need of aggression, his need to dominate the environment. If one drive is strong enough, it can substitute for another. There are times when the animal is content merely to kill. It has been said that "there is more pleasure in seeking truth than in finding it"[a] and that, as the saying goes, "the fruits are for the vulgar." The reason for this is that the effort at need reduction calls out all the powers of the organism, more than does attainment, which is in a way anticlimactic, since it brings the effort to an end.

The hypothesis of the nature of pleasure which I have been developing invites comparison with that of Hebb,[3] who defined pleasure as "a directed *growth* or *development in cerebral organization.*" And he continued: "Those sensory conditions are called pleasant which contribute to the current development in the cerebrum, or which consist of the decline of a sensory process that interferes with development." Hebb pointed out that in the case of music, dissonance, which at first is the cause of displeasure, with repetition is recognized as pleasant, then becomes "dull and boring," i.e., unpleasant. Hebb's theory and mine seem to be supported by the fact that the repetition of experience after a while produces no pleasure, for novelty is not maintained by it and consistency is not increased. Evidently, cerebral development must depend upon novelty of input, and this would be consistent with the idea of growth which is central to Hebb's thesis, for the growth of A must be at the expense of non-A. If knowledge is an exception to this, it can only be because knowledge is to some extent representative, the cerebral growth taking place in terms of replicas or images. Again, by growth here must be meant increases in convolutions or in the amount of retention of experienced material. Hebb's theory fails to take account of the variations in stimuli and their meaning in terms of responses. But its merit is to recognize that pleasure is a kind of disturbance and that such disturbance is not necessarily disruptive of living systems. Hebb recognized also that moral approval or disapproval on the part of the organism experiencing the pleasure is not involved.

I conclude that disturbances are painful, but unless they end in the death of the organism, they are productive of pleasure, for they are bound to end, and one consequence of their ending is pleasure. Pleasure, in short, is much more prevalent than we have been led to suppose by considering only its moral aspects. An organism is a living system if and only if it is alive and is a system, in other words, if it is active and has an organization. Its awareness of this basic set of conditions is the source of its pleasure. Human individuals are able to add another dimension through knowledge, which, in turn, intensifies the pleasure.

REFERENCES

1. ADRIAN, E. D. *The Physical Background of Perception.* Oxford, Clarendon Press, 1947, p. 21.
2. FEIBLEMAN, J. K. *Foundations of Empiricism.* The Hague, Nijhoff, 1962, III (D).
3. HEBB, D. O. *The Organization of Behavior.* New York, Wiley, 1959, pp. 232–234.
4. KIRK, G. S., and RAVEN, J. E. *The Presocratic Philosophers.* London, Cambridge, 1957, p. 340.
5. MILL, J. S. *Examination of Sir William Hamilton's Philosophy,* Vol. 1, Boston, 1865, p. 14.
6. PAULHAN, F. *The Laws of Feeling,* tr. by Ogden, C. K. New York, Harcourt, 1930, pp. 20, 82.
7. PLATO. *Philebus,* tr. by Fowler, H. N. 31 D, 32B, 32C, 33C.
8. SPENCER, H. *The Principles of Psychology,* Vol. 2. New York, Appleton, 1886, p. 514.
9. *Timaeus,* 69D.
10. WALTER, W. G. "A Statistical Approach to the Theory of Conditioning," in *Moscow Colloquium on Electroencephalography of Higher Nervous Activity.* Moscow, 1958.

SANDOR RADO, M.D., D.POL.SC.

The New York School of Psychiatry

Hedonic Self-Regulation of the Organism

ADAPTATIONAL PSYCHODYNAMICS IS an introspectional branch of human bi-ology[8, 11, 12] which deals with the part played in the organization of behavior by the organismic and societal mechanisms of motivation and control. Its development began some 20 years ago with the revival of the foundations laid by Freud in his early work (1892–1905) and the introduction of a methodology appropriate to an observational discipline. Its investigative methods are communicated *deep* introspection, developed from Freud's "free association," and communicated *surface* introspection, based on the routine psychiatric technic of verbal examination. Both are supplemented by introspectional interpretation of those phases of behavior that are accessible to inspection, such as motor activity in general and emotional expression in particular, and by evaluation of biographic observations on the subject obtained from others. Adaptational psychodynamics looks forward to the cross interpretation of its findings, i.e., of the psychodynamics of behavior with behavioral physiology and behavioral genetics. Accordingly, its ultimate goal is to supply the introspectional component for the construction of a correlated dynamics of human behavior.

To achieve this goal, adaptational psychodynamics was forced to depart from orthodox psychoanalytic theory because, after 1905, Freud inadvertently shifted from his originally mechanistic concepts to animistic notions. Several passages in his later work (1905–1939) show that he was unaware of the methodologic difference between animistic and mechanistic thought or of the impossibility of correlating animistic psychodynamics with mechanistic physiology. Thus, while clinging theoretically to his original intention, in fact he moved further and further away from it.

The basic working theory proposed by adaptational psychodynamics assumes a central "integrative apparatus" located in the psychocerebral system (or, as we also call it, the "reporting brain system"). Confirming phylogenetic history, clinical observation suggests that this apparatus includes at least

257

four major subdivisions—levels or units—that are hierarchically arranged around a common axis or stem. The most ancient of the hierarchically arranged levels is that of hedonic self-regulation or hedonic control. In ascending order, reflecting the evolutionary appearance of more developed means of central integration, there follow the levels of preverbal brute emotion, emotional thought, unemotional (impartial, realistic, scientific) thought. The common stem constitutes the organism's action-self. The hypothetical outlines of the entire structure are shown in Figure 1.

The conscious organism's awareness of itself is the central phenomenon of human existence. Ontogenetically, self-awareness appears to be brought into

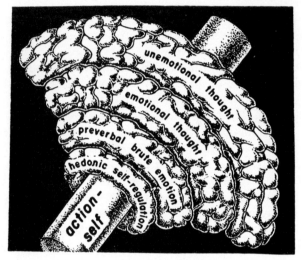

Fig. 1. Integrative apparatus of psychodynamic cerebral system. (This figure is reproduced by courtesy of Grune & Stratton, Inc.)

being through proprioceptive (kinesthetic) sensations. Perceiving his own muscular activities, the infant discovers himself as the one who acts. The circular pattern of willed action and self-awareness appears to be the foundation upon which the organism builds up its action-self by combining proprioceptive and other sensory information in communicative interchange with its human environment. In this development, the infant's sensory experience brings presumably innate nervous circuits into play. The action-self includes representation in the integrative apparatus of the entire acting organism. The development of its self-image begins with the "omnipotent primordial self," which differentiates into the "tested-self" and the "desired-self." The fact that the action-self serves as the organism's highest decision-making unit explains its axial location and consequent central position at each of the hierarchical levels.

The theory of integrative apparatus just indicated includes the unit of hedonic self-regulation. Its evolutionary forerunner may have been present already in one-celled animals (phylum of protozoans). This evolutionary extrapolation suggests a search for the physiologic (biochemical) mechanism of what appears to be a basic central self-regulation of all animal behavior. The design of this central self-regulation makes the organism move *toward* the source of pleasure and *away* from the cause of pain. Clearly, the organism relies on the expectation that pleasure signals the presence of needed supplies or of conditions otherwise favorable to its survival and that pain denotes the presence of a threat to its organic integrity. The fact that primitive species survived and evolved into higher ones proves the biologic effectiveness of this system of response. Where the system failed, the individual (species) died.

In man, discovery of the singular significance of pleasure is traceable at least to Aristotle[1] (384–322 B.C.): "Happiness being found to be something final and self-sufficient, is the End at which all actions aim." In the Declaration of Independence (adopted 1776) Thomas Jefferson solemnified the same idea as "man's unalienable right to the pursuit of happiness." Jeremy Bentham[2] (1748–1832) formulated it with admirable precision: "Nature has placed mankind under the governance of two sovereign masters, *pain* and *pleasure*. It is for them alone to point out what we ought to do as well as to determine what we shall do." In psychoanalysis, the same introspectional discovery became known as Freud's[5] pleasure principle; in adaptational psychodynamics, we call it hedonic self-regulation or hedonic control. The new terminology is in accord with our biologic approach based on the established fact that introspectional (traditionally called "mental") phenomena are produced by the living brain.

To see hedonic self-regulation in the biologic perspective, we have already cast a glance at its evolutionary effectiveness. Now let us attempt to indicate its place in the over-all functional design of the organism.

The organism is a biologic system that perpetuates itself and its kind by means of its environment. Self-perpetuation is the outcome of self-regulation governed by the hereditary instructions for response coded in the organism's complement of genes, copies of which control the life activities of each of its cells. The geneticist calls the totality of response potentials coded in the complement of genes the organism's genotype.[4] The organism in its entirety, including the countless replicas of its original complement of genes, is called the phenotype. Every element of the phenotype's structural (biochemical) composition, of its functional organization, action, and reaction is an outcome of the perpetual interaction between its genotype and the series of environments in which the total organism, i.e., the perpetually changing phenotype, lives. The patterns of the continuous genotype-environment interaction may be improved through ontogenetic adaptations: (1) changes wrought upon the environment by the organism—alloplastic adaptations, and (2) changes undergone by the organism itself—autoplastic adaptations. The master mechanisms of ontogenetic adaptation are learning, creative imagination, and goal-directed activity.

Psychodynamics deals, of course, only with those phases of the life process that are integrated in the psychocerebral system. Some of the organism's systemic requirements produce psychodynamic signals known as tensions, urges, and needs, which may appear in aboriginal form or show varying degrees of acculturation. These signals make the organism aware of its requirements and stir it to action aimed at supplying them: the pleasant ones toward securing pleasure and the unpleasant ones toward riddance of pain or the threat of pain. Consequently, in its encounters with the environment the organism is guided by its responses of pleasure and pain. The former signals "yes," the latter "no." As we have seen, pleasure makes it move toward, and pain away from, the encountered stimulus. Pleasure then becomes the reward for successful performance, and the memory of pleasure incites repetition of the successful activity. Pain becomes the punishment for failure, and the memory of pain deters the organism from repeating the self-harming activity. Nature has placed massive pleasure rewards on the operations that supply the organism's aboriginal needs (intake of food, evacuation of waste, reproduction). Under the modifying influence of the higher levels—brute emotion, emotional thought, unemotional thought, action-self—hedonic self-regulation may be elaborated to highly complex and long-drawn-out patterns, but the ultimate direction of the organism's behavioral activity remains the same. Accordingly, cultural development constantly seeks to extend this natural pleasure-reward and pain-punishment system to the activities that are to become the organism's acculturated needs.[7]

We see now that the sensorimotor sequences governed by the use of pleasure as reward and of pain as punishment constitute the foundation for the self-regulation of the organism's behavior. A brief survey of the major behavioral areas, previously published, confirms this fact.[9]

1. The organism's "emergency control is based on the effective use of pain as a warning signal of damage;

"2. In its pursuit of prosperity, effort and performance are spurred by the pains of deprivation and are directed, facilitated, and rewarded by a variety of pleasures; at the physiological level, the search for and the intake of food are accompanied by pleasures climaxing in satiety called alimentary orgasm; at the biocultural level, activities toward cultural self-realization are greatly eased by the joys of performance culminating in the self-satisfaction of pride;

"3. Its primary incentive for reproduction is sexual orgasm attendant upon insemination, the act of integration which renders evolutionary sex differentiation biologically effective;

"4. Its conscience and conduct are shaped by an educational system based on reward and punishment, that is, on offering pleasure and inflicting pain.

"Hedonic self-regulation advanced from a biological to a cultural stage of development. In the infant, its design is still much the same as in sub-human species; however, during the period of growth and maturation this innate design undergoes highly significant cultural adaptations reflecting the cumulative influence of intelligence and learning, education and experience. In the last analysis, these biocultural modifications of hedonic control are traceable to the increasing power of foresight which forces the organism to accept *delayed* reward in lieu of *immediate* reward. The extent to which such enlightened hedonic responses supplant the purely biological ones is a measure of the adult's fitness for cultural cooperation."

The evidence just outlined shows that continued search for the mechanisms of hedonic self-regulation is a highly promising task. With the same end in view, I shall sketch a few further propositions of general significance advanced by adaptational psychodynamics and shall discuss briefly what are perhaps the two most conspicuous results of the inquiry into hedonic pathology.

Above the hedonic level is the level of preverbal brute emotion. Viewing the emotions as central mechanisms both for arousal of the peripheral organism and for peripheral disposal of superabundant central excitation, we divide them into two classes. The welfare emotions—such as pleasurable desire, joy, affection, love, and self-satisfaction or pride—are differentiated elaborations of the experiencing and the expectation of pleasure. The emergency emotions—such as agony, fear, rage, retroflexed rage, guilty fear, and guilty rage—are differentiated elaborations of the experiencing and the expectation of pain. Walter B. Cannon[3] has shown that the emergency emotions mobilize the organism's physiologic resources for muscular effort: fear for escape and rage for combat. Extension of this view from animal to man and from the organism's peripheral systems to the central integrative apparatus leads to the concept of emergency control. Obviously, the tasks of emergency control take precedence over all other motivations; the warning "safety first" is well founded. Whereas love and affection differentiate the retaining and uniting motor trends of pleasure, rage elaborates the riddance mechanism of pain, tending to use violence for the removal (if not annihilation) of its cause. In the child's relation to authority, fear and guilty fear lead to obedience (submission) and rage and guilty rage to defiance.

In man the psychodynamic order of the next two levels of integration (emotional thought and unemotional thought, respectively) contrasts with that in subhuman species. In nonhumans, realistic thinking is a matter of life and death, but in the human species the young, kept alive by parental care, are free to indulge in emotional thinking that slows down their absorption of the cultural forms and contents of realistic thought. The early predominance of emotional thinking explains the adult's readiness to relapse at a moment's notice to this primitive level, as seen in group behavior as well as in almost all psychiatric disorders. The significance of this fact can hardly be overstated. Emotional thought is selective, tending to justify and strengthen the emotion from which it springs and by which it is controlled. Unemotional thinking enables us to grasp what we are actually exposed to and to decide what to do. Emotional thought culminates in religion, art, and aesthetic pleasure; unemotional thought in science, technology, and wisdom.

The organization of restraining and facilitating mechanisms traditionally known as conscience regulates conduct in human relations by means of anticipatory self-punishment and anticipatory self-reward. Anticipatory self-punishment is carried out by means of retroflexed rage, i.e., defeated rage that has automatically turned against the self. It leads to the self-reward of moral pride that restores the troubled organism to its emotional security.

My studies in schizophrenia[6, 10] and in narcotic bondage[9, 13] have revealed two extreme disorders of hedonic self-regulation. In schizophrenia, one of the two innate (i.e., genetically transmitted) damages has been called integrative pleasure deficiency. The other innate damage is tentatively designated as proprioceptive diathesis. These damages and their far-reaching conseqences are summed up in the concepts of schizotypal organization and schizotypal behavior. The various schizotypal disorders may be viewed as so many experiments of Nature, showing what happens to central integration in the person whose pleasure resources are inherently deficient.

A predisposed individual is thrown into narcotic bondage through the superpleasure produced in him by a narcotic drug. Narcotic superpleasure is composed of three elements: narcotic riddance (from unpleasant feelings), a specific quality of narcotic pleasure, and a feeling of narcotic grandeur rooted in the "magical" effect of the drug. The mechanism is interpreted as a corruption of the organism's hedonic self-regulation.

Much work will have to be done in adaptational psychodynamics before the detailed mechanisms of hedonic self-regulation will be adequately explored in every behavioral area. Advances along this line no less than the information already available may be expected to pose the significant problems to the behavioral physiologist and thus offer him the necessary guidance. We may look forward to a physiologic psychodynamics or, more precisely, to a physiology of motivation and control, in which the psycho-dynamics of hedonic self-regulation will play a crucial part. Although studies in the physiology of pain began some time ago, serious investigations in the physiology of pleasure have only recently been initiated by the Tulane Department of Psychiatry and Neurology and by James Olds, working independently.

The Department of Psychiatry and Neurology of Tulane University was the first medical institution to use adaptational psychodynamics in its extensive research program. The present symposium is but one example of this sustained interest. In closing, I should like to express my gratitude to Robert G. Heath, Chairman of the department, and to the dedicated group of his coworkers.

REFERENCES

1. ARISTOTLE. *Nicomachean Ethics*. Loeb Classical Library. Cambridge, Mass., Harvard, 1939, p. 31.
2. BENTHAM, J. "An Introduction to the Principles of Morals and Legislation," in *The English Philosophers from Bacon to Mill*, ed. by Burtt, E. A. New York Modern Library, 1939, pp. 791–852.
3. CANNON, W. B. *Bodily Changes in Pain, Hunger, Fear and Rage*. New York, Appleton, 1934.
4. DOBZHANSKY, T. *Genetics and the Origin of Species*. New York, Columbia, 1951.
5. FREUD, S. "Formulations in the Two Principles of Mental Functioning" (1911), in *Freud's Complete Psychological Works, Standard Edition*, Vol. 12. London, Hogarth, 1958, pp. 218–226.
6. RADO, S. "Dynamics and Classification of Disordered Behavior" (1953), in *Psychoanalysis of Behavior: Collected Papers*, Vol. I, 1922–1955. New York, Grune & Stratton, 1956, pp. 268–285.
7. RADO, S. "Hedonic Control, Action-Self, and the Depressive Spell" (1954), in *Psychoanalysis of Behavior: Collected Papers*, Vol. I, 1922–1955. New York, Grune & Stratton, 1956, pp. 286–311.
8. RADO, S. "Development of Adaptational Psychodynamics," in *Psychoanalysis of Behavior: Collected Papers*, Vol. I, 1922–1955. New York, Grune & Stratton, 1956, pp. 167–357.
9. RADO, S. "Narcotic Bondage: A General Theory of the Dependence on Narcotic Drugs" (1957), in *Psychoanalysis of Behavior: Collected Papers*, Vol. II, 1956–1961. New York, Grune & Stratton, 1962, pp. 21–29.
10. RADO, S. "Theory and Therapy: The Theory of Schizotypal Organization and Its Application to the Treatment of Decompensated Schizotypal Behavior" (1960), in *Psychoanalysis of Behavior: Collected Papers*, Vol. II, 1956–1961. New York, Grune & Stratton, 1962, pp. 127–140.

11. RADO, S. *Psychoanalysis of Behavior: Collected Papers,* Vol. II, 1956–1961. New York, Grune & Stratton, 1962.
12. RADO, S. "On the retransformation of psychoanalysis into a medical science. *Compr. Psychiat. 3*:317, 1962.
13. RADO, S. Fighting narcotic bondage and other forms of narcotic disorder. *Compr. Psychiat. 4*:160, 1963.

NEIL R. BURCH, M.D.
Baylor University College of Medicine

Discussion

CONJOINTLY, THE TWO PRECEDING PAPERS represent explorations into what I consider to be the single most important problem in psychiatry. Analysis of the logic or, as I should prefer, the analogic, of the human affect system will lead to deeper and more refined understanding of psychodynamics than we have at this time. It will become clear that I take exception to two cardinal ideas presented by Professor Feibleman and Professor Rado: respectively, the nature of the logical model appropriate for describing the relations and operators within the affect-emotional system and the function of emotional thought in the hierarchy of the integrative apparatus.

Taking pleasure as a prototypal component of the affect system, I should not argue with the thesis set forth by Professor Feibleman that consistency and completeness are necessary attributes of the affect system. Also acceptable are the postulates that affect is body-wide, that it involves self-consciousness, and that consciousness itself is a function of the affect system. Pleasure or positive affect defined as the "qualitative concomitant of drive reduction," or even as "the feeling of attainment that accompanies a completion," strips this aspect of the affect system of its operational meaning. Similarly, the contention that pleasurable experience is always basically the same is an oversimplification which actually obscures the operational characteristics of affect. Such a sameness of quality implies a single dimension which is restricted to more than–less than relations.

The operational relations within the affect system and between the affect system and the symbolic thought system are again obscured by arranging the component parts in hierarchical levels of ascending order in the manner of Professor Rado. Whereas such a hierarchy is of heuristic interest and may grossly reflect phylogeny, the division is in the nature of a value judgment and implies that each succeeding level mediates progressively more advanced operations in the thought process. Professor Rado makes this formulation explicit when he suggests that "the early predominance of emotional thinking explains the adult's readiness to relapse at a moment's notice to this primitive level, as seen in group behavior as well as in almost all psychiatric disorders." The conclusion forced by such a hierarchy is that "emotional thought culminates in religion, art, and aesthetic pleasure; un-emotional thought in science, technology, and wisdom." I do not agree with this use of the hierarchical concept or with the conclusions it forces. This concept largely ignores the vertical integration of the central nervous system stressed by recent advances in neurophysiology[7] and does an injustice to the function and importance of the affect system as the substrate of intuitive, analogic thought.

With the understanding that all models by their very nature are con-structed in an "as if" world, I should propose a more conventional model of the total affect system which divides it into levels with fairly well-defined operational characteristics. The levels can be compared in terms of intensity and duration of subjective experience and stimulus-response correspond-ence. Again with pleasure considered as the prototype of affect, the levels are as follows:

LEVEL I: MOOD.   The mood of euphoria or the general feeling of well-being is a tenuous cloak. The intensity of our subjective experience to a mood is relatively weak and on a graded scale might be assigned a rank of 1+. The external referent, i.e., the event or events in the external uni-verse which invoke this mood, is usually poorly defined and often not within awareness. The correspondence between the mood and any given stimulus is usually very low. I may find it impossible to identify any one thing that accounts for my mood of today, or perhaps of the last few days. At this level, a chronic background affect modulation is part of and feeds into all other levels.

LEVEL II: FEELING TONE.   The feeling tone of "like," or "good for me," is experienced with a 2+ intensity, but for a much shorter duration than level I. This will, of course, move me toward the "encountered stimulus" which Professor Rado describes in his discussion of hedonic self-regulation, but here again the stimulus which has generated the feeling tone, although more specific than at the level of the mood, often does not have a well-defined stimulus-response relation.

LEVEL III: EMOTION.   An emotion such as love is strongly experienced at the 3+ level on my arbitrary scale and, although of relatively short dura-tion, has a much stronger stimulus-response correspondence than the pre-vious levels. I can generally identify the stimulus field leading me to the subjective experience of love even if the most significant individual stimulus is not within my awareness.

LEVEL IV: THE ANALOG UNIT.   I should propose a final and most important level within the affect system. At the level of the analog, the affect unit is specific for an external referent and stands in almost a 1:1 correspondence with the external event. Although the duration of the experience is fleeting, as fleeting as thought, the subjective intensity is 4+ on my scale. The analog or discrete affect unit which is associated with the name of a man I am trying to remember but which is just outside of awareness—on the tip of my tongue—is specific for that name. In a hundred names guessed, some will have almost the right analog, but only the correct name fits this affect experience in such a way that the symbol-analog match feels just right.

The analog might be visualized in somewhat the same fashion as the substituted benzene ring of the organic chemist. The various symbols are associated as groupings of various elements attached to complex side chains by single, double, or triple bonds. A chair-table association might be interpreted as having a triple bond: The symbol for chair first generates the analog for chair and the analog in turn has a strong bond with the symbol table and therefore high probability of yielding this symbol in association. Because of the 4+ intensity assumed to exist at this level of the analog unit, it follows that a great deal of energy is required to break the stronger bonds. The triple bond would be ruptured only in the severest pathologic situations. The weaker single bonds of the side-chain groups might well be opened under moderate stress, fatigue, or toxic states, and different groups might be substituted. Work in our laboratory has indicated that the higher level and more complex operation in the analog system is especially sensitive to minimal changes in the state of consciousness.

For the last few years I have been presenting to my students in psychiatry material which identifies the two separate but equally important types of thought process as analogic thought and digital thought. The terminology embarrasses me somewhat because it so patently trades on the current fad of computer terminology. I use these terms because there is a striking similarity between the characteristics of analog-digital machines and analog-digital thought. As with the machines, analogic thought is considerably faster and can handle a far more complex array of inputs and variables, but at the price of approximate solutions rather than exact logical, digital results. I would emphasize that it is in the interaction and integration of these two types of thought—both always present, always active—that human intelligence is epitomized. For certain tasks digital logic is more appropriate than analogic, but there must be a continuous cycling back and forth between the two systems. I am of the opinion that the core psychopathology of the schizophrenic process is dissociation—the dissociation or split of the analog affect unit from its appropriate digital symbolic correspondent. This fragmentation of the analog-digital valence or bonding is nowhere more lucidly set forth than in the following excerpt from Bleuler:[2] "It appears as if those pathways of association and inhibition, established by experience, had lost their meaning and significance. Associations seem to take new pathways more easily, and thus no longer follow the old preferred ways, that is the logical pathways indicated by past experience. Jung has drawn attention to the fact that even in the healthy, similar unusual pathways of association are opened up during moments of confusion, distraction, and unconscious thinking. But in such people, it never goes quite so far as it does in schizophrenics. (In the healthy psyche, only the dream forms a sufficient analogy to what goes on in schizophrenia.) Especially in acute conditions of schizophrenia, one often finds so complete a fragmentation of the thinking processes that they cannot result in a complete idea or action, but merely in vague movements. In this way, even concepts such as 'father' and 'mother' become vague and obscure." Properly developed, fragmentation of the analog-digital bonding may be used to illustrate the process underlying such phenomena as predicate identification, archaic thought, and *déjà vu*. Not only do I conceptualize schizophrenia in terms of analog-digital bonding, but I have come to view personality structure as identifiable in terms of its analog-digital ratio and innate capability describable as the relative balance and degree of analog-digital I.Q.

I suggest that Freud offered a disservice to psychiatry in his emphasis on the distortion of pure, logical thought by the primary process. The same sort of negative feeling tone, of course, pervaded his investigations of the entire unconscious process. Neo-Freudians have partially rescued the affect system, and even theoretical physicists are coming to recognize the use of the analogic "regulative principle"[4] as legitimate, but our system of formal education still lauds the digital and derogates the analogic. Much of this repudiation of intuitive thought, interpreted only as the intuitive flash of insight, probably derives from the fact that the analogic system operates largely at a different level of abstraction than the symbolic level of rational thought. Aristotelian logic and the later calculus of Boolean algebra[8] were constructed and are eminently appropriate for the manipulation of symbols. The symbolic is the highest level of abstraction; the symbol bears no physical connection or relation to the physical event symbolized. Symbols are essentially "not-things" which stand for or represent "things." It is this essential quality of complete physical independence of the symbol and the symbolized that allows precise manipulation and formalized communication. The analogic thought process operates principally not at the symbolic level or even at the level of the signal, but rather at the level of the sign, which requires a vastly more complex representation of the physical event being coded. (Abstractions at the level of the sign would seem to be similar in many ways to "quality" as analyzed by Professor Feibleman.) Operating at the level of the sign presents the same difficulty in communicating the affect-coded representation as the difficulty Susanne Langer[5] so effectively described in the communication of "non-discursive symbols": "Non-discursive form in art has a different office, namely to articulate knowledge that cannot be rendered discursively because it concerns experiences that are not *formally* amenable to the discursive projection. Such experiences are the rhythms of life, organic, emotional, and mental (the rhythm of attention is an interesting link among them all), which are not simply periodic, but endlessly complex, and sensitive to every sort of influence. All together they compose the dynamic pattern of feeling. It is this pattern that only non-discursive symbolic forms can present, and that is the point and purpose of artistic construction." I may communicate my symbols to you with fair ease, but to communicate widely my feeling tone or analog requires the transmission of such a complex pattern and such vast amounts of information that, literally, a new language must be created and its rules formalized.

My proposition is that the analogic thought process can and does manipulate and calculate data at all levels identified by measurement theory,[9] the nominal level through the ratio level, although many of the analogic operations are probably in terms of ordinal and interval relations. Because of the complex pattern of sign manipulation, the most appropriate mathematical models for analogic processes may well turn out to be within the domain of topology.[1] The topologic postulate that two surfaces remain identical under any transform that maintains a 1:1 correspondence in the mapping from one surface to another is the sort of relational operator that may be necessary in formalizing these processes. The sheet of graph paper which has been crumpled into a ball is topologically still identical with the flat, uncrumpled surface; the analog may be understood as coding the topology of functional surfaces or that interface of operational relations which joins one event with another. What is an ashtray? What are the dynamic characteristics and functional surfaces, and what is its shape in my analog? The ashtray is a vehicle for ashes, but perhaps for other small objects too. I am in a room without ashtrays; an empty coffee cup may take on the functional shape of an ashtray. I am in a room without such shapes; the floor may assume for me the characteristics of a holder of ashes. In the set, ashtrays, there are many physical shapes but a limited family of functional surfaces which defines the set. Group theory, a special case of set theory, which emphasizes the investigation of operators and transforms, per se, may well enter into the future of psychiatry in much the same way in which set theory[6] has been used in the analysis of learning theory. The feeling of an ashtray and the multiple relations implicit in its function as a holder of ashes have not been formally described within logic, philosophy, or Boolian algebra as we know them today.

Finally, I should like to address myself to the problem of novelty and novel stimuli introduced by Dr. Feibleman. I should take the position that the reduction of novelty in the stimulus field is the primary work of the human thought process. This is not to say that complete lack of stimuli, such as in experimental sensory deprivation, may not produce dysphoria for the same reason that excessive and overwhelming stimuli are uncomfortable; the limits of the system have been exceeded. I should question the logical step from "consciousness breaks down with monotony of input" to "thus pleasure, upon some degree of which consciousness depends, itself depends in turn upon novelty among the stimuli." Human intelligence, with its maze of negative feedback to inhibit total response and to facilitate discrete appropriate reaction, has as its task the generation of multiple subjective universes. These universes extend in time throughout the past, the present, and the future. We constantly check the subjective universe against the objective universe of reality. The optimum subjective universe may well be the one which best matches current reality and which best predicts the future of the next minute, month, or year. Insofar as the subjective universe predicts reality as it unfolds, it has reduced the statistical informational content and novelty of the external stimulus to the organism.[3] It may well be that the action and work of constructing a subjective universe, building up its pattern and complexity, are pleasurable; such pleasure would certainly be consistent with the survival value of reducing the number of unexpected external events and therefore the informational content of future reality. Life is in the business of replicating itself, not only by organically repeating itself in kind, but also by replicating and propagating the subjective universe even at the expense and pain of superposition on others or on objective reality.

At the end of a volume primarily devoted to neurophysiologic exploration of pleasure and pain, the place of the philosopher and psychiatric theoretician might be questioned. The understanding of human behavior should increase exponentially with advances in the technics and methodology set before you in this symposium, but the understanding of human behavior in terms of higher order abstractions such as mind, value system, and even soul remains our final need.

REFERENCES

1. BERGAMINI, D., and the editors of *Life. Mathematics*. Life Science Library. New York, Time Inc., 1963.
2. BLEULER, E. *Dementia Praecox or the Group of Schizophrenias*. New York, International Universities Press, 1950, pp. 349–350.
3. GOLDMAN, S. *Information Theory*. Englewood Cliffs, N. J., Prentice-Hall, 1953.
4. KÖRNER, S. (ed.). *Observation and Interpretation*. New York, Academic Press, 1957.
5. LANGER, S. K. *Feeling and Form*. New York, Scribner, 1953, pp. 240–241.

6. LUCE, R. D. (ed.). *Developments in Mathematical Psychology,* New York, Free Press, 1960.
7. MORUZZI, G., and MAGOUN, H. W. Brain stem reticular formation and activation of the EEG. *Electroenceph. Clin. Neurophysiol. 1*:455, 1949.
8. NEWMAN, J. R. (ed.). *The World of Mathematics,* Vol. 3. New York, Simon & Schuster, 1956.
9. TORGERSON, W. S. *Theory and Methods of Scaling.* New York, Wiley, 1958.